186/6

D1493236

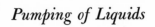

Pumping of Liquids

Pumping of Liquids

F. A. HOLLAND
Royal College of Advanced Technology
Salford, Lancs
England

and

F. S. CHAPMAN
Lever Brothers Company
New York, N. Y.

New York
REINHOLD PUBLISHING CORPORATION

Preface

The pumping of liquids through pipelines of circular cross-section is the subject of this book. Liquids at both ambient and above ambient temperatures are considered. Liquids at temperatures below ambient are not treated, since they belong to the specialized field of cryogenics.

Chapter 1 provides an introduction to fluid flow theory and includes a brief description of vector analysis. A theoretical treatment of Newtonian and non-Newtonian liquid flow in pipelines is given in Chapters 2 and 3, respectively. In the remainder of the text, the more practical aspects of liquid pumping are presented.

Chapter 4 describes the common valves used in pipelines, and Chapters 5 and 6 treat positive displacement and centrifugal pumps, respectively. Although centrifugal pumps are more common than positive displacement pumps, the latter are considered first, since this arrangement better illustrates the important factors in liquid pumping.

Liquid flow measurement is discussed in Chapter 7, the flow of slurries in Chapter 8, and the prevention of heat losses from pipelines in Chapter 9. Chapter 10 and the Appendix deal with piping and piping systems.

The authors are indebted to Mrs. Frances I. Chapman and Mrs. Vera R. Holland for typing and proofreading the manuscript. They also wish to thank Mrs. Alberta Gordon and Mrs. Florence Poillon of Reinhold Publishing Corporation for editing and processing the book.

A substantial portion of Chapters 5, 6 and 9 and their illustrations has already appeared as articles published in *Chemical Engineering*. The authors are grateful to the editors of that magazine for permission to publish this material.

It is hoped that this book will prove useful to both practicing engineers and those about to begin their careers in the processing industries.

F. A. HOLLAND
F. S. CHAPMAN

CHAPTER 1

General Considerations in Liquid Transport

Energy Relationships

The total energy of a flowing liquid consists of the following component parts: internal, potential, pressure and kinetic energies. It is convenient to consider each of these energies with reference to an arbitrary base level and to make all calculations on unit mass of liquid.

Internal Energy. This is the energy associated with the physical state of the liquid, i.e., the energy that the atoms and molecules of the liquid possess as a result of their configuration and motion.[7] Internal energy is a function of temperature. It can be written as U per unit mass of liquid.

Potential Energy. This is the energy a liquid possesses because of its position in the earth's gravitational field. The work required to raise a unit mass of liquid to a height z above an arbitrary level is zg, where g is the gravitational acceleration. This work is the potential energy of the liquid above the arbitrarily chosen base level.

Pressure Energy. This energy is a measure of the work required to introduce the liquid into the system without a change in volume. If P is the pressure in the system and V is the volume of a mass m of liquid, then PV/m is the pressure energy per unit mass of liquid. Since the ratio m/V is the density ρ, the pressure energy per unit mass of liquid can be written as P/ρ.

Kinetic Energy. This is the energy associated with motion. The kinetic energy per unit mass of liquid is $v^2/2$, where v is the linear velocity relative to some fixed body, e.g., the earth.

Total Energy. In addition to the energies listed above, other forms of energy, e.g., electrical, magnetic, etc., exist. However, it is not necessary to consider these latter forms of energy in this treatment.

The total energy E per unit mass of liquid may thus be written as

$$E = U + zg + \frac{P}{\rho} + \frac{v^2}{2}$$
(1-1)

where each of the terms has the dimensions of force times distance per unit mass, i.e., $(ML/T^2) \times L/M$.

Consider the liquid flow from a point 1 to a point 2. Between these two points, let an amount Δq of heat energy be added to the liquid and let the liquid do a net amount of work ΔW on its surroundings, where Δq and ΔW refer to unit mass of liquid. An energy balance equation can be written on the liquid as follows:

$$E_2 - E_1 = \Delta q - \Delta W$$

which can be written in full as

$$\left(U_2 + z_2 g + \frac{P_2}{\rho} + \frac{v_2^2}{2} \right) - \left(U_1 + z_1 g + \frac{P_1}{\rho} + \frac{v_1^2}{2} \right)$$

$$= \Delta q - \Delta W$$
(1-2)

If the temperature of the flowing liquid remains constant, the internal energy does not change. If no heat is added to the liquid, $\Delta q = 0$. For these two conditions, Equation (1-2) can be rewritten as

$$\left(z_2 g + \frac{P_2}{\rho} + \frac{v_2^2}{2} \right) - \left(z_1 g + \frac{P_1}{\rho} + \frac{v_1^2}{2} \right) = -\Delta W$$
(1-3)

A flowing liquid is required to do work in order to overcome frictional forces. This component of the net work term ΔW is therefore positive. If the liquid flows through a pump situated between points 1 and 2, then the component of the net work term ΔW supplied by the pump is negative. In most cases, these are the only two work components involved and ΔW can be written as follows:

$$\Delta W = \text{work required to overcome friction} - \text{energy supplied by}$$
$$\text{a pump}$$
(1-4)

Equation (1–3) can be rewritten in the form

$$\left(z_2 + \frac{P_2}{\rho g} + \frac{v_2^2}{2g}\right) - \left(z_1 + \frac{P_1}{\rho g} + \frac{v_1^2}{2g}\right) = -\Delta W/g \qquad (1–5)$$

where each of the terms in Equation (1–5) has the dimension of length. In Equation (1–5), the terms z, $P/\rho g$ and $v^2/2g$ are known as the potential, pressure and velocity heads, respectively. The term $\Delta W/g$ can be written as

$$\Delta W/g = h_f - \Delta h \qquad (1–6)$$

where h_f is the head loss due to friction and Δh is the head imparted to the liquid by the pump. The term Δh is known as the total head of the pump. Both h_f and Δh have the dimensions of length.

Substitute Equation (1–6) into Equation (1–5) to give

$$\left(z_2 + \frac{P_2}{\rho g} + \frac{v_2^2}{2g}\right) - \left(z_1 + \frac{P_1}{\rho g} + \frac{v_1^2}{2g}\right) = \Delta h - h_f \qquad (1–7)$$

Equation (1–7) is commonly referred to as the Bernoulli equation where all the terms have the dimension of length. The Bernoulli equation is simply an energy balance written for convenience in terms of length. The various forms of energy are interchangeable, and the equation enables the magnitude of these changes to be calculated in a given system.

Flow Patterns

In general, flowing liquids have different velocities at different points in a line perpendicular to the direction of flow. A particular distribution of velocities depends on the nature of the flow which in turn is a function of the geometry of the container, the physical properties of the liquid, and its mass flow rate.

For the most part, flow can be characterized either as laminar or as turbulent flow.

Laminar Flow. This is also called viscous or streamline flow. In this type of flow, layers of liquid move relative to each other without any macroscopic intermixing. Laminar flow systems are commonly represented graphically by streamlines. There is no liquid flow across these lines. A velocity distribution results from shear stresses which in turn are present because of viscous frictional forces.

Turbulent Flow. In turbulent flow, there is an irregular random movement of liquid in directions transverse to the main flow. This irregular fluctuating motion can be regarded as superimposed on the mean motion.

Consider liquid flow with reference to an ordinary rectangular Cartesian coordinate system x, y, z. A point velocity at any instant in the x direction can be written as

$$v_x = \bar{v}_x + v_x' \tag{1-8}$$

where $\bar{v}_x$, the mean point velocity, is defined as

$$\bar{v}_x = \frac{1}{\Delta t} \int_0^{\Delta t} v_x \, dt \tag{1-9}$$

In Equation (1–9), Δt is a time interval which need be only a few seconds, since the irregular fluctuations are extremely rapid. If the mean velocity $\bar{v}_x$ is constant with time, the motion in the x direction is said to be in steady state. If motions exist in the y and z directions, they can similarly be expressed as the sum of a mean and a fluctuating velocity.

Momentum Transfer

In a liquid in streamline flow, fast-moving molecules diffuse into slow-moving streams and vice versa, resulting in a transfer of momentum in a direction perpendicular to the direction of flow.

For Newtonian liquids, the rate of momentum transfer is given by the equation

$$R_{zx} = -\mu \frac{dv_x}{dz} \tag{1-10}$$

where v_x is the linear velocity of liquid in the x direction at a point z, R_{zx} is the rate of transfer of momentum per unit area in the z direction, and μ is the coefficient of viscosity. The rate of momentum transfer R_{zx} is also known as the shear stress, and the velocity gradient $-dv_x/dz$ as the shear rate.

For Newtonian liquids, the coefficient of viscosity μ is not a function of the shear stress or rate. Equation (1–10) is known as Newton's law of momentum transfer.

Equation (1–10) may also be written as

$$R_{zx} = -\eta \rho \frac{dv_x}{dz} \tag{1-11}$$

where $\eta = \mu/\rho$, the viscous diffusivity or kinematic viscosity.

In turbulent flow, momentum transfer takes place by the movement of eddies imposed on the ordinary molecular motion. An equation for momentum transfer through regions of turbulent flow analogous to Equation (1–11) for laminar flow can be written as follows:

$$R_{zx} = - (\eta + \eta_e)\rho \frac{dv_x}{dz} \tag{1-12}$$

where η_e is defined as the eddy viscous diffusivity. In turbulent flow, the eddy viscous diffusivity η_e is much greater than the molecular viscous diffusivity η. Thus large shear stresses exist in turbulent liquids.

Consider unsteady state molecular momentum transfer in one direction as shown in Figure 1–1. Since R_{zx} is the rate of momentum transfer across unit area in the z direction, a momentum balance can be written on the volume element $1 \times \Delta z$ as follows:

$$\frac{\partial}{\partial t}(\rho v_x)\Delta z \qquad = \qquad R_{zx}|_z \qquad - \qquad R_{zx}|_{z+\Delta z} \tag{1-13}$$

$$\begin{pmatrix} \text{rate of accu-} \\ \text{mulation of} \\ \text{momentum in} \\ \text{the volume ele-} \\ \text{ment } 1 \times \Delta z \end{pmatrix} = \begin{pmatrix} \text{rate of transfer} \\ \text{of momentum} \\ \text{into the vol-} \\ \text{ume element } 1 \\ \times \Delta z \text{ by mo-} \\ \text{lecular motion} \end{pmatrix} - \begin{pmatrix} \text{rate of transfer} \\ \text{of momentum} \\ \text{out of the vol-} \\ \text{ume element } 1 \\ \times \Delta z \text{ by mo-} \\ \text{lecular motion} \end{pmatrix}$$

Equation (1–13) can be rewritten as

$$\frac{\partial}{\partial t}(\rho v_x)\Delta z = \frac{(R_{zx}|_z - R_{zx}|_{z+\Delta z})\,\Delta z}{\Delta z} \tag{1-14}$$

which in the limit $\Delta z \to 0$ becomes

$$\frac{\partial}{\partial t}(\rho v_x)\,\Delta z = -\frac{\partial R_{zx}}{\partial z}\Delta z$$

or

$$\frac{\partial}{\partial t}(\rho v_x) = -\frac{\partial R_{zx}}{\partial z} \tag{1-15}$$

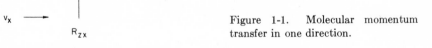

Figure 1-1. Molecular momentum transfer in one direction.

For a Newtonian liquid obeying Equation (1–10), Equation (1–15) becomes

$$\frac{\partial}{\partial t}(\rho v_x) = \frac{\partial}{\partial z}\left(\mu \frac{\partial v_x}{\partial z}\right)$$

which for a constant density ρ and viscosity coefficient μ can be written either as

$$\rho \frac{\partial v_x}{\partial t} = \mu \frac{\partial^2 v_x}{\partial z^2}$$

or as

$$\frac{\partial v_x}{\partial t} = \eta \frac{\partial^2 v_x}{\partial z^2} \tag{1–16}$$

Equation (1–16) is a partial differential equation requiring the specification of boundary conditions for its solution.

Many liquids used in industry do not obey Newton's law of momentum transfer given in Equation (1–10). These are the so-called non-Newtonian liquids. A number of mathematical models have been proposed to describe their behavior.[8] However, the simplest and most widely applicable model is the power law equation

$$R_{zz} = K_p\left(-\frac{dv_x}{dz}\right)^n \tag{1–17}$$

In Equation (1–17), K_p is called the consistency coefficient and n the power law index.[4] For Newtonian liquids, $n = 1$ and K_p the consistency coefficient becomes the coefficient of viscosity. In this case, Equation (1–17) becomes identical with Equation (1–10). Although not all non-Newtonian liquids obey the power law equation [Equation (1–17)], the majority do—at least over limited ranges. The differential term dv_x/dz in Equation (1–17) is negative so that the term in parentheses is always positive.

For power law liquids, Equation (1–15) becomes

$$\frac{\partial}{\partial t}(\rho v_x) = -\frac{\partial}{\partial z}\left[K_p\left(-\frac{\partial v_x}{\partial z}\right)^n\right]$$

which can be written

$$\frac{\partial}{\partial t}(\rho v_x) = K_p n\left(-\frac{\partial v_x}{\partial z}\right)^{n-1}\frac{\partial^2 v_x}{\partial z^2} \tag{1–18}$$

For a constant density ρ this can be written in the form

$$\frac{\partial v_x}{\partial t} = \left(\frac{K_p n}{\rho}\right)\left(-\frac{\partial v_x}{\partial z}\right)^{n-1}\frac{\partial^2 v_x}{\partial z^2} \tag{1–19}$$

For Newtonian liquids, i.e., where $n = 1$ and $K_p = \mu$, Equation (1–19) becomes identical with Equation (1–16).

So far, momentum transfer in one direction only has been considered. For more complicated cases, vector analysis is required.

Vector Analysis

Scalars possess only magnitude; vectors have both magnitude and direction. A vector will be signified by boldface type to distinguish it from a scalar.

Consider the velocity vector $\mathbf{v}$ with reference to the right-handed rectangular coordinate system shown in Figure 1–2. Define unit vectors $\mathbf{i}, \mathbf{j}$ and $\mathbf{k}$ in the positive x, y and z directions, respectively, so that

$$\mathbf{v} = \mathbf{i}v_x + \mathbf{j}v_y + \mathbf{k}v_z \tag{1-20}$$

where v_x, v_y and v_z are the scalar components of the velocity $\mathbf{v}$ in the x, y and z directions, respectively.

Multiplication of Vectors. Vectors can be multiplied together to give either (1) the dot or inner product, or (2) the cross or outer product.

(1) The dot or inner product of two vectors $\mathbf{a}$ and $\mathbf{b}$ is a scalar quantity

$$\mathbf{a} \cdot \mathbf{b} = ab \cos \theta \tag{1-21}$$

where θ is the angle between the positive directions of the two vectors.

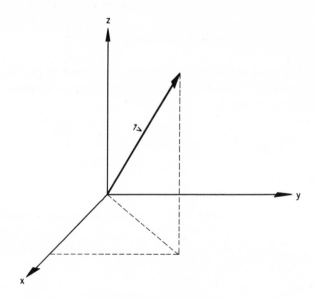

Figure 1-2. Geometric representation of a vector in Cartesian coordinates.

Obviously when two vectors are perpendicular, i.e., $\theta = 90°$,

$$\mathbf{a} \cdot \mathbf{b} = 0$$

and when two vectors are parallel, i.e., $\theta = 0$,

$$\mathbf{a} \cdot \mathbf{b} = ab$$

Thus the following relationships exist between the unit vectors in the x, y and z directions:

$$\mathbf{i} \cdot \mathbf{i} = \mathbf{j} \cdot \mathbf{j} = \mathbf{k} \cdot \mathbf{k} = 1$$
$$\mathbf{i} \cdot \mathbf{j} = \mathbf{i} \cdot \mathbf{k} = \mathbf{j} \cdot \mathbf{k} = 0$$

Therefore, since

$$\mathbf{a} = \mathbf{i}a_x + \mathbf{j}a_y + \mathbf{k}a_z$$
$$\mathbf{b} = \mathbf{i}b_x + \mathbf{j}b_y + \mathbf{k}b_z$$
$$\mathbf{a} \cdot \mathbf{b} = a_x b_x + a_y b_y + a_z b_z \qquad (1\text{--}22)$$

(2) The cross or outer product of two vectors $\mathbf{a}$ and $\mathbf{b}$ is a vector quantity

$$\mathbf{a} \times \mathbf{b} = \mathbf{a}\mathbf{b} \sin \theta = \mathbf{c} \qquad (1\text{--}23)$$

where θ is the angle between the positive directions of the two vectors; $\mathbf{c}$ is perpendicular to the plane of $\mathbf{a}$ and $\mathbf{b}$ as shown in Figure 1–3 and its

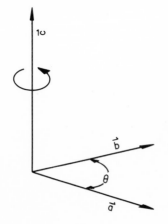

Figure 1-3. Graphical illustration of the cross product of two vectors.

direction is governed by the rotation of **a** into **b** by the right-handed rule. Obviously when two vectors are perpendicular, i.e., $\theta = 90°$,

$$\mathbf{a} \times \mathbf{b} = ab = c$$

and when the two vectors are parallel, i.e., $\theta = 0$,

$$\mathbf{a} \times \mathbf{b} = 0$$

Thus the following relationships exist between the unit vectors in the x, y and z directions:

$$\mathbf{i} \times \mathbf{i} = \mathbf{j} \times \mathbf{j} = \mathbf{k} \times \mathbf{k} = 0$$
$$\mathbf{i} \times \mathbf{j} = \mathbf{k}, \qquad \mathbf{j} \times \mathbf{i} = -\mathbf{k}$$
$$\mathbf{j} \times \mathbf{k} = \mathbf{i}, \qquad \mathbf{k} \times \mathbf{j} = -\mathbf{i}$$
$$\mathbf{k} \times \mathbf{i} = \mathbf{j}, \qquad \mathbf{i} \times \mathbf{k} = -\mathbf{j}$$

Therefore, since $\mathbf{a} = \mathbf{i}a_x + \mathbf{j}a_y + \mathbf{k}a_z$ and $\mathbf{b} = \mathbf{i}b_x + \mathbf{j}b_y + \mathbf{k}b_z$;

$$\mathbf{a} \times \mathbf{b} = \mathbf{i}(a_y b_z - a_z b_y) - \mathbf{j}(a_x b_z - a_z b_x) + \mathbf{k}(a_x b_y - a_y b_x) \qquad (1\text{--}24)$$

Equation (1–24) is the determinant of the matrix

$$\mathbf{a} \times \mathbf{b} = \begin{vmatrix} \mathbf{i} & \mathbf{j} & \mathbf{k} \\ a_x & a_y & a_z \\ b_x & b_y & b_z \end{vmatrix}$$

The Vector Operator **∇**. This is also called "del" and is defined as

$$\mathbf{\nabla} = \mathbf{i}\frac{\partial}{\partial x} + \mathbf{j}\frac{\partial}{\partial y} + \mathbf{k}\frac{\partial}{\partial z} \qquad (1\text{--}25)$$

in rectangular coordinates.

Consider a scalar quantity such as pressure P. $\mathbf{\nabla}P$ is known as grad P, where

$$\mathbf{\nabla}P = \mathbf{i}\frac{\partial P}{\partial x} + \mathbf{j}\frac{\partial P}{\partial y} + \mathbf{k}\frac{\partial P}{\partial z} \qquad (1\text{--}26)$$

∇ is treated as an ordinary vector, so that the dot product

$$\mathbf{\nabla} \cdot \mathbf{v} = \frac{\partial v_x}{\partial x} + \frac{\partial v_y}{\partial y} + \frac{\partial v_z}{\partial z} \qquad (1\text{--}27)$$

Equation (1–27) is analogous to Equation (1–22). $\nabla \cdot \mathbf{v}$ is called the divergence of the velocity vector $\mathbf{v}$. Similarly, by analogy with Equation (1–24), the cross product

$$\nabla \times \mathbf{v} = \begin{vmatrix} \mathbf{i} & \mathbf{j} & \mathbf{k} \\ \dfrac{\partial}{\partial x} & \dfrac{\partial}{\partial y} & \dfrac{\partial}{\partial z} \\ v_x & v_y & v_z \end{vmatrix} \tag{1–28}$$

where $\nabla \times \mathbf{v}$ is known as the curl of the velocity vector $\mathbf{v}$.

The Vector Operator ∇^2. This is known as the Laplacian operator. It is defined as

$$\nabla^2 = \frac{\partial^2}{\partial x^2} + \frac{\partial^2}{\partial y^2} + \frac{\partial^2}{\partial z^2} \tag{1–29}$$

in rectangular coordinates.

The vector operators ∇ and ∇^2 enable the basic fluid flow equations to be written in a conveniently short form.

Equation of Continuity

Although only liquids are being considered in this text, the equation of continuity will be derived first for the general case of a fluid.

Consider a small volume element $\Delta x \, \Delta y \, \Delta z$ of fluid in Figure 1–4 having a density $\rho(x,y,z,t)$ at a particular point (x,y,z) and time t. Let the components of the velocity vector $\mathbf{v}$ be v_x, v_y and v_z in the positive x, y and z directions, respectively.

The rate of mass flow into the volume element in the y direction across the surface of area $\Delta x \, \Delta z$ is $\Delta x \, \Delta z \, \rho v_y |_y$.

The rate of mass flow out of the volume element in the y direction across the surface of area $\Delta x \, \Delta z$ is $\Delta x \, \Delta z \, \rho v_y |_{y+\Delta y}$. The rate of accumulation of mass in the y direction is therefore

$$\Delta x \, \Delta z (\rho v_y |_y - \rho v_y |_{y+\Delta y})$$

which can be written as

$$\Delta x \, \Delta y \, \Delta z \, \frac{(\rho v_y |_y - \rho v_y |_{y+\Delta y})}{\Delta y}$$

which in the limit $\Delta y \rightarrow 0$ becomes

$$- \Delta x \, \Delta y \, \Delta z \, \frac{\partial (\rho v_y)}{\partial y}$$

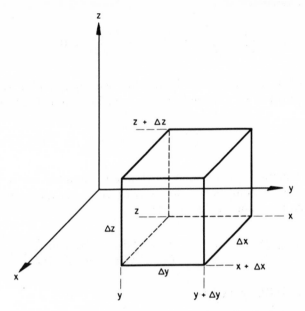

Figure 1-4. A small element of volume in Cartesian coordinates.

Similarly, the rates of accumulation of mass in the x and z directions are

$$- \Delta x \, \Delta y \, \Delta z \, \frac{\partial (\rho v_x)}{\partial x}$$

and

$$- \Delta x \, \Delta y \, \Delta z \, \frac{\partial (\rho v_z)}{\partial z}$$

respectively. Since the total mass in the volume element is $\Delta x \, \Delta y \, \Delta z \, \rho$, its rate of change is

$$\Delta x \, \Delta y \, \Delta z \, \frac{\partial \rho}{\partial t}$$

The rate of change of mass in the volume element is equal to the total rate of accumulation of mass inside the volume element. Therefore,

$$\Delta x \, \Delta y \, \Delta z \, \frac{\partial \rho}{\partial t} = - \Delta x \, \Delta y \, \Delta z \, \frac{\partial (\rho v_x)}{\partial x} - \Delta x \, \Delta y \, \Delta z \, \frac{\partial (\rho v_y)}{\partial y} - \Delta x \, \Delta y \, \Delta z \, \frac{\partial (\rho v_z)}{\partial z}$$

which can be rewritten as

$$\frac{\partial \rho}{\partial t} + \frac{\partial (\rho v_x)}{\partial x} + \frac{\partial (\rho v_y)}{\partial y} + \frac{\partial (\rho v_z)}{\partial z} = 0 \qquad (1\text{--}30)$$

Equation (1–30) is commonly known as the equation of continuity. Equation (1–30) can be written in the form of Equation (1–27) as

$$\frac{\partial \rho}{\partial t} + \mathbf{\nabla} \cdot \rho \mathbf{v} = 0 \qquad (1\text{--}31)$$

which is the equation of continuity written in the familiar vector notation.

The equation of continuity may be written in an alternate form by differentiating Equation (1–30) to give

$$\frac{\partial \rho}{\partial t} + v_x \frac{\partial \rho}{\partial x} + v_y \frac{\partial \rho}{\partial y} + v_z \frac{\partial \rho}{\partial z} + \rho \left(\frac{\partial v_x}{\partial x} + \frac{\partial v_y}{\partial y} + \frac{\partial v_z}{\partial z} \right) = 0 \qquad (1\text{--}32)$$

The operator D/Dt, defined as

$$\frac{\partial}{\partial t} + v_x \frac{\partial}{\partial x} + v_y \frac{\partial}{\partial y} + v_z \frac{\partial}{\partial z}$$

is known as the substantial derivative. Therefore, Equation (1–32) can be written as

$$\frac{D\rho}{Dt} + \rho \mathbf{\nabla} \cdot \mathbf{v} = 0 \qquad (1\text{--}33)$$

Equation (1–31) is written from the viewpoint of a stationary observer, while Equation (1–33) is written from the viewpoint of an observer moving along at the velocity of the stream $\mathbf{v}$.

In a normal liquid, the density ρ is not a function of the coordinates x, y, z or of the time t. In this case, the equation of continuity can be written either as

$$\frac{\partial v_x}{\partial x} + \frac{\partial v_y}{\partial y} + \frac{\partial v_z}{\partial z} = 0 \qquad (1\text{--}34)$$

or as

$$\mathbf{\nabla} \cdot \mathbf{v} = 0 \qquad (1\text{--}35)$$

Momentum Conservation Equations

A momentum balance

$$\begin{pmatrix} \text{rate of ac-} \\ \text{cumulation} \\ \text{of} \\ \text{momentum} \end{pmatrix} = \begin{pmatrix} \text{rate of ac-} \\ \text{cumulation} \\ \text{of convec-} \\ \text{tion} \\ \text{momentum} \end{pmatrix} + \begin{pmatrix} \text{rate of ac-} \\ \text{cumulation} \\ \text{of momentum} \\ \text{due to sur-} \\ \text{face forces} \end{pmatrix} + \begin{pmatrix} \text{sum of} \\ \text{forces} \\ \text{on} \\ \text{system} \end{pmatrix}$$

can be written for the volume element in Figure 1–5 where R_{xx}, R_{yx}, R_{zx} are the fluxes of the x component of momentum resulting from surface forces through the faces perpendicular to the x, y and z directions, respectively.

The rate of flow of the x component of momentum due to surface forces into the volume element in the y direction across the surface of area $\Delta x \, \Delta z$ is

$$\Delta x \; \Delta z \; R_{yx}|_y$$

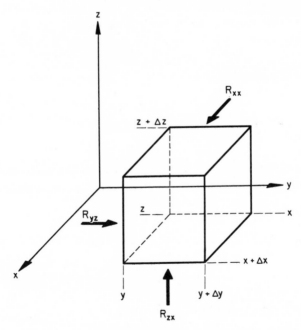

Figure 1-5.   Fluxes of momentum into a small element
of volume.

The corresponding rate of flow out of the volume element in the y direction across the surface of area $\Delta x \, \Delta z$ is

$$\Delta x \; \Delta z \; R_{yx}|_{y+\Delta y}$$

The rate of accumulation in the y direction of the x component of momentum due to surface forces is therefore

$$\Delta x \; \Delta z (R_{yx}|_y - R_{yx}|_{y+\Delta y})$$

which can be written as

$$\Delta x \; \Delta y \; \Delta z \; \frac{(R_{yx}|_y - R_{yx}|_{y+\Delta y})}{\Delta y}$$

which in the limit $\Delta y \to 0$ becomes

$$- \; \Delta x \; \Delta y \; \Delta z \; \frac{\partial R_{yx}}{\partial y}$$

Similarly, the rates of accumulation in the x and z directions of the x component of momentum due to surface forces are

$$- \; \Delta x \; \Delta y \; \Delta z \; \frac{\partial R_{xx}}{\partial x}$$

and

$$- \; \Delta x \; \Delta y \; \Delta z \; \frac{\partial R_{zx}}{\partial x}$$

respectively.

The rate of flow of the x component of convection momentum into the volume element in the y direction across the surface of area $\Delta x \, \Delta z$ is

$$\Delta x \; \Delta z \; \rho v_x v_y|_y$$

The corresponding rate of flow out of the volume element in the y direction across the surface area $\Delta x \, \Delta z$ is

$$\Delta x \; \Delta z \; \rho v_x v_y|_{y+\Delta y}$$

The rate of accumulation of the x component of convection momentum in the y direction is therefore

$$\Delta x \; \Delta z (\rho v_x v_y|_y - \rho v_x v_y|_{y+\Delta y})$$

which can be written as

$$\Delta x \ \Delta y \ \Delta z \ \frac{(\rho v_x v_y|_y - \rho v_x v_y|_{y+\Delta y})}{\Delta y}$$

which in the limit $\Delta y \to 0$ becomes

$$- \ \Delta x \ \Delta y \ \Delta z \ \frac{\partial \rho v_x v_y}{\partial y}$$

Similarly the rates of accumulation of the x component of convection momentum in the x and z directions are

$$- \ \Delta x \ \Delta y \ \Delta z \ \frac{\partial \rho v_x v_x}{\partial x}$$

and

$$- \ \Delta x \ \Delta y \ \Delta z \ \frac{\partial \rho v_x v_z}{\partial z}$$

respectively.

The pressure and gravitational forces on the volume element in the y direction can be written as

$$\Delta x \ \Delta z (P|_y - P|_{y+\Delta y}) + \rho g_y \ \Delta x \ \Delta y \ \Delta z$$

which can be written as

$$\Delta x \ \Delta y \ \Delta z \ \frac{(P|_y - P|_{y+\Delta y})}{\Delta y} + \rho g_y \ \Delta x \ \Delta y \ \Delta z$$

which in the limit $\Delta y \to 0$ becomes

$$- \ \Delta x \ \Delta y \ \Delta z \ \frac{\partial P}{\partial y} + \rho g_y \ \Delta x \ \Delta y \ \Delta z$$

Similarly, the pressure and gravitational forces on the volume element in the x and z directions can be written as

$$- \ \Delta x \ \Delta y \ \Delta z \ \frac{\partial P}{\partial x} + \rho g_x \ \Delta x \ \Delta y \ \Delta z$$

and

$$- \ \Delta x \ \Delta y \ \Delta z \ \frac{\partial P}{\partial z} + \rho g_z \ \Delta x \ \Delta y \ \Delta z$$

respectively.

Since the x component of momentum in the volume element is

$$\Delta x \; \Delta y \; \Delta z \; \rho v_x$$

its rate of change is

$$\Delta x \; \Delta y \; \Delta z \; \frac{\partial \rho v_x}{\partial t}$$

The rate of change of x component momentum in the volume element is equal to the total rate of accumulation of x component momentum inside the volume element.

For convenience, $\Delta x \; \Delta y \; \Delta z$ can be canceled from all terms and a momentum balance on the x component written as follows:

$$\frac{\partial \rho v_x}{\partial t} = -\left(\frac{\partial \rho v_x v_x}{\partial x} + \frac{\partial \rho v_x v_y}{\partial y} + \frac{\partial \rho v_x v_z}{\partial z} \right) - \left(\frac{\partial R_{xx}}{\partial x} + \frac{\partial R_{yx}}{\partial y} + \frac{\partial R_{zx}}{\partial z} \right)$$

$$- \frac{\partial P}{\partial x} + \rho g_x \qquad (1\text{-}36)$$

The differentiations in Equation (1–36) can be carried out to give

$$\rho\left(\frac{\partial v_x}{\partial t} + v_x \frac{\partial v_x}{\partial x} + v_y \frac{\partial v_x}{\partial y} + v_z \frac{\partial v_x}{\partial z} \right) = - v_x \left[\frac{\partial \rho}{\partial t} + \frac{\partial (\rho v_x)}{\partial x} + \frac{\partial (\rho v_y)}{\partial y} \right.$$

$$\left. + \frac{\partial (\rho v_z)}{\partial z} \right] - \left(\frac{\partial R_{xx}}{\partial x} + \frac{\partial R_{yx}}{\partial y} + \frac{\partial R_{zx}}{\partial z} \right) - \frac{\partial P}{\partial x} + \rho g_x \qquad (1\text{-}37)$$

The first term on the right-hand side of Equation (1–37) is zero because of the equation of continuity [Equation (1–30)]. In addition, since

$$\frac{D}{Dt} = \frac{\partial}{\partial t} + v_x \frac{\partial}{\partial x} + v_y \frac{\partial}{\partial y} + v_z \frac{\partial}{\partial z} = \frac{\partial}{\partial t} + \mathbf{v} \cdot \boldsymbol{\nabla}$$

Equation (1–37) can be written as

$$\rho \frac{Dv_x}{Dt} = -\left(\frac{\partial R_{xx}}{\partial x} + \frac{\partial R_{yx}}{\partial y} + \frac{\partial R_{zx}}{\partial z} \right) - \frac{\partial P}{\partial x} + \rho g_x \qquad (1\text{-}38)$$

Equation (1–38) is completely general and applies to both compressible and non-Newtonian viscous fluids in isothermal flow. Unfortunately, this equation cannot be solved for turbulent flow. However, it can be solved for laminar flow, provided simplifying conditions are introduced.

For a liquid of constant density ρ and constant viscosity μ in laminar flow, Equation (1–38) can be written as

$$\rho \frac{Dv_x}{Dt} = \mu\left(\frac{\partial^2 v_x}{\partial x^2} + \frac{\partial^2 v_x}{\partial y^2} + \frac{\partial^2 v_x}{\partial z^2}\right) - \frac{\partial P}{\partial x} + \rho g_x \qquad (1-39)$$

The transformation of Equation (1–38) to Equation (1–39) is fairly lengthy; also, the details are of limited interest. However, a description of the derivation can be found in a number of texts.[1,2,6]

Equations similar to Equation(1–39) can be written for the y and z components of momentum as follows:

$$\rho \frac{Dv_y}{Dt} = \mu\left(\frac{\partial^2 v_y}{\partial x^2} + \frac{\partial^2 v_y}{\partial y^2} + \frac{\partial^2 v_y}{\partial z^2}\right) - \frac{\partial P}{\partial y} + \rho g_y \qquad (1-40)$$

for the y component and

$$\rho \frac{Dv_z}{Dt} = \mu\left(\frac{\partial^2 v_z}{\partial x^2} + \frac{\partial^2 v_z}{\partial y^2} + \frac{\partial^2 v_z}{\partial z^2}\right) - \frac{\partial P}{\partial z} + \rho g_z \qquad (1-41)$$

for the z component.

Since the velocity and gravitational acceleration vectors can be written, respectively, in terms of their components as follows:

$$\mathbf{v} = \mathbf{i}v_x + \mathbf{j}v_y + \mathbf{k}v_z$$

and

$$\mathbf{g} = \mathbf{i}g_x + \mathbf{j}g_y + \mathbf{k}g_z$$

and since

$$\nabla P = \mathbf{i}\frac{\partial P}{\partial x} + \mathbf{j}\frac{\partial P}{\partial y} + \mathbf{k}\frac{\partial P}{\partial z}$$

Equations (1–39), (1–40) and (1–41) can be combined to give the equation

$$\rho \frac{D\mathbf{v}}{Dt} = \mu\nabla^2\mathbf{v} - \nabla P + \rho\mathbf{g} \qquad (1-42)$$

Equations (1–39), (1–40), (1–41) and (1–42) are the modified Navier-Stokes equations for liquids in laminar flow, having a constant density and viscosity.

Transformation of Coordinate Systems

Consider the transformation of (x,y,z) coordinates to a new coordinate system (x_1,x_2,x_3) where

$$x = f_1\,(x_1,x_2,x_3)$$
$$y = f_2\,(x_1,x_2,x_3)$$
$$z = f_3\,(x_1,x_2,x_3)$$

Assume orthogonal coordinates, i.e., the coordinate curves x_1, x_2 and x_3, are mutually perpendicular at each point in space. The x_1 curve is the curve generated when x_2 and x_3 are held constant. Therefore,

$$\mathbf{i}_1\cdot\mathbf{i}_2 = 0$$
$$\mathbf{i}_1\cdot\mathbf{i}_3 = 0$$
$$\mathbf{i}_2\cdot\mathbf{i}_3 = 0$$

where $\mathbf{i}_1$, $\mathbf{i}_2$ and $\mathbf{i}_3$ are unit vectors along the x_1, x_2 and x_3 curves, respectively.

Consider the position vector $\mathbf{r}$ of a point P in Figure 1–6.

$$\frac{\partial \mathbf{r}}{\partial x_1} = \frac{\partial \mathbf{r}}{\partial s_1}\frac{ds_1}{dx_1} = \mathbf{i}_1\left(\frac{ds_1}{dx_1}\right)$$

Since the absolute value of $d\mathbf{r}$, i.e., $|d\mathbf{r}|$, $= ds_1$ in the limit, where s_1 is the arc length along the x_1 curve, then

$$\frac{\partial \mathbf{r}}{\partial x_1} = \mathbf{i}_1\,h_1 \text{ where } h_1 = \frac{ds_1}{dx_1} = \left|\frac{\partial \mathbf{r}}{\partial x_1}\right|$$

and

$$h_k = \frac{ds_k}{dx_k} \text{ where } k = 1,2,3$$

h is a measure of how much a coordinate system stretches. All three h's are unity in the Cartesian system. Therefore, since

$$\frac{d\mathbf{r}}{ds} = \frac{\partial \mathbf{r}}{\partial x_1}\frac{dx_1}{ds} + \frac{\partial \mathbf{r}}{\partial x_2}\frac{dx_2}{ds} + \frac{\partial \mathbf{r}}{\partial x_3}\frac{dx_3}{ds}$$

where s is the arc length along a curve in any direction, then

$$\frac{d\mathbf{r}}{ds} = \mathbf{i}_1 h_1\frac{dx_1}{ds} + \mathbf{i}_2 h_2\frac{dx_2}{ds} + \mathbf{i}_3 h_3\frac{dx_3}{ds}$$

or

$$d\mathbf{r} = \mathbf{i}_1 h_1\, dx_1 + \mathbf{i}_2 h_2\, dx_2 + \mathbf{i}_3 h_3\, dx_3$$

Consider a scalar quantity q. In Cartesian coordinates the following equations can be written:

$$\nabla q = \mathbf{i}\frac{\partial q}{\partial x} + \mathbf{j}\frac{\partial q}{\partial y} + \mathbf{k}\frac{\partial q}{\partial z}$$

and

$$d\mathbf{r} = \mathbf{i}\, dx + \mathbf{j}\, dy + \mathbf{k}\, dz$$

Therefore,

$$\nabla q \cdot d\mathbf{r} = \frac{\partial q}{\partial x}\, dx + \frac{\partial q}{\partial y}\, dy + \frac{\partial q}{\partial z}\, dz$$

since $\mathbf{i}\cdot\mathbf{i} = \mathbf{j}\cdot\mathbf{j} = \mathbf{k}\cdot\mathbf{k} = 1$ and $\mathbf{i}\cdot\mathbf{j} = \mathbf{i}\cdot\mathbf{k} = \mathbf{j}\cdot\mathbf{k} = 0$. Since

$$dq = \frac{\partial q}{\partial x}\, dx + \frac{\partial q}{\partial y}\, dy + \frac{\partial q}{\partial z}\, dz$$

therefore

$$dq = \nabla q \cdot d\mathbf{r}$$

Write

$$\nabla q = \mathbf{i}_1\lambda_1 + \mathbf{i}_2\lambda_2 + \mathbf{i}_3\lambda_3$$

in terms of the new coordinate system. Since

$$d\mathbf{r} = \mathbf{i}_1 h_1\, dx_1 + \mathbf{i}_2 h_2\, dx_2 + \mathbf{i}_3 h_3\, dx_3$$

and

$$dq = \frac{\partial q}{\partial x_1}\, dx_1 + \frac{\partial q}{\partial x_2}\, dx_2 + \frac{\partial q}{\partial x_3}\, dx_3$$

in terms of the new coordinate system, the following equation can be written

$$dq = \nabla q \cdot d\mathbf{r} = \lambda_1 h_1\, dx_1 + \lambda_2 h_2\, dx_2 + \lambda_3 h_3\, dx_3$$

$$= \frac{\partial q}{\partial x_1}\, dx_1 + \frac{\partial q}{\partial x_2}\, dx_2 + \frac{\partial q}{\partial x_3}\, dx_3$$

i.e.,

$$\frac{\partial q}{\partial x_k} = \lambda_k h_k \text{ or } \lambda_k = \frac{1}{h_k}\frac{\partial q}{\partial x_k}$$

Therefore,

$$\nabla = \frac{\mathbf{i}_1}{h_1}\frac{\partial}{\partial x_1} + \frac{\mathbf{i}_2}{h_2}\frac{\partial}{\partial x_2} + \frac{\mathbf{i}_3}{h_3}\frac{\partial}{\partial x_3} \qquad (1\text{-}43)$$

By other vector manipulations,[3] it may be shown that

$$\nabla \cdot \mathbf{v} = \frac{1}{h_1 h_2 h_3} \left[\frac{\partial (h_2 h_3 v_1)}{\partial x_1} + \frac{\partial (h_3 h_1 v_2)}{\partial x_2} + \frac{\partial (h_1 h_2 v_3)}{\partial x_3} \right] \qquad (1\text{-}44)$$

where v_1, v_2 and v_3 are the scalar components of the vector $\mathbf{v}$ in the 1, 2 and 3 directions.

$$\nabla^2 = \frac{1}{h_1 h_2 h_3} \left[\frac{\partial}{\partial x_1} \left(\frac{h_2 h_3}{h_1} \frac{\partial}{\partial x_1} \right) + \frac{\partial}{\partial x_2} \left(\frac{h_3 h_1}{h_2} \frac{\partial}{\partial x_2} \right) \right.$$

$$\left. + \frac{\partial}{\partial x_3} \left(\frac{h_1 h_2}{h_3} \frac{\partial}{\partial x_3} \right) \right] \qquad (1\text{-}45)$$

and

$$\nabla \times \mathbf{v} = \frac{1}{h_1 h_2 h_3} \begin{vmatrix} \mathbf{i}_1 h_1 & \mathbf{i}_2 h_2 & \mathbf{i}_3 h_3 \\ \dfrac{\partial}{\partial x_1} & \dfrac{\partial}{\partial x_2} & \dfrac{\partial}{\partial x_3} \\ h_1 v_1 & h_2 v_2 & h_3 v_3 \end{vmatrix} \qquad (1\text{-}46)$$

In the expressions for ∇, ∇^2 and $\nabla \times \mathbf{v}$, the h's cannot be factored out since they are functions of all three coordinates. In the Cartesian system, $h_1 = h_2 = h_3 = 1$.

Cylindrical Coordinates

Consider the transformation of (x, y, z) coordinates to a new coordinate system (x_1, x_2, x_3): where $x_1 = r$, $x_2 = \theta$ and $x_3 = x$. In this system, r is the distance from the x axis and should not be confused with the position vector $\mathbf{r}$ of Figure 1-6. Since

$$x = f_1 (x_1, x_2, x_3) = r \cos \theta$$
$$y = f_2 (x_1, x_2, x_3) = r \sin \theta$$
$$z = f_3 (x_1, x_2, x_3) = x$$

Then

$$\mathbf{r} = \mathbf{i}x + \mathbf{j}y + \mathbf{k}z = \mathbf{i}r \cos \theta + \mathbf{j}r \sin \theta + \mathbf{k}x$$

Therefore,

$$\frac{\partial \mathbf{r}}{\partial x_1} = \frac{\partial \mathbf{r}}{\partial r} = \mathbf{i} \cos \theta + \mathbf{j} \sin \theta = \mathbf{i}_1 h_1$$

$$\frac{\partial \mathbf{r}}{\partial x_2} = \frac{\partial \mathbf{r}}{\partial \theta} = - \mathbf{i}r \sin \theta + \mathbf{j}r \cos \theta = \mathbf{i}_2 h_2$$

$$\frac{\partial \mathbf{r}}{\partial x_3} = \frac{\partial \mathbf{r}}{\partial x} = \mathbf{k} = \mathbf{i}_3 h_3$$

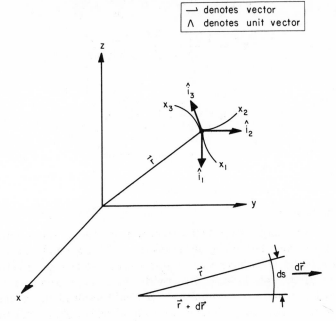

Figure 1-6. Graphical representation of the transformation of orthogonal coordinates.

Since

$$h_1 = \left| \frac{\partial \mathbf{r}}{\partial x_1} \right|, \text{ etc.,}$$

and the absolute value $|\mathbf{a}|$ of a vector $\mathbf{a} = \mathbf{i}a_x + \mathbf{j}a_y + \mathbf{k}a_z$ is the square root of $a_x{}^2 + a_y{}^2 + a_z{}^2$, then $h_1 = 1, h_2 = r$, and $h_3 = 1$. Therefore,

$$\mathbf{i}_1 = \mathbf{i} \cos \theta + \mathbf{j} \sin \theta$$

$$\mathbf{i}_2 = -\mathbf{i} \sin \theta + \mathbf{j} \cos \theta$$

$$\mathbf{i}_3 = \mathbf{k}$$

Therefore, writing r, θ and x for the subscripts 1, 2 and 3 in Equation (1–43) through Equation (1–46) gives the following equations for cylindrical coordinates:

$$\nabla = \mathbf{i}_r \frac{\partial}{\partial r} + \mathbf{i}_\theta \frac{1}{r} \frac{\partial}{\partial \theta} + \mathbf{i}_x \frac{\partial}{\partial x} \tag{1–47}$$

$$\nabla \cdot \mathbf{v} = \frac{1}{r} \frac{\partial}{\partial r} (r \, v_r) + \frac{1}{r} \frac{\partial v_\theta}{\partial \theta} + \frac{\partial v_x}{\partial x} \qquad (1\text{--}48)$$

$$\nabla^2 = \frac{1}{r} \frac{\partial}{\partial r} \left(r \frac{\partial}{\partial r} \right) + \frac{1}{r^2} \frac{\partial^2}{\partial \theta^2} \frac{\partial^2}{\partial x^2} \qquad (1\text{--}49)$$

and

$$\nabla \times \mathbf{v} = \frac{1}{r} \begin{vmatrix} \mathbf{i}_r & r\mathbf{i}_\theta & \mathbf{i}_x \\ \frac{\partial}{\partial r} & \frac{\partial}{\partial \theta} & \frac{\partial}{\partial x} \\ v_r & rv_\theta & v_x \end{vmatrix} \qquad (1\text{--}50)$$

The Boundary Layer

Although only liquids are being treated in this text, the following discussion on the boundary layer also holds true for the general case of fluids.

When a liquid flows over a solid surface, its velocity in direct contact with the surface must be zero. Otherwise, the velocity gradient would be infinite at this point and an infinite shear would result at the solid surface. This is readily seen with reference to a liquid which obeys Newton's law of momentum transfer:

$$R_{zx} = -\mu \frac{dv_x}{dz} \qquad (1\text{--}10)$$

It should be noted with reference to the above equation that if the liquid has no viscosity, i.e., $\mu = 0$, then the limitation of no slip at the wall does not apply. Liquids with no viscosity are the so-called ideal liquids which in practice do not exist. However, when dealing with liquids of low viscosity, it is sometimes convenient to consider them as ideal liquids in regions not directly affected by a solid surface.

In the region of immediate proximity to the solid surface, the liquid is directly affected by the solid surface. This region is known as the boundary layer. Prandtl[5] considered a liquid flowing over a solid surface as being divided into two regions: one directly affected by the surface and one unaffected by the surface.

In general, the boundary layer is thin, and since for a Newtonian liquid the shear stress is given by Equation (1–10), its magnitude at a solid surface can be quite high. Outside the boundary layer, velocity gradients and hence shear stresses are small. The concept of the boundary layer leads to a considerable simplification of the theoretical analysis of flow over solid surfaces.

Consider a liquid flowing at a uniform velocity entering a pipe. A boundary layer forms at the pipe wall. This layer grows progressively thicker until it meets the layer from the opposite wall at the axis of the pipe. The thickness of the fully developed boundary layer is thus the radius of the pipe. The type of liquid flow, i.e., streamline or turbulent, in the boundary layer at this point persists in the fully developed flow region. The nature of the fully developed flow in the pipe depends on the density, viscosity and velocity of the flowing liquid and the diameter of the pipe. At first, the flow in the boundary layer is streamline. If the streamline boundary layer has not filled the pipe after a certain distance from the point of entry, the flow starts to become turbulent. However, even after full turbulence develops, a laminar sublayer remains in the immediate region of the pipe wall.

Units

The two most common systems of units in engineering work are the foot pound-mass second system and the foot pound-mass pound-weight second system.

The foot pound-mass second system has a length L, mass M, time T basis. The unit of force is the poundal, defined as that force which will impart an acceleration of 1 ft/sec^2 to a mass of 1 lb. In this system, 1 horsepower (hp) = 17,710 ft poundals/sec.

The foot pound-mass pound-weight second system has a length L, mass M, force F, time T basis. In this system,

$$1 \text{ lb weight} \div g_c = 1 \text{ poundal}$$

where g_c is a constant having the dimensions ML/FT^2 and is numerically almost equal to the gravitational acceleration, i.e., 32.2; 1 hp = 550 ft lb$_f$/sec where the pound refers to 1 lb weight or force. The latter is equal to 32.2 poundals.

NOMENCLATURE

a	quantity in Equation (1–21)
b	quantity in Equation (1–21)
E	total energy per unit mass
F	force
g_c	conversion factor, 32.174 lb$_m$ ft/lb$_f$ sec^2
g	gravitational acceleration
h	quantity in Equation (1–43)
h	head
hp	horsepower
h_f	frictional head loss

$\mathbf{i}$ unit vector
$\mathbf{j}$ unit vector
$\mathbf{k}$ unit vector
K_p consistency coefficient in Equation (1–17)
L length
m mass
M mass
n power law index (dimensionless) in Equation (1–17)
P pressure
q a scalar quantity
q heat energy per unit mass
$\mathbf{r}$ position vector
R shear stress
s arc length along a curve
T time
t time
U internal energy per unit mass
v linear velocity
V volume
W work per unit mass
z height
η kinematic viscosity of liquid
θ an angle
λ a scalar quantity
μ viscosity of liquid
ρ density of liquid
∇ vector operator in Equations (1–25), (1–43) and (1–47)

REFERENCES

1. Bennett, C.O., and Myers, J.E., "Momentum, Heat and Mass Transfer," p. 98, New York, McGraw-Hill Book Co. Inc., 1962.
2. Bird, R.B., Stewart, W.E., and Lightfoot, E.N., "Transport Phenomena," p. 80, New York, John Wiley & Sons, Inc., 1960.
3. Hildebrand, F.B., "Advanced Calculus for Applications," p. 302, Englewood Cliffs, N.J., Prentice-Hall Inc., 1962.
4. Holland, F. A., *Chem. Eng.*, **71**, No. 17 (1964).
5. Prandtl, L., *Proc. III International Math. Congress*, Heidelberg (1904).
6. Rohsenow, W.M., and Choi, H.Y., "Heat, Mass and Momentum Transfer," p. 50, Englewood Cliffs, N.J., Prentice-Hall Inc., 1961.
7. Smith, J.M., "Introduction to Chemical Engineering Thermodynamics," p. 6, New York, McGraw-Hill Book Co. Inc., 1949.
8. Wilkinson, W.L., "Non-Newtonian Fluids," p. 56, London, Pergamon Press, 1960.

CHAPTER 2

Newtonian Liquid Flow in Pipelines

Liquid Flow Patterns in a Pipe

The first published work on liquid flow patterns in pipes and tubes was done by Reynolds.[18] He observed the flow patterns of liquids in circular tubes by injecting dye into the moving stream. Reynolds correlated his data by using a dimensionless group N_{Re} later known as the Reynolds number.

$$N_{Re} = \frac{\rho u d_i}{\mu} \tag{2-1}$$

where ρ and μ are the density and the viscosity of the liquid, respectively, d_i is the inside diameter of the tube and u is the mean linear velocity of liquid in the tube. Any consistent system of units can be used in Equation (2-1).

Throughout this text, the mean linear velocity of liquid in a pipe or tube will be represented by the symbol u, while the linear velocity at a point will be written as v.

Reynolds found that as he increased the liquid velocity in the tube, the flow pattern changed from laminar to turbulent at an N_{Re} of about 2100. Other investigators[7] have shown that under certain conditions, e.g., with very smooth pipes, laminar flow can exist at very much higher Reynolds numbers.

It is frequently stated in the literature that turbulent flow is more common than laminar in practical engineering applications. In liquid processing, this is not the case. This is demonstrated in Figure 2-1 which is a plot of viscosity in centipoises (cp) vs inside pipe diameter in inches for a liquid of density 60 lb/cu ft flowing at a typical mean velocity of 5 ft/sec and a Reynolds number of 2100. For example, on this basis, a liquid of density 60 lb/cu ft flowing at a mean velocity of 5 ft/sec inside a pipe with an internal diameter of 3.0 inches is in laminar flow if its viscosity is 60 cp. It is in turbulent flow if its viscosity is 50 cp where 1 cp = 0.000672 lb/ft sec.

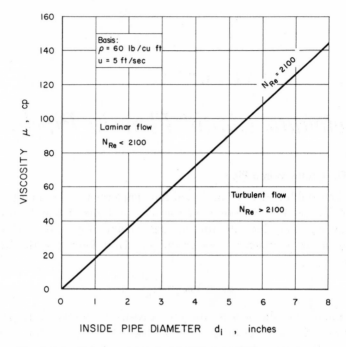

Figure 2-1. Laminar to turbulent flow transition point as a function of viscosity and pipe diameter.

Navier-Stokes Equations Applied to Laminar Liquid Flow in a Pipe

In Chapter 1 it was shown that the modified Navier-Stokes equations for liquids in laminar flow can be conveniently written in the vector form as

$$\rho \frac{D\mathbf{v}}{Dt} = \mu \nabla^2 \mathbf{v} - \nabla P + \rho \mathbf{g} \qquad (1\text{-}42)$$

Consider liquid flowing through a circular pipe with a linear velocity parallel to the axis of the pipe of v_x at a radial distance of r from the center of the pipe. The liquid is assumed to be Newtonian, the rate steady and the flow pattern laminar. Since the vector operator

$$\frac{D}{Dt} = \frac{\partial}{\partial t} + \mathbf{v} \cdot \nabla$$

and the vector operators ∇ and ∇^2 can be written as

$$\nabla = \mathbf{i}_r \frac{\partial}{\partial r} + \mathbf{i}_\theta \frac{1}{r} \frac{\partial}{\partial \theta} + \mathbf{i}_x \frac{\partial}{\partial x} \qquad (1\text{-}47)$$

and

$$\mathbf{\nabla}^2 = \frac{1}{r}\frac{\partial}{\partial r}\left(r\frac{\partial}{\partial r}\right) + \frac{1}{r^2}\frac{\partial^2}{\partial \theta^2} + \frac{\partial^2}{\partial x^2} \qquad (1\text{--}49)$$

in cylindrical coordinates. Equation (1–42) can be written as

$$\rho\left(\frac{\partial v_x}{\partial t} + v_r\frac{\partial v_x}{\partial r} + \frac{v_\theta}{r}\frac{\partial v_x}{\partial \theta} + v_x\frac{\partial v_x}{\partial x}\right) = \mu\left[\frac{1}{r}\frac{\partial}{\partial r}\left(r\frac{\partial v_x}{\partial r}\right) + \frac{1}{r^2}\frac{\partial^2 v_x}{\partial \theta^2}\right.$$
$$\left. + \frac{\partial^2 v_x}{\partial x^2}\right] - \frac{\partial P}{\partial x} + \rho g_x \qquad (2\text{--}2)$$

for the direction parallel to the axis of the pipe.

In Equations 1–47), (1–49) and (2–2), θ is the angle any radial line makes with a fixed radial line. Assume that there is no radial or angular velocity in the liquid, i.e., $v_r = 0$ and $v_\theta = 0$. Thus Equation (2–2) can be written as

$$\rho\left(\frac{\partial v_x}{\partial t} + v_x\frac{\partial v_x}{\partial x}\right) = \mu\left[\frac{1}{r}\frac{\partial}{\partial r}\left(r\frac{\partial v_x}{\partial r}\right) + \frac{\partial^2 v_x}{\partial x^2}\right] - \frac{\partial P}{\partial x} + \rho g_x \qquad (2\text{--}3)$$

Since the flow through the pipe is steady, Equation (2–3) can be further reduced to

$$\mu\left[\frac{1}{r}\frac{\partial}{\partial r}\left(r\frac{\partial v_x}{\partial r}\right)\right] - \frac{\partial P}{\partial x} + \rho g_x = 0 \qquad (2\text{--}4)$$

Consider a long horizontal pipe of length ℓ and inside diameter d_i. Let the pressure drop across the pipe be ΔP. For this case, the gravitational term $g_x = 0$ and Equation (2–4) becomes

$$\mu\left[\frac{1}{r}\frac{\partial}{\partial r}\left(r\frac{\partial v_x}{\partial r}\right)\right] + \frac{\Delta P}{\ell} = 0 \qquad (2\text{--}5)$$

since the pressure gradient $\partial P/\partial x = -\Delta P/\ell$. The negative sign is used with the pressure gradient term since the pressure decreases along the pipe as the distance x increases.

Equation (2–5) can be integrated twice with respect to the radius r to give

$$v_x = -\frac{1}{\mu}\left(\frac{\Delta P}{\ell}\right)\frac{r^2}{4} + C_1\log_e r + C_2 \qquad (2\text{--}6)$$

where C_1 and C_2 are constants.

From the boundary conditions $v_x =$ finite at $r = 0$ and $v_x = 0$ at $r = d_i/2$,

$$C_1 = 0 \text{ and } C_2 = \frac{1}{\mu}\left(\frac{\Delta P}{\ell}\right)\frac{d_i^2}{16}$$

Equation (2–6) can therefore be written as

$$v_x = \left(\frac{\Delta P}{\ell}\right)\frac{d_i^2}{16\mu}[1 - (2r/d_i)^2] \tag{2-7}$$

Equation (2–7) shows the velocity profile to be parabolic for the laminar flow of Newtonian liquids through pipes.

The linear velocity v_x is a maximum at the center of the pipe, i.e., when $r = 0$. Therefore,

$$v_{\max} = \left(\frac{\Delta P}{\ell}\right)\frac{d_i^2}{16\mu} \tag{2-8}$$

The mean linear velocity u of the liquid in the pipe is calculated as follows. Consider an annulus of radius r to $r + dr$ as shown in Figure 2–2. The volumetric rate of flow dQ in the annulus is

$$dQ = 2\pi r\, dr\, v_x = 2\pi\left(\frac{\Delta P}{\ell}\right)\frac{d_i^2}{16\mu}\left(r - \frac{4r^3}{d_i^2}\right)dr \tag{2-9}$$

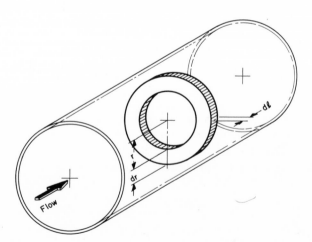

Figure 2-2.   Annulus of flow in a pipe.

The total volumetric flow rate Q through the pipe is obtained by integrating Equation (2–9) between the limits $r = 0$ and $r = d_i/2$ to give

$$Q = \pi\left(\frac{\Delta P}{\ell}\right)\frac{d_i{}^2}{128\mu} \tag{2-10}$$

The mean linear velocity u of the liquid in the pipe is simply the volumetric flow rate Q from Equation (2–10) divided by the cross-sectional flow area in the pipe $\pi d_i{}^2/4$. Therefore,

$$u = \left(\frac{\Delta P}{\ell}\right)\frac{d_i{}^2}{32\mu} \tag{2-11}$$

Equation (2–11) is the well-known Hagen-Poiseuille equation for the steady state streamline flow of Newtonian liquids in pipes and tubes.

Equation (2–7), which gives the linear velocity v_x at any point, and Equation (2–11), which gives the mean linear velocity u for a Newtonian liquid in steady flow in a pipe, can also be derived from a shell momentum balance. It is frequently more convenient to use shell momentum balances rather than the general equations of momentum transfer for steady state flow systems.

Shell Momentum Balance for Laminar Liquid Flow in a Pipe

Consider a liquid in steady state laminar flow in a horizontal circular pipe of length ℓ and inside diameter d_i. A momentum balance can be written as follows on the annular shell of thickness Δr at radius r shown in Figure 2–3:

$$\begin{pmatrix} \text{rate of ac-} \\ \text{cumula-} \\ \text{tion of} \\ \text{momentum} \end{pmatrix} = \begin{pmatrix} \text{rate of ac-} \\ \text{cumula-} \\ \text{tion of} \\ \text{convection} \\ \text{momentum} \end{pmatrix} + \begin{pmatrix} \text{rate of ac-} \\ \text{cumula-} \\ \text{tion of} \\ \text{momentum} \\ \text{due to sur-} \\ \text{face forces} \end{pmatrix} +$$

$$\begin{pmatrix} \text{sum of} \\ \text{forces} \\ \text{on sys-} \\ \text{tem} \end{pmatrix} \tag{2-12}$$

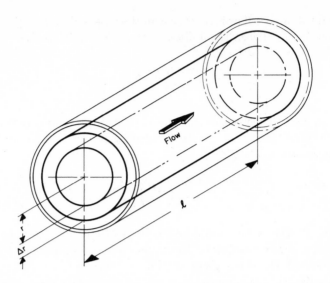

Figure 2-3.   Annular shell in a pipe.

The shell is taken to be the length of the tube ℓ and the end effects are neglected.

For steady state flow, the various terms in Equation (2–12) can be written as follows:

$$\begin{pmatrix} \text{rate of} \\ \text{accumulation} \\ \text{of} \\ \text{momentum} \end{pmatrix} = 0$$

$$\begin{pmatrix} \text{rate of} \\ \text{accumulation} \\ \text{of convection} \\ \text{momentum} \end{pmatrix} = 2\pi r\ \Delta r[v_x(\rho v_x)|_0 - v_x(\rho v_x)|_\ell] = 0$$

$$\begin{pmatrix} \text{rate of} \\ \text{accumulation} \\ \text{of momen-} \\ \text{tum due to} \\ \text{surface forces} \end{pmatrix} = 2\pi r\ell(R_{rx}|_r - R_{rx}|_{r+\Delta r}) \qquad (2\text{–}13)$$

Equation (2–13) can also be written in the form

$$\begin{pmatrix} \text{rate of} \\ \text{accumulation} \\ \text{of momen-} \\ \text{tum due to} \\ \text{surface forces} \end{pmatrix} = 2\pi \ \Delta r \ \ell \ \frac{(rR_{rz}|_r - rR_{rz}|_{r+\Delta r})}{\Delta r}$$

which in the limit $\Delta r \to 0$ becomes

$$\begin{pmatrix} \text{rate of} \\ \text{accumulation} \\ \text{of momen-} \\ \text{tum due to} \\ \text{surface forces} \end{pmatrix} = - \ 2\pi \ \Delta r \ \ell \ \frac{d(rR_{rz})}{dr} \qquad (2\text{--}14)$$

$$\begin{pmatrix} \text{sum of} \\ \text{forces on} \\ \text{system} \end{pmatrix} = 2\pi r \ \Delta r (P|_0 - P|_\ell) = 2\pi r \ \Delta r \ \Delta P \qquad (2\text{--}15)$$

Substitute Equations (2–14) and (2–15) into Equation (2–12) to give

$$- \ 2\pi \ \Delta r \ \ell \ \frac{d(rR_{rz})}{dr} + 2\pi r \ \Delta r \ \Delta P = 0$$

which can be rewritten as

$$\frac{d}{dr} \ (rR_{rz}) = \left(\frac{\Delta P}{\ell} \right) r \qquad (2\text{--}16)$$

Integrate Equation (2–16) to give

$$R_{rz} = \left(\frac{\Delta P}{\ell} \right) \frac{r}{2} + \frac{C}{r}$$

where C is a constant. Since the rate of momentum transfer or shear stress R_{rz} is finite at r = 0, the constant C is zero. Therefore,

$$R_{rz} = \left(\frac{\Delta P}{\ell} \right) \frac{r}{2} \qquad (2\text{--}17)$$

Equation (2–17) gives the rate of momentum transfer or shear stress R_{rz} at a radius r in the pipe.

In the derivation of Equation (2–17), no assumptions have been made about the nature of the liquid. Thus Equation (2–17) is valid for both Newtonian and non-Newtonian liquids.

For flow in a pipe, the rate equation for momentum transfer in Newtonian liquids [Equation (1–10)] can be written as

$$R_{rx} = - \mu \frac{dv_x}{dr} \qquad (2\text{–}18)$$

Substitute Equation (2–18) into Equation (2–17) to give

$$\frac{dv_x}{dr} = - \left(\frac{\Delta P}{\ell} \right) \frac{r}{2\mu}$$

which on integration becomes

$$v_x = - \left(\frac{\Delta P}{\ell} \right) \frac{r^2}{4\mu} + C \qquad (2\text{–}19)$$

Since the linear velocity $v_x = 0$ at $r = d_i/2$, the constant

$$C = \left(\frac{\Delta P}{\ell} \right) \frac{d_i^2}{16\mu}$$

Thus Equation (2–19) can be written in the form

$$v_x = \left(\frac{\Delta P}{\ell} \right) \frac{d_i^2}{16\mu} [1 - (2r/d_i)^2]$$

which is identical with Equation (2–7) derived from the simplified Navier-Stokes equations.

Universal Velocity Distribution for Turbulent Liquid Flow in a Pipe

Consider fully developed turbulent flow inside a circular pipe with a thin laminar sublayer immediately adjacent to the wall. In the laminar sublayer, the shear stress arises from molecular viscosity.

Assume that the shear stress or rate of momentum transfer has a constant value of R throughout the laminar sublayer. Let z be the distance from the wall in a radial direction. In the laminar sublayer, the rate equation for momentum transfer in Newtonian liquids [Equation (1–10)] can be written as

$$R = \mu \frac{dv_x}{dz} \qquad (2\text{–}20)$$

The right-hand side of Equation (2–20) is written with a positive sign since the velocity gradient dv_x/dz is positive.

Since the shear stress R in the laminar sublayer is constant, Equation (2-20) can be integrated to give

$$Rz = \mu v_x + C \tag{2-21}$$

where C is a constant. Since the linear velocity $v_x = 0$ at $z = 0$, the constant C is zero.

Therefore, Equation (2-21) can be rewritten as

$$v_x = \frac{Rz}{\mu} = \frac{Rz}{\rho\eta} \tag{2-22}$$

where η is the kinematic viscosity.

In Equation (2-22), R/ρ is a constant and has the dimensions of velocity squared. Thus a velocity $v^* = \sqrt{R/\rho}$ can be defined. This is commonly called either the friction velocity or the shear stress velocity.

In terms of v^*, Equation (2-22) can be rewritten as

$$\frac{v_x}{v^*} = \frac{v^*z}{\eta} = \frac{\rho v^*z}{\mu} \tag{2-23}$$

A dimensionless velocity can be defined as $v^+ = v_x/v^*$ and a dimensionless distance as $z^+ = v^*z/\eta = \rho v^*z/\mu$. In terms of v^+ and z^+, Equation (2-23) becomes

$$v^+ = z^+$$

The dimensionless distance z^+ has the form of a Reynolds number.

In the laminar sublayer, the velocity increases proportionally to the distance from the wall in contrast to the parabolic profile for fully developed laminar flow in a circular pipe. The equation $v^+ = z^+$ fits the experimental data in the range $0 < z^+ < 5$.

The shear stress in a turbulent liquid is given by Equation (1-12). Since the eddy viscous diffusivity η_e is much greater than the molecular viscous diffusivity η, the shear stress R in the turbulent flow region in the pipe can be written as

$$R = \eta_e\rho\frac{dv_x}{dz} \tag{2-24}$$

where in this case the velocity gradient is positive.

Prandtl[16] made the assumption that in turbulent flow, eddies move around in a similar manner to molecules in a gas. He defined a mixing length L for turbulent flow analogous to the mean free path in the kinetic theory of gases.

It can be shown[1] that

$$\eta_e = L^2 \frac{dv_x}{dz}$$

Therefore, Equation (2-24) can be rewritten as

$$R = \rho L^2 \left(\frac{dv_x}{dz} \right)^2 \tag{2-25}$$

Prandtl also assumed that L is proportional to the distance z away from the solid surface. This is reasonable, since L would have to be zero at the wall.

Write $L = Kz$, where K is a proportionality constant, and substitute into Equation (2-25) to give

$$\frac{R}{\rho} = K^2 z^2 \left(\frac{dv_x}{dz} \right)^2 \tag{2-26}$$

Since the friction velocity $v^* = \sqrt{R/\rho}$, Equation (2-26) can be rewritten in the form

$$v^* = Kz \frac{dv_x}{dz} \tag{2-27}$$

Integrate Equation (2-27) to give

$$v_x = v^* \left(\frac{1}{K} \log_e z + C_1 \right) \tag{2-28}$$

where C_1 is a constant. Equation (2-28) can be rewritten in the modified form

$$v_x = v^* \left(\frac{1}{K} \log_e \frac{\rho v^* z}{\mu} + C_2 \right) \tag{2-29}$$

where C_2 is another constant. Equation (2-29) cannot be applied near the walls, since it gives a linear velocity $v_x = -\infty$ instead of $v_x = 0$ at the wall.

In terms of $v^+ = v_x/v^*$ and $z^+ = \rho v^* z/\mu$, Equation (2-29) can be rewritten as

$$v^+ = \frac{1}{K} \log_e z^+ + C \tag{2-30}$$

where C is a constant which differs from C_1 and C_2.

Equation (2-30) fits the experimental data for turbulent flow in smooth round pipes for $z^+ > 30$ when written in the form

$$v^+ = 2.5 \log_e z^+ + 5.5 \tag{2-31}$$

For the buffer region $5 < z^+ < 30$, the appropriate equation is

$$v^+ = 5.0 \log_e z^+ - 3.05 \tag{2-32}$$

Equations (2–31) and (2–32) and the equation $v^+ = z^+$ enable the velocity distribution to be calculated for turbulent flow in a pipe.[2] These equations can also be used to calculate the velocity distribution over a plane surface. They are only approximate and lead to discontinuities at $z^+ = 5$ and $z^+ = 30$.

Pressure Drop Calculations in Pipelines

Consider a liquid flowing with a mean linear velocity u through a pipe of length ℓ and inside diameter d_i. Let ΔP be the pressure drop across the length of pipe ℓ and let R be the shear stress per unit area at the pipe wall. Assume that there is no slip at the wall.

A force balance over the pipe gives

$$\Delta P \, \pi \frac{d_i{}^2}{4} = R\ell\pi d_i \tag{2-33}$$

which reduces to

$$\Delta P = 4R \frac{\ell}{d_i} \tag{2-34}$$

Equation (2–34) can be rewritten in the form

$$\Delta P = 8\left(\frac{R}{\rho u^2}\right) \left(\frac{\ell}{d_i}\right) \left(\frac{\rho u^2}{2}\right) \tag{2-35}$$

where $R/\rho u^2$ is the dimensionless basic friction factor. Equations (2–34) and (2–35) are valid for both steady state laminar and turbulent flow in circular pipes and tubes.

For laminar flow, experimental investigations[3] have shown the basic friction factor to be related to the Reynolds number by the equation

$$\frac{R}{\rho u^2} = \frac{8}{N_{Re}} = \frac{8\mu}{\rho u d_i} \tag{2-36}$$

The substitution of the experimentally determined Equation (2–36) into Equation (2–35) gives

$$u = \left(\frac{\Delta P}{\ell}\right) \frac{d_i^2}{32\mu} \tag{2-11}$$

which is the Hagen-Poiseuille equation for the steady state streamline flow of Newtonian liquids in pipes and tubes. This equation was previously derived from the simplified Navier-Stokes equations. Thus the Hagen-Poiseuille solution of the Navier-Stokes equations is in agreement with experimental data.

Equation (2–36) shows that for laminar flow, the basic friction factor depends only on the value of the Reynolds number and not on the roughness of the pipe. In contrast, the basic friction factor for turbulent flow depends on both the Reynolds number and a dimensionless roughness factor ϵ/d_i where ϵ is a linear quantity representing the roughness of the pipe surface. Values of ϵ for various kinds of pipes are given in Table 2–1.[6]

For turbulent flow in smooth circular pipes, the basic friction factor is approximately related to the Reynolds number[4] by the equation

$$\frac{R}{\rho u^2} = \frac{0.0396}{N_{Re}^{0.25}} \tag{2-37}$$

Equation (2–37) is an empirical equation which holds for Reynolds numbers up to 10^5.

A plot of the basic friction factor $R/\rho u^2$ vs the Reynolds number N_{Re} for pipeline flow is shown in Figure 2–4. This plot covers the laminar, transition and turbulent flow regions. In the turbulent flow region, the friction factor increases with pipe roughness.

The pressure drop over a length of pipe is obtained as follows:

(1) Calculate the dimensionless Reynolds number $N_{Re} = \rho u d_i/\mu$ in the pipe, knowing the density ρ, viscosity μ and mean linear velocity u of the liquid and the inside diameter d_i of the pipe.

TABLE 2–1 Roughness of Pipe Surfaces[6]

	Values of Absolute Roughness, ϵ (ft)
Drawn tubing	0.000005
Commercial steel and wrought iron	0.00015
Asphalted cast iron	0.0004
Galvanized iron	0.0005
Cast iron	0.00085
Wood stave	0.0006–0.003
Concrete	0.001–0.01
Riveted steel	0.003–0.03

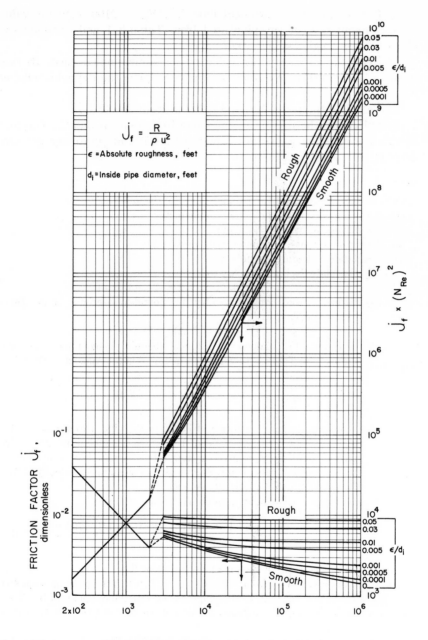

Figure 2-4. Friction factor vs Reynolds number chart.

(2) If the liquid is in turbulent flow, i.e., $N_{Re} > 2100$, read the value of the roughness ϵ for the pipe used from Table 2–1 and calculate the dimensionless roughness factor ϵ/d_i.

(3) Read the corresponding value of the dimensionless basic friction factor $R/\rho u^2$ from Figure 2–4 for the known value of the Reynolds number N_{Re}.

(4) Calculate the terms ℓ/d_i and $\rho u^2/2$ in Equation (2–35).

(5) Substitute the friction factor value from step (3) and the ℓ/d_i and $\rho u^2/2$ values from step (4) into Equation (2–35) and obtain the pressure drop ΔP over a length of pipe ℓ.

EXAMPLE

Calculate the pressure drop in poundals/sq ft for the following system:
(1) A 100 ft long, 2 inch schedule 40 commercial steel pipe.
(2) Liquid transfer rate, 40 U.S. gpm.
(3) Liquid of viscosity 10 cp and specific gravity 1.2.
The calculation procedure is as follows:
(1) (a) Calculate the liquid density to be
$$\rho = 62.4 \times 1.2 = 74.9 \text{ lb/cu ft}$$
(b) Estimate the liquid viscosity in pound-foot-second units. Since 1 cp = 0.000672 lb/ft sec,
$$10 \text{ cp} = 0.00672 \text{ lb/ft sec}$$
(c) Read the inside diameter of a 2 inch schedule 40 steel pipe to be 2.067 inches from Table A–1, which can be found in the Appendix. Therefore,
$$d_i = \frac{2.067}{12} = 0.1725 \text{ ft}$$

(d) Calculate the linear velocity of liquid in the pipe. From Table A–1, a mean linear velocity of liquid of 1 ft/sec in a 2 inch schedule 40 steel pipe is given by a volumetric flow rate of 10.45 U.S. gpm. Thus a volumetric flow rate of 40 U.S. gpm gives a mean linear velocity of 3.83 ft/sec in a 2 inch schedule 40 steel pipe.
(e) Calculate the Reynolds number N_{Re} in the pipe to be

$$N_{Re} = \frac{\rho u d_i}{\mu} = \frac{(74.9 \text{ lb/cu ft}) (3.83 \text{ ft/sec}) (0.1725 \text{ ft})}{0.00672} = 7360$$

Thus the liquid in the pipe is in turbulent flow.
(2) Read the roughness ϵ from Table 2–1 to be 0.00015 ft for commercial steel pipe. Since the 2 inch schedule 40 steel pipe has an internal diameter of 0.1725 ft, calculate the dimensionless roughness factor ϵ/d_i to be 0.00015 ft/0.1725 ft = 0.000869.
(3) Read the basic friction factor $R/\rho u^2 = 0.0042$ from Figure 2–4 corresponding to $N_{Re} = 7360$ and $\epsilon/d_i = 0.000869$.

(4)   Calculate the dimensionless ℓ/d_i ratio.

$$\ell/d_i = \frac{100 \text{ ft}}{0.1725 \text{ ft}} = 580$$

Calculate the term $\rho u^2/2$.

$$\frac{\rho u^2}{2} = \frac{(74.9 \text{ lb/cu ft}) (3.83 \text{ ft/sec})^2}{2}$$

$$= 550 \text{ lb/ft sec}^2 = 550 \text{ poundals/sq ft}$$

(5)   Substitute $R/\rho u^2$, ℓ/d_i and $\rho u^2/2$ into Equation (2–35) to give the pressure drop

$$\Delta P = 8 \ (0.0042) \ (580) \ (550) = 10{,}700 \text{ poundals/sq ft}$$

Equation (2–35) can be rewitten in terms of the frictional head loss h_f as

$$h_f = 8\left(\frac{R}{\rho u^2}\right) \left(\frac{\ell}{d_i}\right) \left(\frac{u^2}{2g}\right) \tag{2–38}$$

where g is the gravitational acceleration.[5] If the linear velocity u is in ft/sec and g is in ft/sec^2, the frictional head loss h_f is in ft.

EXAMPLE

Calculate the frictional head loss h_f over the pipe length in the previous example.
(1)   Calculate the velocity head $u^2/2g$.

$$u = 3.83 \text{ ft/sec and } g = 32.2 \text{ ft/sec}^2$$

Therefore,

$$u^2/2g = 0.228 \text{ ft.}$$

(2)   Substitute $R/\rho u^2 = 0.0042$, $\ell/d_i = 580$, and $u^2/2g = 0.228$ ft into Equation (2–38) to give

$$h_f = 8(0.0042) \ (580) \ (0.228) = 4.45 \text{ ft}$$

Frequently the pressure drop is required in psi. For this case, equation (2–35) is rewritten in the form

$$\Delta P \text{ (psi)} = \frac{8}{144} \left(\frac{R}{\rho u^2}\right) \left(\frac{\ell}{d_i}\right) \left(\frac{\rho u^2}{2g_c}\right) \tag{2–39}$$

where the density ρ is in lb/cu ft, the mean linear velocity u is in ft/sec and the constant g_c is approximately 32.2.

The basic friction factor $R/\rho u^2$ is more conveniently written as j_f. Figure 2–4 contains a plot of $j_f(N_{Re})^2$ vs N_{Re}. This plot enables the mean linear velocity u in a pipe to be estimated for a given pressure drop, since the term $j_f(N_{Re})^2$ does not contain velocity.

$$j_f(N_{Re})^2 = \frac{R}{\rho u^2}\left(\frac{\rho u d_i}{\mu}\right)^2 = \frac{R\rho d_i^2}{\mu^2} \tag{2-40}$$

Combine Equations (2–34) and (2–40) to give

$$j_f(N_{Re})^2 = \frac{\Delta P\rho d_i^3}{4\ell\mu^2} \tag{2-41}$$

If ΔP, ρ, d_i, ℓ and μ in Equation (2–41) are all known, the dimensionless term $j_f(N_{Re})^2$ may be calculated. If the dimensionless roughness factor ϵ/d_i for the pipe is also known, the corresponding Reynolds number $N_{Re} = \rho u d_i/\mu$ can be read from Figure 2–4. The mean linear velocity u can then be calculated from N_{Re} knowing ρ, d_i, and μ.

EXAMPLE

For the pipe system in the previous example, calculate the mean liquid velocity u ft/sec in the pipe, knowing the pressure drop ΔP to be 10,700 poundals/sq ft. In this system,

> liquid density $\rho = 74.9$ lb/cu ft
> liquid viscosity $\mu = 0.00672$ lb/ft sec
> pipe length $\ell = 100$ ft
> inside pipe diameter $d_i = 0.1725$ ft
> the dimensionless roughness factor $\epsilon/d_i = 0.000869$

The calculation procedure is as follows:
(1) Calculate the dimensionless factor

$$j_f(N_{Re})^2 = \frac{\Delta P\rho d_i^3}{4\ell\mu^2}$$

Therefore,

$$\frac{\Delta P\rho d_i^3}{4\ell\mu^2} = \frac{(10,700 \text{ poundals/sq ft}) (74.9 \text{ lb/cu ft}) (0.1725 \text{ ft})^3}{4 (100 \text{ ft}) (0.00672 \text{ lb/ft sec})^2}$$

$$= 2.27 \times 10^5$$

(2) Read the Reynolds number $N_{Re} = 7400$ from Figure 2–4 for $j_f(N_{Re})^2 = 2.27 \times 10^5$ and $\epsilon/d_i = 0.000869$.
(3) Calculate the mean linear velocity u ft/sec from the Reynolds number N_{Re}. Since $N_{Re} = \rho u d_i/\mu$,

$$u = N_{Re}(\mu/\rho d_i)$$

Therefore,

$$u = \frac{(7400) (0.00672 \text{ lb/ft sec})}{(74.9 \text{ lb/cu ft}) (0.1725 \text{ ft})}$$

$$= 3.85 \text{ ft/sec}$$

The slight difference between this value and the assumed velocity in the previous example is due to error in reading the graph in Figure 2–4.

Figure 2–5 shows a plot of $N_{Re}/(\epsilon/d_i)$ vs $8j_f(N_{Re})^2(\epsilon/d_i)^3$. This graph is the work of Ramalho, Tiller and Berry.[17] It enables the inside pipe diameter d_i to be calculated for a given pressure drop ΔP and volumetric flow rate $Q = \pi d_i^2 u/4$.

$$\frac{N_{Re}}{\epsilon/d_i} = \frac{\rho u d_i^2}{\mu \epsilon} = \frac{4Q\rho}{\pi \mu \epsilon} \tag{2-42}$$

$$8j_f(N_{Re})^2 (\epsilon/d_i)^3 = \frac{2\Delta P \rho \epsilon^3}{\ell \mu^2} \tag{2-43}$$

EXAMPLE

For the pipe system in the previous example, calculate the inside pipe diameter d_i in ft, knowing the pressure drop ΔP to be 10,700 poundals/sq ft and the volumetric flow rate Q of the liquid in the pipe to be 40 U.S. gpm or 0.0892 cu ft/sec. For this system,

liquid density $\rho = 74.9$ lb/cu ft
liquid viscosity $\mu = 0.00672$ lb/ft sec
pipe length $\ell = 100$ ft
the roughness $\epsilon = 0.00015$ ft or 1.5×10^{-4} ft

The calculation procedure is as follows:

(1) Calculate the dimensionless factor

$$\frac{N_{Re}}{\epsilon/d_i} = \frac{\rho u d_i^2}{\mu \epsilon} = \frac{4Q\rho}{\pi \mu \epsilon}$$

Therefore,

$$\frac{4Q\rho}{\pi \mu \epsilon} = \frac{4(0.0892 \text{ cu ft/sec}) (74.9 \text{ lb/cu ft})}{3.14 (0.00672 \text{ lb/ft sec}) (1.5 \times 10^{-4} \text{ ft})}$$

$$= 8.43 \times 10^{-6}$$

(2) Calculate the dimensionless factor

$$8j_f(N_{Re})^2 (\epsilon/d_i)^3 = \frac{2\Delta P \rho \epsilon^3}{\ell \mu^2}$$

Therefore,

$$\frac{2\Delta P \rho \epsilon^3}{\ell \mu^2} = \frac{2(10,700 \text{ poundals/sq ft}) (74.9 \text{ lb/cu ft}) (1.5 \times 10^{-4} \text{ ft})^3}{(100 \text{ ft}) (0.00672 \text{ lb/ft sec})^2}$$

$$= 1.195 \times 10^{-3}$$

(3) For $N_{Re}/(\epsilon/d_i) = 8.43 \times 10^6$ and $8j_f(N_{Re})^2 (\epsilon/d_i)^3 = 1.195 \times 10^{-3}$, read the value of $\epsilon/d_i = 0.00087$ from Figure 2–5.

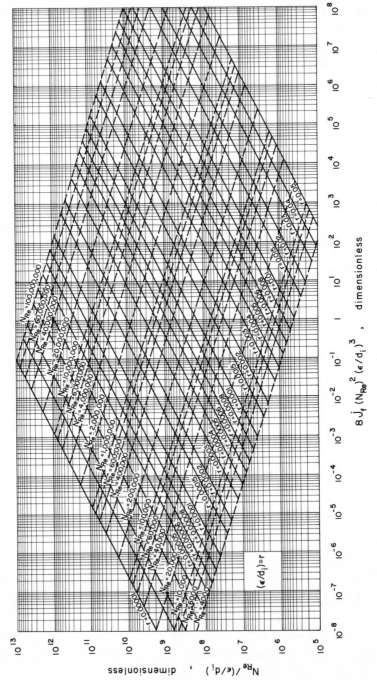

Figure 2-5.   Modified friction factor vs Reynolds number chart.[17]

(4) Since $\epsilon = 0.00015$ ft, calculate the inside pipe diameter d_i to be $d_i = 0.00015/0.00087 = 0.1725$ ft. Therefore, use a 2 inch schedule 40 steel pipe.

Two other dimensionless friction factors are in common use besides the basic friction factor j_f. These are the Fanning friction factor f which equals $2j_f$ and a friction factor F which equals $8j_f$. The friction factor F is widely used by equipment supply companies. In terms of the friction factors j_f, f and F, the appropriate equations for calculating the frictional head loss h_f in a pipe are, respectively:

$$h_f = 8j_f \left(\frac{\ell}{d_i}\right)\left(\frac{u^2}{2g}\right) \qquad (2\text{-}44)$$

$$h_f = 4f \left(\frac{\ell}{d_i}\right)\left(\frac{u^2}{2g}\right) \qquad (2\text{-}45)$$

and

$$h_f = F \left(\frac{\ell}{d_i}\right)\left(\frac{u^2}{2g}\right) \qquad (2\text{-}46)$$

So far, only the pressure drop in straight lengths of circular pipe has been discussed. The pressure drop in pipelines containing valves and fittings can be obtained in the same way as already described by using the equivalent lengths listed in Table 4–1.

The corrections for pipe entrance and exit losses can be calculated from Figure 2–6 for Newtonian liquids.

Comparison of Velocity Profiles in Laminar and Turbulent Flow in Pipes

Combine Equations (2–7) and (2–8) for steady state laminar flow in a circular pipe to give

$$\frac{v_x}{v_{\max}} = 1 - \left(\frac{2r}{d_i}\right)^2 \qquad (2\text{-}47)$$

Combine Equations (2–8) and (2–11) for steady state laminar liquid flow in a circular pipe to give

$$\frac{u}{v_{\max}} = 0.5 \qquad (2\text{-}48)$$

Equation (2–47) gives the linear velocity at any radial position in the pipe v_x in terms of the maximum linear velocity $v_{\max}$ at the pipe center. Equation (2–48) gives the mean linear velocity u in the pipe in terms of the maximum linear velocity $v_{\max}$ at the pipe center.

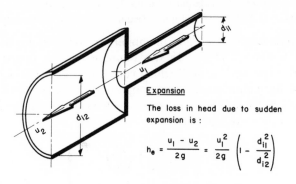

Expansion

The loss in head due to sudden expansion is:

$$h_e = \frac{u_1 - u_2}{2g} = \frac{u_1^2}{2g}\left(1 - \frac{d_{i1}^2}{d_{i2}^2}\right)$$

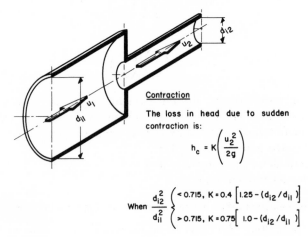

Contraction

The loss in head due to sudden contraction is:

$$h_c = K\left(\frac{u_2^2}{2g}\right)$$

When $\dfrac{d_{i2}^2}{d_{i1}^2}\begin{cases} < 0.715, \ K = 0.4\left[1.25 - (d_{i2}/d_{i1})\right] \\ > 0.715, \ K = 0.75\left[1.0 - (d_{i2}/d_{i1})\right] \end{cases}$

Figure 2-6. Expansion and contraction head losses for
liquids in pipes.

For steady state turbulent liquid flow in a pipe, the corresponding equations to Equations (2–47) and (2–48) are

$$\frac{v_x}{v_{max}} = \left(\frac{d_i - 2r}{d_i}\right)^{1/7} = \left(\frac{2z}{d_i}\right)^{1/7} \tag{2–49}$$

and

$$\frac{u}{v_{max}} = 0.8 \tag{2–50}$$

respectively, where z is the distance from the pipe wall.

Equation (2–49) was found to fit the experimental data of Nikuradse[14,15] on the radial velocity distribution for turbulent flow in a pipe, with a fair degree of accuracy. This equation is known as the one-seventh power velocity distribution equation for turbulent flow.

A comparison of Equations (2–48) and (2–50) illustrates the flattened velocity profile of turbulent flow relative to laminar flow in pipes.

Differentiate Equation (2–49) to give

$$\frac{dv_x}{dz} = \frac{v_{\max}}{7} \, (2/d_i)^{1/7} (z)^{-6/7} \qquad (2\text{--}51)$$

At the wall of the pipe, i.e., $z = 0$, Equation (2–51) indicates that an infinite velocity gradient and, hence, shear stress exist. This is not the case. Thus the turbulent velocity profile equation [Equation (2–49)] is only true for the bulk of the liquid. It does not hold true for the liquid region in immediate proximity to the wall.

Unsteady Laminar Liquid Flow in a Pipe

A long horizontal pipe of length ℓ and inside diameter d_i contains a Newtonian liquid of constant density ρ and constant viscosity μ at rest. At a time $t = 0$, a pressure drop ΔP is applied across the length of pipe ℓ which causes the liquid in the pipe to flow. The momentum transfer equations can be used to determine the variation of the velocity profile across the pipe as a function of time.

Consider a point velocity v_x in the direction of the axis of the pipe at a radius r from the center. The appropriate momentum transfer equation in cylindrical coordinates is

$$\rho\!\left(\frac{\partial v_x}{\partial t} + v_r \frac{\partial v_x}{\partial r} + \frac{v_\theta}{r}\frac{\partial v_x}{\partial \theta} + v_x \frac{\partial v_x}{\partial x}\right) = \mu\!\left[\frac{1}{r}\frac{\partial}{\partial r}\!\left(r\frac{\partial v_x}{\partial r}\right) + \frac{1}{r^2}\frac{\partial^2 v_x}{\partial \theta^2}\right.$$

$$\left. + \frac{\partial^2 v_x}{\partial x^2}\right] - \frac{\partial P}{\partial x} + \rho g_x \qquad (2\text{--}2)$$

Assume that there is no radial or angular velocity in the liquid, i.e., $v_r = 0$ and $v_\theta = 0$. Also assume that the velocity v_x in the x direction is a function only of the radial position in the pipe r and the time t, i.e., $v_x = v_x(r,t)$. Since the pipe is horizontal, the gravitational term $g_x = 0$.

The pressure gradient

$$\frac{\partial P}{\partial x} = -\frac{\Delta P}{\ell}$$

The negative sign is used with the pressure gradient term since the pressure decreases along the pipe as the distance x increases. For these conditions, Equation (2–2) becomes

$$\rho \frac{\partial v_x}{\partial t} = \frac{\Delta P}{\ell} + \frac{\mu}{r} \frac{\partial}{\partial r}\left(r \frac{\partial v_x}{\partial r}\right)$$

which can be rewritten

$$\frac{\partial v_x}{\partial t} = \frac{\Delta P}{\rho\ell} + \frac{\mu}{\rho}\left[\frac{1}{r} \frac{\partial}{\partial r}\left(r \frac{\partial v_x}{\partial r}\right)\right] \tag{2–52}$$

After a time, the liquid flow in the pipe will become steady and a constant velocity $\bar{v}_x$ will be attained at each point across the diameter of the pipe. In terms of this constant velocity, the velocity v_x at any time t can be written as follows:

$$v_x(r,t) = \bar{v}_x(r) - v_t(r,t) \tag{2–53}$$

where the transient velocity function $v_t \to 0$ as $t \to \infty$. As $t \to \infty$, $\partial v_x/\partial t \to 0$ and $v_x \to \bar{v}_x$. Thus for the steady state, Equation (2–52) becomes

$$0 = \frac{\Delta P}{\rho\ell} + \frac{\mu}{\rho}\left[\frac{1}{r} \frac{\partial}{\partial r}\left(r \frac{\partial \bar{v}_x}{\partial r}\right)\right] \tag{2–54}$$

which, when integrated, gives the parabolic distribution of velocity across the pipe characteristic of laminar flow. The derivation is the same as for Equation (2–7).

Differentiate Equation (2–53) with respect to t, to give

$$\frac{\partial v_x}{\partial t} = - \frac{\partial v_t}{\partial t} \tag{2–55}$$

and with respect to r, to give

$$\frac{\partial v_x}{\partial r} = \frac{\partial \bar{v}_x}{\partial r} - \frac{\partial v_t}{\partial r} \tag{2–56}$$

Rewrite Equation (2–54) as

$$-\frac{\Delta P r}{\mu\ell} = \frac{\partial}{\partial r}\left(r \frac{\partial \bar{v}_x}{\partial r}\right) \tag{2–57}$$

and integrate to give

$$-\left(\frac{\Delta P}{\mu\ell}\right)\frac{r^2}{2} + C = r \frac{\partial \bar{v}_x}{\partial r}$$

which can be rewritten as

$$-\left(\frac{\Delta P}{\mu \ell}\right)\frac{r}{2} + \frac{C}{r} = \frac{\partial \bar{v}_x}{\partial r} \qquad (2\text{-}58)$$

where C is a constant. Since the velocity gradient $\partial \bar{v}_x / \partial r$ is finite at the center of the pipe where $r = 0$, $C = 0$. Therefore,

$$\frac{\partial \bar{v}_x}{\partial r} = -\left(\frac{\Delta P}{\mu \ell}\right)\frac{r}{2} \qquad (2\text{-}59)$$

Substitute Equation (2–53) into Equation (2–52) to give

$$\frac{\partial v_x}{\partial t} = \frac{\Delta P}{\rho \ell} + \frac{\mu}{\rho}\left[\frac{1}{r}\frac{\partial}{\partial r}\left(r\frac{\partial \bar{v}_x}{\partial r} - r\frac{\partial v_t}{\partial r}\right)\right] \qquad (2\text{-}60)$$

Combine Equation (2–59) with Equation (2–60) to give

$$\frac{\partial v_x}{\partial t} = \frac{\Delta P}{\rho \ell} - \frac{\mu}{\rho}\left[\frac{1}{r}\frac{\partial}{\partial r}\left(\frac{\Delta P\, r^2}{2\mu \ell}\right)\right] - \frac{\mu}{\rho}\left[\frac{1}{r}\frac{\partial}{\partial r}\left(r\frac{\partial v_t}{\partial r}\right)\right]$$

$$= -\frac{\mu}{\rho}\left[\frac{1}{r}\frac{\partial}{\partial r}\left(r\frac{\partial v_t}{\partial r}\right)\right]$$

which, when combined with Equation (2–55), becomes

$$\frac{\partial v_t}{\partial t} = \frac{\mu}{\rho}\left[\frac{1}{r}\frac{\partial}{\partial r}\left(r\frac{\partial v_t}{\partial r}\right)\right] \qquad (2\text{-}61)$$

Substitute the kinematic viscosity $\eta = \mu/\rho$ in Equation (2–61) and expand in the form

$$\frac{\partial v_t}{\partial t} = \eta\left(\frac{\partial^2 v_t}{\partial r^2} + \frac{1}{r}\frac{\partial v_t}{\partial r}\right) \qquad (2\text{-}62)$$

Solve the partial differential equation [Equation (2–62)] by the separation of variables technique as follows. Assume a solution:

$$v_t(r,t) = Z(r)T(t) \qquad (2\text{-}63)$$

Differentiate Equation (2–63) with respect to t, to give

$$\frac{\partial v_t}{\partial t} = Z\frac{dT}{dt} \qquad (2\text{-}64)$$

and with respect to r, to give

$$\frac{\partial v_t}{\partial r} = T\frac{dZ}{dr} \tag{2-65}$$

and

$$\frac{\partial^2 v_t}{\partial r^2} = T\frac{d^2 Z}{dr^2} \tag{2-66}$$

Substitute Equation (2–65) and (2–66) in Equation (2–62) to give

$$Z\frac{dT}{dt} = \eta\left(T\frac{d^2 Z}{dr^2} + \frac{T}{r}\frac{dZ}{dr}\right)$$

which can be written in the form

$$\frac{1}{T}\frac{dT}{dt} = \eta\left[\frac{1}{Z}\frac{d^2 Z}{dr^2} + \frac{1}{Z}\left(\frac{1}{r}\frac{dZ}{dr}\right)\right] \tag{2-67}$$

The right-hand side of Equation (2–67) is independent of t and the left-hand side is independent of r. This is only possible if both sides are independent of r and t, i.e., equal to a constant. Let this constant be $-\alpha$. Combine this constant with Equation (2–67) to give the following two ordinary differential equations:

$$\frac{dT}{dt} + \alpha T = 0 \tag{2-68}$$

and

$$\frac{d^2 Z}{dr^2} + \frac{1}{r}\frac{dZ}{dr} + \left(\frac{\alpha}{\eta}\right)Z = 0 \tag{2-69}$$

Put $\alpha/\eta = \beta^2$ and rewrite Equation (2–69) first as

$$\frac{d^2 Z}{dr^2} + \frac{1}{r}\frac{dZ}{dr} + \beta^2 Z = 0$$

and then as

$$r^2\frac{d^2 Z}{dr^2} + r\frac{dZ}{dr} + \beta^2 r^2 Z = 0 \tag{2-70}$$

Substitute[11] $s = \beta r$ in Equation (2–70) to give

$$s^2\frac{d^2 Z}{ds^2} + s\frac{dZ}{ds} + s^2 Z = 0 \tag{2-71}$$

Equation (2–71) is the well-known Bessel equation of zero order.

Equation (2–68) has a solution:

$$T = C_1 e^{-\alpha t} \tag{2-72}$$

where C_1 is a constant.

Equation (2–71) can be readily solved using the method of Frobenius.[9] The solution can be written as

$$Z = C_2 \, J_0(s) + C_3 Y_0(s) \tag{2-73}$$

where C_2 and C_3 are constants. The first solution $J_0(s)$ in Equation (2–73) is the most commonly encountered Bessel function.[12] It represents the converging power series expansion

$$J_0(s) = \sum_{n=0}^{\infty} \frac{(-1)^n}{(n!)^2} \left(\frac{s}{2}\right)^{2n} = 1 - \frac{s^2}{2^2} + \frac{s^4}{2^2 \cdot 4^2} - \frac{s^6}{2^2 \cdot 4^2 \cdot 6^2} + \cdots \tag{2-74}$$

which is graphically illustrated in Figure 2–7. The other solution in Equation (2–73), $Y_0(s)$, is also converging and is graphically illustrated in Figure 2–8.

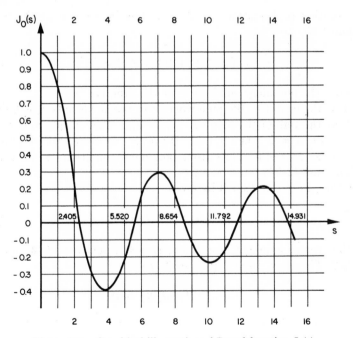

Figure 2-7.   Graphical illustration of Bessel function $J_0(s)$.

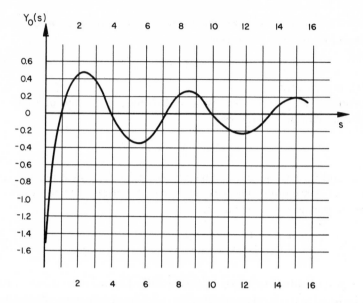

Figure 2-8.   Graphical illustration of Bessel function $Y_0(s)$.

The solution of Equation (2–62) can thus be written in the form of Equation (2–63) as

$$v_t = C_1 e^{-\alpha t}[C_2 J_0(s) + C_3 Y_0(s)] \qquad (2\text{--}75)$$

Consider the boundary conditions for the problem:
B.C.1 at the center of the pipe where $r = 0$, the velocity v_t is finite.
B.C.2 at the wall of the pipe where $r = d_i/2$, the velocity v_t is zero.
Since $s = \beta r$, $s = 0$ when $r = 0$. However, as seen from Figure 2–8, $Y_0(s) \rightarrow -\infty$ as $s \rightarrow 0$. Thus from boundary condition 1, the constant C_3 in Equation (2–75) must be zero.
Therefore, Equation (2–75) becomes

$$v_t = C_1 C_2 e^{-\alpha t} J_0(s) \qquad (2\text{--}76)$$

From the second boundary condition, $v_t = 0$ where $r = d_i/2$ and hence $s = \beta d_i/2$. Therefore, from Equation (2–75).

$$C_1 C_2 e^{-\alpha t} J_0(\beta d_i/2) = 0$$

i.e.,

$$J_0(\beta d_i/2) = 0 \qquad (2\text{--}77)$$

Thus $\beta d_i/2$ has the values of s in Figure 2–7 where $J_0(s)$ cuts the abscissa. Let

$$\beta d_i/2 = \lambda_n \qquad (2\text{--}78)$$

where $\lambda_1 = 2.405$, $\lambda_2 = 5.520$, $\lambda_3 = 8.654$, $\lambda_4 = 11.792$, $\lambda_5 = 14.931$, $\lambda_6 = 18.071$, and so on.

From Equation (2–78) write

$$\beta = 2\lambda_n/d_i \qquad (2\text{--}79)$$

Since $\alpha = \eta\beta^2$, combine this with Equation (2–79) to give

$$\alpha = \eta(2\lambda_n/d_i)^2 \qquad (2\text{--}80)$$

Substitute Equations (2–79) and (2–80) and $s = \beta r$ in Equation (2–76) to give

$$v_t = \sum_{n=1}^{\infty} C_{1n}C_{2n}e^{-\eta(2\lambda_n/d_i)^2 t}J_0(2\lambda_n r/d_i) \qquad (2\text{--}81)$$

where all the values of n are included. Equation (2–81) can be simplified by substituting an overall constant $C = C_1C_2$ to give

$$v_t = \sum_{n=1}^{\infty} C_n e^{-\eta(2\lambda_n/d_i)^2 t}J_0(2\lambda_n r/d_i) \qquad (2\text{--}82)$$

where the values of C_n are arbitrary constants.

Since the velocity $v_x = 0$ at time $t = 0$, Equation (2–53) shows that $v_t = \bar{v}_x$ at $t = 0$. Substitute this value in Equation (2–82) to give

$$\bar{v}_x = \sum_{n=1}^{\infty} C_n J_0(2\lambda_n r/d_i) \qquad (2\text{--}83)$$

The constants C_n can be evaluated by making use of the orthogonality properties of Bessel functions.[10,13] The procedure is as follows:

Multiply both sides of Equation (2–83) by $rJ_0(2\lambda_m r/d_i)$ and integrate from 0 to $d_i/2$ with respect to r. Therefore,

$$\int_0^{d_i/2} r\bar{v}_x J_0(2\lambda_m r/d_i) \, dr = \sum_{n=1}^{\infty} C_n \int_0^{d_i/2} rJ_0(2\lambda_n r/d_i)J_0(2\lambda_m r/d_i)dr$$

$$= C_n \frac{d_i^2}{8} J_1^2(\lambda_n) \qquad (2\text{--}84)$$

since

$$\int_0^{d_i/2} J_0(2\lambda_n r/d_i) J_0(2\lambda_m r/d_i) = 0 \text{ for } n \neq m$$

and

$$\int_0^{d_i/2} r J_0(2\lambda_n r/d_i) J_0(2\lambda_m r/d_i) dr = \frac{d_i^2}{8} [J_1(\lambda_n)]^2 \delta_{nm}$$

where δ_{nm} is the Kronecker delta[13], $\delta_{nm} = +1$ if $n = m$, and $\delta_{nm} = 0$ if $n \neq m$.

Equation (2–84) can be rewritten as

$$C_n = \frac{8}{d_i^2 J_1^2(\lambda_n)} \int_0^{d_i/2} r \bar{v}_x J_0(2\lambda_n r/d_i) dr \qquad (2\text{–}85)$$

In Equation (2–85)

$$\bar{v}_x = \left[\left(\frac{\Delta P}{\ell}\right)\left(\frac{d_i^2}{16\mu}\right)\right][1 - (2r/d_i)^2]$$

This is the steady state velocity distribution in a pipe for laminar liquid flow derived in Equation (2–7).

The evaluation of the integral of the right-hand side of Equation (2–85) can be shown to be[3]

$$C_n = \left[\left(\frac{\Delta P}{\ell}\right)\left(\frac{d_i^2}{16\mu}\right)\right] \cdot \frac{8}{\lambda_n^3 J_1(\lambda_n)} \qquad (2\text{–}86)$$

Substitute the value of C_n from Equation (2–86) into Equation (2–82) to give

$$v_t = 8\left[\left(\frac{\Delta P}{\ell}\right)\left(\frac{d_i^2}{16\mu}\right)\right] \sum_{n=1}^{\infty} \frac{J_0(2\lambda_n r/d_i) e^{-\eta(2\lambda_n/d_i)^2 t}}{\lambda_n^3 J_1(\lambda_n)} \qquad (2\text{–}87)$$

which is the solution to the transient part of Equation (2–53).

The full solution of Equation (2–53) is therefore

$$v_x = \left[\left(\frac{\Delta P}{\ell}\right)\left(\frac{d_i^2}{16\mu}\right)\right]\left[1 - (2r/d_i)^2\right.$$

$$\left. - 8\sum_{n=1}^{\infty} \frac{J_0(2\lambda_n r/d_i) e^{-\eta(2\lambda_n/d_i)^2 t}}{\lambda_n^3 J_1(\lambda_n)}\right] \qquad (2\text{–}88)$$

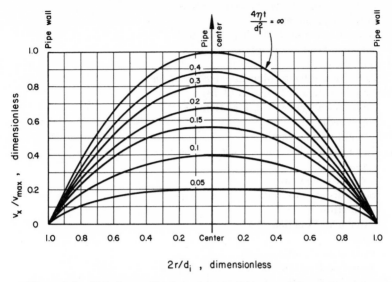

Figure 2-9.   Velocity profiles in a pipe as a function of time from rest.

Equation (2–88) gives the local velocity v_x of an incompressible Newtonian liquid at any point in a circular pipe at a distance r from the center as a function of the liquid viscosity μ, the kinematic viscosity η, the pressure gradient $\Delta P/\ell$ impressed on the liquid, the inside pipe diameter d_i and the time t.

As the time $t \rightarrow \infty$, Equation (2–88) reduces to the steady state equation

$$v_x = \left[\left(\frac{\Delta P}{\ell} \right) \left(\frac{d_i^{\,2}}{16\mu} \right) \right] [1 - (2r/d_i)^2] \qquad (2\text{-}7)$$

The unsteady state velocity profiles calculated from Equation (2–88) are shown[19] in Figure 2–9 in relation to the steady state velocity profile for a Newtonian liquid flowing inside a circular pipe.

The mathematics in this section could have been simplified slightly by using dimensionless parameters in place of the variables velocity, radius and time. However, the use of reduced parameters has the disadvantage of obscuring the physical meaning of the various terms.

NOMENCLATURE

C constant
d_i inside pipe diameter
f Fanning friction factor (dimensionless) $= 2R/\rho u^2$

F friction factor (dimensionless) $= 8R/\rho u^2$
g gravitational acceleration
g_c conversion factor, 32.174 lb_m ft/lb_f sec^2
h_f frictional head loss in a pipe
i unit vector
j_f basic friction factor (dimensionless) $= R/\rho u^2$
$J_0(s)$ Bessel solution in Equation (2–73)
K proportionality factor in Equation (2–27)
ℓ pipe length
L Prandtl mixing length
N_{Re} Reynolds number (dimensionless) $= \rho u d_i/\mu$
P pressure
Q volumetric flow rate
r radial distance from the center of a pipe
R shear stress
s variable in Equation (2–71) $= \beta r$
t time
T variable in Equation (2–63)
u mean linear velocity of liquid inside a pipe
v linear velocity of liquid at a point in a pipe
x distance in the axial direction along a pipe
$Y_0(s)$ Bessel solution in Equation (2–73)
z distance from pipe wall in a radial direction
Z variable in Equation (2–63)
α factor in Equation (2–72)
β proportionality factor between s and r
δ_{nm} Kronecker delta
ϵ absolute roughness
μ viscosity of liquid
ρ density of liquid
η kinematic viscosity of liquid
θ angle between a radial line and a fixed radial line
λ_n product in Equation (2–78) $= \beta d_i/2$
∇ vector operator in Equation (1–47)

REFERENCES

1. Bennet, C.O., and Myers, J.E., "Momentum, Heat and Mass Transfer," p. 131, New York, McGraw-Hill Book Co. Inc., 1962.
2. *Ibid.*, p. 135.
3. Bird, R. B., Stewart, W.E., and Lightfoot, E.N., "Transport Phenomena," p. 129, New York, John Wiley & Sons, Inc., 1960.
4. Blasius, H., *Forsch. Ver. Deut. Ing.*, 131 (1913).
5. Coulson, J. M., and Richardson, J. F., "Chemical Engineering," Vol. 1, p. 50, New York, The Macmillan Co., 1964.

6. *Ibid.*, p. 51
7. Ekman, V. W., *Arch. Math. Astr. och Fys.*, **VI**, 12 (1910).
8. Hagen, G., *Ann. Phys. (Pogg. Ann.)*, **46**, 423 (1839).
9. Hildebrand, F. B., "Advanced Calculus for Applications," p. 129, Englewood Cliffs, N.J., Prentice-Hall, Inc., 1962.
10. *Ibid.*, p. 488.
11. Miller, K. S., "Partial Differential Equations in Engineering Problems," p. 179, Englewood Cliffs, N.J., Prentice-Hall, Inc., 1953.
12. *Ibid.*, p. 205.
13. *Ibid.*, p. 206.
14. Nikuradse, J., *Forschungs-Arb Ing-Wesen*, 356 (1932).
15. Nikuradse, J., *Forschungs-Arb Ing-Wesen*, 361 (1933).
16. Prandtl, L., *Z. Angew. Math. Mech.*, **5**, 136 (1925).
17. Ramalho, R. S., Tiller, F. M., and Berry, V. J., *Chem. Eng.*, **71**, No. 15 (1964).
18. Reynolds, O., *Proc. Royal Soc. (London)*, A, **174**, 935 (1883).
19. Szymanski, P., *J. Math. Pures Appl.*, **11**, 67 (1932).

CHAPTER 3

Non-Newtonian Liquid Flow in Pipelines

Time Independent Non-Newtonian Liquids

The rheological character of a time independent non-Newtonian liquid is commonly illustrated on a Cartesian plot of shear stress R_s vs shear rate $\dot\gamma$ as shown in Figure 3–1. The apparent viscosity μ_a at a particular shear rate $\dot\gamma$ is defined by the equation

$$\mu_a = \frac{R_s}{\dot\gamma} \tag{3-1}$$

The term viscosity has no meaning for a non-Newtonian liquid unless it is related to a particular shear rate $\dot\gamma$.

If the apparent viscosity μ_a decreases with increasing shear rate $\dot\gamma$, the liquid is said to be pseudoplastic. Conversely, if μ_a increases with increasing $\dot\gamma$, the liquid is called dilatant. For a Newtonian liquid, the ratio $R_s/\dot\gamma$ is constant.

A third type of time independent non-Newtonian liquid is the Bingham plastic. The plot of shear stress against shear rate on Cartesian coordinates for a Bingham plastic is a straight line having an intercept R_b on the shear stress axis. R_b, which is called the yield stress, is the stress which must be exceeded before flow starts. The liquid at rest contains a three dimensional structure of sufficient rigidity to resist any stress less than the yield stress.

When this stress is exceeded, the system behaves as a Newtonian liquid under a shear stress of $R_s - R_b$. For Bingham plastics, the slope of the shear stress, shear rate plot is called the coefficient of rigidity.

Time Dependent Non-Newtonian Liquids

The apparent viscosity of a pseudoplastic liquid decreases immediately when the rate of shear is increased. For some liquids, the apparent vis-

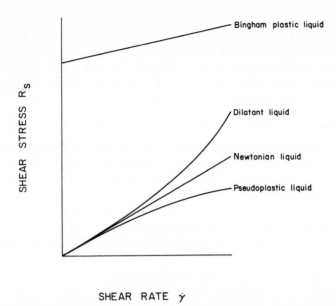

Figure 3-1. Shear stress vs shear rate on Cartesian coordinates.

cosity continues to decrease further with the time for which the particular rate of shear is applied. These liquids are called thixotropic. Their structure progressively breaks down with time at a constant shear rate. Thixotropy is a reversible process. Eventually a dynamic equilibrium is reached where the rate of structural breakdown is balanced by the simultaneous rate of reformation.[11] Thus a minimum value of the apparent viscosity is reached at any constant rate of shear. Many materials show thixotropic behavior in addition to being pseudoplastic or even dilatant.[4]

Most thixotropic liquids will recover their original viscosity if allowed to stand for a sufficient length of time. Some liquids will revert almost immediately, while others might take several hours.

A plot of shear stress R_s against shear rate $\dot{\gamma}$ for thixotropic liquids shows a hysteresis effect when the shear rate is changed at regular time intervals. The curve obtained for increasing shear rates does not coincide with the curve for decreasing shear rates.

The apparent viscosity of a dilatant liquid increases immediately when the rate of shear is increased. For some liquids the apparent viscosity continues to increase further with the time for which the particular rate of shear is applied. These liquids are called rheopectic. Small shearing motions facilitate the formation of structure. Above a critical point, breakdown occurs. If the shearing rate is rapid, the structure does not form. In general, the apparent viscosity of rheopectic liquids increases with time to a maximum value at a constant rate of shear. Most rheopectic liquids revert very quickly to their original viscosity if left to stand.

In practice, truly time dependent non-Newtonian liquids are rare. They will not be discussed again in this chapter.

Shear Rate at a Pipe Wall for Time Independent Non-Newtonian Liquids

Consider a liquid in steady state flow in a pipe of inside diameter d_i. Figure 2–2 shows an annular element of the flowing liquid. The radius and width of this element are r and dr, respectively. Let the tangential shear stress per unit area over the element be R_{rx} and the linear velocity of the liquid in the element be v_x. Let the tangential shear stress per unit area at the wall be R, i.e., at the point where the radius $r = d_i/2$.

In Equation (2–9) it was stated that the volumetric liquid flow rate in the element

$$dQ = 2\pi r\, dr\, v_x$$

Therefore, the volumetric flow rate Q through the whole pipe is obtained by integrating between the limits $r = 0$ and $r = d_i/2$.

$$Q = \int_0^{d_i/2} 2\pi r v_x\, dr \tag{3-2}$$

Equation (3–2) can be integrated by parts to

$$Q = (\pi r^2 v_x)_0^{d_i/2} - \int_0^{d_i/2} \pi r^2 \left(\frac{dv_x}{dr}\right) dr \tag{3-3}$$

The first term on the right-hand side of Equation (3–3) is zero, since v_x is zero at the pipe wall where $r = d_i/2$. Therefore, the volumetric flow rate through the pipe is

$$Q = -\int_0^{d_i/2} \pi r^2 \left(\frac{dv_x}{dr}\right) dr \tag{3-4}$$

where $-dv_x/dr$ is the shear rate at a radius r in the pipe.

Consider a length of pipe ℓ and a pressure drop ΔP over this length. Consider the forces acting on a liquid core of radius r.

A force balance over the liquid core gives

$$\Delta P\, \pi r^2 = 2\pi r \ell R_{rx} \tag{3-5}$$

which reduces to

$$\Delta P = 2R_{rx}\ell/r \qquad (3\text{--}6)$$

The shear stress R_{rx} at a radius r in the pipe can be related to the shear stress R at the wall by combining Equations (3–6) and (2–34) to give

$$r = \left(\frac{d_i}{2R} \right) R_{rx} \qquad (3\text{--}7)$$

Equation (3–7) can also be written in the differential form

$$dr = \left(\frac{d_i}{2R} \right) dR_{rx} \qquad (3\text{--}8)$$

Since the shear rate $- dv_x/dr$ at a radius r in the pipe is a function of the shear stress R_{rx}, write

$$-\frac{dv_x}{dr} = \mathfrak{f}(R_{rx}) \qquad (3\text{--}9)$$

The minus sign is used in Equation (3–9) since the point linear velocity v_x decreases as the radius r increases.

Substitute Equations (3–7), (3–8) and (3–9) into Equation (3–4) to give

$$Q = -\int_0^{d_i/2} \pi r^2 \left(\frac{dv_x}{dr} \right) dr = \left(\frac{\pi d_i^3}{8R^3} \right) \int_0^R (R_{rx})^2 \mathfrak{f}(R_{rx}) dR_{rx} \qquad (3\text{--}10)$$

Since the volumetric flow rate

$$Q = \frac{\pi d_i^2 u}{4} \qquad (3\text{--}11)$$

where u is the mean linear velocity of liquid in the pipe,

$$u = \frac{4Q}{\pi d_i^2} \qquad (3\text{--}12)$$

Combine Equations (3–12) and (3–10) to give

$$\frac{8u}{d_i} = 8\left(\frac{4Q}{\pi d_i^3} \right) = \left(\frac{4}{R^3} \right) \int_0^R (R_{rx})^2 \mathfrak{f}(R_{rx}) dR_{rx} \qquad (3\text{--}13)$$

The term $8u/d_i$ is known as the flow characteristic. It is a function of the shear stress R at the wall; therefore, write

$$\frac{8u}{d_i} = \phi(R) \tag{3-14}$$

Substitute Equation (3–14) into Equation (3–13) and rearrange to give

$$R^3\phi(R)/4 = \int_0^R (R_{rx})^2 \, \mathfrak{f}(R_{rx})dR_{rx} \tag{3-15}$$

Differentiate Equation (3–15) with respect to R, to give

$$\frac{[3R^2\phi(R) + R^3\phi'(R)]}{4} = R^2\mathfrak{f}(R) \tag{3-16}$$

Rearrange Equation (3–16) to give

$$\mathfrak{f}(R) = \frac{3\phi(R)}{4} + \left(\frac{R}{4}\right)\phi'(R) \tag{3-17}$$

which can be rewritten as

$$\mathfrak{f}(R) = \frac{3\phi(R)}{4} + \left[\frac{\phi(R)}{4}\right]\left[\frac{\phi'(R)}{\phi(R)}\right]\frac{R}{dR}\,dR$$

$$= \frac{3\phi(R)}{4} + \left[\frac{\phi(R)}{4}\right]\left[\frac{d\log_e \phi(R)}{d\log_e R}\right] \tag{3-18}$$

Since from Equation (3–9)

$$-\frac{dv_x}{dr}\Big|_{\text{wall}} = \mathfrak{f}(R) \tag{3-19}$$

Equations (3–17) and (3–18) relate the shear rate at the wall $\mathfrak{f}(R)$ to the shear stress R at the wall and the flow characteristic $\phi(R) = 8u/d_i$.

The shear stress R at the wall is related to the pressure drop ΔP in the pipe length by the equation

$$\Delta P = \frac{4R\ell}{d_i} \tag{2-34}$$

which can be rewritten in the form

$$R = \frac{\Delta P}{4\ell/d_i} \tag{3-20}$$

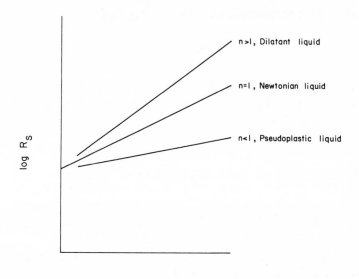

Figure 3-2. Shear stress vs shear rate on log-log coordinates.

Substitute Equations (3–14) and (3–20) into Equation (3–29) to give

$$R = K_p[\phi(R)]^n \qquad (3\text{–}30)$$

Equation (3–30) can be rewritten in a logarithmic form as

$$\log_e R = \log_e K_p + n \log_e \phi(R) \qquad (3\text{–}31)$$

which may be differentiated and written in the form

$$\frac{1}{n} = \frac{d \log_e \phi(R)}{d \log_e R} \qquad (3\text{–}32)$$

A comparison of Equations (3–22) and (3–32) shows that for power law liquids $n = n'$. Thus for power law liquids, Equation (3–23) becomes

$$-\left.\frac{dv_x}{dr}\right|_{\text{wall}} = \left(\frac{8u}{d_i}\right)\left(\frac{3n + 1}{4n}\right) \qquad (3\text{–}33)$$

Equation (3–33) relates the shear rate at the wall to the flow characteristic $(8u/d_i)$ and the power law index n,

Equation (3–29) can also be written in the form

$$\frac{\Delta P}{4\ell/d_i} = [K_p(8u/d_i)^{n-1}](8u/d_i) \qquad (3\text{–}34)$$

A comparison of Equation (3–34) for power law liquids and Equation (3–24) for Newtonian liquids enables an apparent viscosity for pipe flow to be defined as follows:

$$(\mu_a)_{p1} = K_p(8u/d_i)^{n-1} \qquad (3\text{–}35)$$

For Newtonian liquids, $n = 1$ and Equation (3–35) reduces to $(\mu_a)_{p1} = K_p$.

$$\text{apparent viscosity } (\mu_a)_{p1} = \frac{\text{shear stress at the pipe wall}}{\text{flow characteristic}}$$

The apparent viscosity $(\mu_a)_{p1}$ is the simulated Newtonian liquid viscosity at the particular flow characteristic $8u/d_i$.

For pipeline flow, the Reynolds number is defined as:

$$N_{Re} = \frac{\rho u d_i}{\mu} \qquad (2\text{–}1)$$

for Newtonian liquids.

On the basis of the definition of apparent viscosity given in Equation (3–35), the Reynolds number for pipeline flow of power law liquids can be written as:

$$N_{Re} = \frac{\rho u d_i}{K_p(8u/d_i)^{n-1}} \qquad (3\text{–}36)$$

An alternative definition for the apparent viscosity of a non-Newtonian liquid in a pipeline is as follows:

$$\text{apparent viscosity } (\mu_a)_{p2} = \frac{\text{mean shear stress over the liquid in the pipe}}{\text{mean shear rate over the liquid in the pipe}}$$

An expression for $(\mu_a)_{p2}$ for power law liquids is obtained as follows: Consider an annular element of liquid flowing in a pipe as shown in Figure 2–2. Rearrange Equation (3–6) to read

$$R_{rz} = \left(\frac{\Delta P}{\ell}\right)\frac{r}{2} = \left(\frac{\Delta P}{2\ell}\right)r \qquad (2\text{–}17)$$

Equation (2–17) gives the shear stress R_{rz} at any radial position r in the pipe in terms of the pressure drop ΔP over a pipe length ℓ.

The mean shear stress $\bar{R}_{rz}$ over the liquid in the pipe is easily calculated to be

$$\bar{R}_{rz} = \frac{\displaystyle\int_0^{d_i/2} R_{rz}\, dr}{\displaystyle\int_0^{d_i/2} dr} = \left(\frac{\Delta P}{2\ell}\right)\frac{d_i}{4} \tag{3-37}$$

The shear rate $\dot{\gamma}$ at the annular element is given by the equation:

$$\dot{\gamma} = -\frac{dv_x}{dr} \tag{3-38}$$

The mean shear rate $\dot{\gamma}$ over the pipe is:

$$\bar{\dot{\gamma}} = \frac{\displaystyle\int_0^{d_i/2} \dot{\gamma}\, dr}{\displaystyle\int_0^{d_i/2} dr} \tag{3-39}$$

For a power law liquid obeying Equation (3–27), the following equation can be written for pipeline flow:

$$R_{rz} = K_p(\dot{\gamma})^n \tag{3-40}$$

Therefore,

$$\dot{\gamma} = \left(\frac{R_{rz}}{K_p}\right)^{1/n} \tag{3-41}$$

Combine Equations (2–17) and (3–41) to give:

$$\dot{\gamma} = \left(\frac{\Delta P}{2\ell}\right)^{1/n}\left(\frac{r}{K_p}\right)^{1/n} \tag{3-42}$$

Substitute Equation (3–42) in Equation (3–39) and perform the integration to give:

$$\bar{\dot{\gamma}} = \left(\frac{\Delta P}{2\ell}\right)^{1/n}\left(\frac{1}{K_p{}^{1/n}}\right)\left(\frac{n}{n+1}\right)\left(\frac{d_i}{2}\right)^{1/n} \tag{3-43}$$

Therefore,

$$(\mu_\mathrm{a})_{p2} = \frac{\bar{R}_{rz}}{\dot{\gamma}} = \left(\frac{\Delta P}{2\ell}\right)^{1-(1/n)} \left(\frac{K_\mathrm{p}^{1/n}}{2}\right)\left(\frac{n+1}{n}\right)\left(\frac{d_\mathrm{i}}{2}\right)^{1-(1/n)}$$

$$= \left(\frac{\Delta P}{4\ell/d_\mathrm{i}}\right)^{1-(1/n)} \left(\frac{K_\mathrm{p}^{1/n}}{2}\right)\left(\frac{n+1}{n}\right)$$

$$= [K_p(8u/d_\mathrm{i})^n]^{1-(1/n)} \left(\frac{K_\mathrm{p}^{1/n}}{2}\right)\left(\frac{n+1}{n}\right)$$

Therefore,

$$(\mu_\mathrm{a})_{p2} = \frac{K_\mathrm{p}}{2}(8u/d_\mathrm{i})^{n-1}\left(\frac{n+1}{n}\right) \tag{3-44}$$

for power law liquids.

For Newtonian liquids, $n = 1$ and Equation (3–44) reduces to $(\mu_\mathrm{a})_{p2} = K_\mathrm{p}$.

Laminar Flow Velocity Distribution in a Pipe for Power Law Liquids

Consider a non-Newtonian liquid obeying the power law equation

$$R_{rz} = K_\mathrm{p}(\dot{\gamma})^n \tag{3-40}$$

Substitute Equation (3–38) in Equation (3–40) and write

$$R_{rz} = K_\mathrm{p}\left(-\frac{dv_x}{dr}\right)^n \tag{3-45}$$

From a shell momentum balance for steady state laminar liquid flow in a pipe, the following equation was obtained:

$$R_{rz} = \left(\frac{\Delta P}{\ell}\right)\frac{r}{2} \tag{2-17}$$

Equation (2–17) gives the shear stress or rate of momentum transfer R_{rz} at a radius r in a pipe. Substitute Equation (2–17) into Equation (3–45) and rearrange to give

$$\frac{dv_x}{dr} = -\left(\frac{\Delta P}{2\ell K_\mathrm{p}}\right)^{1/n} r^{1/n} \tag{3-46}$$

which on integration over the whole pipe becomes

$$v_x = \left[\frac{\Delta P}{(K_p 4\ell/d_i)} \right]^{1/n} \left(\frac{n}{n+1} \right) \left(\frac{d_i}{2} \right) \left[1 - \left(\frac{2r}{d_i} \right)^{(n+1)/n} \right] \quad (3\text{-}47)$$

Equation (3–47) gives the linear point liquid velocity at a radial position r in the pipe for a power law liquid. For Newtonian liquids $n = 1$, $K_p = \mu$ and Equation (3–47) becomes

$$v_x = \left(\frac{\Delta P}{\ell} \right) \frac{d_i^2}{16\mu} [1 - (2r/d_i)^2] \quad (2\text{-}7)$$

For the case of steady laminar flow of a power law liquid in a circular pipe, it is very much easier to derive the velocity profile from a shell balance than from the general momentum transfer equations.

Rewrite Equation (3–45) in the form

$$-\frac{dv_x}{dr} = \left(\frac{R_{rx}}{K_p} \right)^{1/n} \quad (3\text{-}48)$$

Combine Equation (3–48) with Equation (3–9) to give

$$f(R_{rx}) = \left(\frac{R_{rx}}{K_p} \right)^{1/n} \quad (3\text{-}49)$$

Substitute Equation (3–49) in Equation (3–13) to give

$$\frac{8u}{d_i} = \left(\frac{4}{R^3} \right) \left(\frac{1}{K_p} \right)^{1/n} \int_0^R R_{rx}^{2+(1/n)} \, dR_{rx} \quad (3\text{-}50)$$

Integrate Equation (3–50) and rearrange in the form

$$\frac{8u}{d_i} = \left(\frac{R}{K_p} \right)^{1/n} \left(\frac{4n}{3n+1} \right) \quad (3\text{-}51)$$

Combine Equations (3–20) and (3–51) to give

$$\frac{8u}{d_i} = \left[\frac{\Delta P}{(K_p 4\ell/d_i)} \right]^{1/n} \left(\frac{4n}{3n+1} \right) \quad (3\text{-}52)$$

and substitute in Equation (3–47) to give

$$v_x = u \left(\frac{3n+1}{n+1} \right) \left[1 - \left(\frac{2r}{d_i} \right)^{(n+1)/n} \right] \quad (3\text{-}53)$$

Equation (3–53) gives the velocity profile for a power law liquid in a circular pipe in terms of the mean linear velocity u in the pipe.

For Newtonian liquids, the power law index $n = 1$ and Equation (3–53) becomes

$$v_x = 2u\left[1 - \left(\frac{2r}{d_i}\right)^2\right] \tag{3–54}$$

Equation (3–54) can also be obtained by combining Equations (2–7) and (2–11).

Figure 3–3 is a plot of the steady state velocity profile equation [Equation (3–53)] showing the effect of the magnitude of the power law index n on the velocity distribution in a circular pipe. The plot illustrates this for

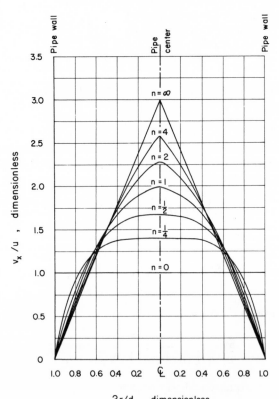

Figure 3-3.   Velocity distribution in a pipe as a function of power law index.

pseudoplastic liquids where $n < 1$ and for dilatant liquids where $n > 1$ with reference to the Newtonian laminar flow velocity profile given by Equation (3–54).

Pressure Drops in Pipes for Liquids in Laminar Flow

Equation (3–24) gives the relationship between pressure drop ΔP and mean linear velocity u in a pipe for the steady state laminar flow of a Newtonian liquid at a fixed temperature. A plot of $\Delta P/(4\ell/d_i)$ vs $(8u/d_i)$ gives a single line independent of pipe size. On Cartesian coordinates, this line is straight and has a slope equal to the coefficient of viscosity μ.

Similarly, for any time independent non-Newtonian liquid, a plot of $\Delta P/(4\ell/d_i)$ vs $(8u/d_i)$ on Cartesian coordinates also gives a single line independent of pipe size. This was pointed out by Alves, Boucher and Pigford.[1] The line curves upward with an increasing slope for dilatant liquids and with a decreasing slope for pseudoplastic liquids.

A plot of $\Delta P/(4\ell/d_i)$ vs $(8u/d_i)$ can be made for particular time independent non-Newtonian liquid using a capillary tube viscometer or a small pilot size pipeline.[8] These data can then be used to predict the pressure drop for the same liquid in laminar flow in a production size pipeline.

A log-log plot of $\Delta P/(4\ell/d_i)$ vs $(8u/d_i)$ has the slope n' given in Equation (3–21). This is only a point value for time independent non-Newtonian liquids which do not obey the power law. For power law liquids, a log-log plot of $\Delta P/(4\ell/d_i)$ vs $(8u/d_i)$ is a straight line of slope n. Thus for power law liquids, n' is not just a point value but is equal to n, the power law index.

Equation (3–21), for a general time independent non-Newtonian liquid, can also be expressed in the form

$$\frac{\Delta P}{4\ell/d_i} = K_p'(8u/d_i)^{n'} \tag{3–55}$$

where K_p' and n' are point values of the consistency coefficient and power law index, respectively. These values of K_p' and n' are only valid in the general case for a particular flow characteristic $(8u/d_i)$.

It is important not to confuse Equation (3–55) for a general time independent non-Newtonian liquid with Equation (3–29) for power law liquids.

A Reynolds number can be defined for general time independent non-Newtonian liquids as follows:

$$N_{\text{Re}} = \frac{\rho u d_i}{K_p'(8u/d_i)^{n'-1}} \tag{3–56}$$

Again Equation (3–56) should not be confused with Equation (3–36) which was the Reynolds number defined for power law liquids.

The basic friction factor j_f can be calculated at a particular flow characteristic $(8u/d_i)$ if corresponding point values of K_p' and n' are known. The required value of j_f is obtained from the following equation valid for laminar flow:

$$j_f = \frac{R}{\rho u^2} = \frac{8}{N_{Re}} \qquad (2\text{--}36)$$

Alternatively, the Fanning friction factor f can be calculated from the following equation:[13]

$$f = \frac{16}{N_{Re}} \qquad (3\text{--}57)$$

The values of j_f and f can then be substituted in Equations (2–44) and (2–45), respectively, to obtain the head loss in a pipe.

The method described above is due to Metzner and Reed.[7]

Consider the steady state laminar flow of Bingham plastics in circular pipes. For this case, Equation (3–9) can be written as:

$$-\frac{dv_x}{dr} = \frac{(R_{rx} - R_b)}{\mu_p} = f(R_{rx}) \qquad (3\text{--}58)$$

where R_{rx} is the shear stress at a radial position r in the pipe, R_b is the yield stress for the Bingham plastic, and μ_p is the coefficient of rigidity.

Substitute $f(R_{rx})$ from Equation (3–58) into Equation (3–13) to give:

$$\frac{8u}{d_i} = \left(\frac{4}{R^3}\right) \int_{R_b}^{R} (R_{rx})^2 \frac{(R_{rx} - R_b)}{\mu_p} \, dR_{rx} \qquad (3\text{--}59)$$

The integration limits in Equation (3–59) are from R_b to R, and not 0 to R, since no flow takes place below the yield shear stress R_b.

The shear stress at the center of a pipe is zero. Thus for the region adjacent to the pipe axis, the shear stress R_{rx} will be less than the yield stress R_b for a Bingham plastic. Therefore, a Bingham plastic moves through a pipe as a solid plug surrounded by liquid.

Integrate Equation (3–59) to give

$$\frac{8u}{d_i} = \frac{R}{\mu_p}\left[1 - \frac{4}{3}\left(\frac{R_b}{R}\right) + \frac{1}{3}\left(\frac{R_b}{R}\right)^4\right] \qquad (3\text{--}60)$$

which is the well-known Buckingham equation.

Substitute Equation (3–20) in Equation (3–60) and rewrite in the form:

$$\frac{8u}{d_i} = \frac{1}{\mu_p} \left\{ \frac{\Delta P}{(4\ell/d_i)} - \frac{4R_b}{3} + \frac{R_b^4}{3\left[\frac{\Delta P}{(4\ell/d_i)} \right]^3} \right\} \qquad (3\text{–}61)$$

Govier[5] has developed a method for solving Equation (3–61) for the pressure drop ΔP. He defines a modified Reynolds number N_{Re}' and a dimensionless yield number Y for Bingham plastics as follows:

$$N_{Re}' = \frac{\rho u d_i}{\mu_p} \qquad (3\text{–}62)$$

$$Y = \frac{R_b d_i}{u \mu_p} \qquad (3\text{–}63)$$

It is interesting to note that the product of N_{Re}' and Y is the dimensionless Hedstrom number N_{He} where

$$N_{He} = N_{Re}'Y = \frac{\rho u d_i}{\mu_p} \times \frac{R_b d_i}{u \mu_p} = \frac{R_b d_i^2}{\mu_p^2} \qquad (3\text{–}64)$$

The pressure drop ΔP is related to the basic friction factor $j_f = R/\rho u^2$ by the equation

$$\Delta P = 8\left(\frac{R}{\rho u^2}\right)\left(\frac{\ell}{d_i}\right)\left(\frac{\rho u^2}{2}\right) \qquad (2\text{–}35)$$

Since the Fanning friction factor $f = 2R/\rho u^2$, it can be expressed in the following form:

$$f = \left[\frac{\Delta P}{(4\ell/d_i)} \right] \div \left(\frac{\rho u^2}{2} \right) = \frac{\Delta P \, d_i}{2u^2\ell\rho} \qquad (3\text{–}65)$$

Govier[5] multiplied both sides of Equation (3–61) by $\mu_p/8u^2\rho$, substituted the values of N_{Re}', Y and f from Equations (3–62), (3–63) and (3–65), respectively, into Equation (3–61), and rearranged the equation in the form:

$$\frac{1}{fN_{Re}'} = \frac{1}{16} - \frac{Y}{6fN_{Re}'} + \frac{Y^4}{3(fN_{Re}')^4} \qquad (3\text{–}66)$$

The product fN_{Re}' is a unique function of Y.[6] Govier[5] has given the corresponding values of fN_{Re}' and Y which are listed in Table 3–1. Values of the

TABLE 3-1. Solutions for the Buckingham Equation

Yield Number Y	Product fN_{Re}
0	16.00
1	18.67
2	21.32
3	23.97
5	29.20
10	41.94
20	66.42
30	90.09
50	136.1
100	247.5
200	463.8
300	676.4
500	1,096
1,000	2,133
2,000	4,186
3,000	6,226
5,000	10,290
10,000	20,410

Fanning friction factor f at any value of the yield number Y may be obtained from Table 3-1 by dividing the product fN_{Re}' by the Reynolds number value N_{Re}'. Then the pressure drop ΔP can be calculated from Equation (3-65).

Pressure Drops in Pipes for Liquids in Turbulent Flow

The theory of turbulent flow in pipelines is far less developed than for laminar flow. Thus turbulent flow pressure drops can be predicted with a much lower degree of accuracy than laminar flow pressure drops. However, since non-Newtonian liquids tend to be relatively viscous, they are rarely in turbulent flow. This is illustrated by Figure 2-1.

The Blasius equation [Equation (2-37)] for the turbulent flow of Newtonian liquids in smooth circular pipes, can be rewritten in terms of the Fanning friction factor f as

$$f = \frac{0.079}{N_{Re}^{0.25}} \qquad (3-67)$$

For the turbulent flow of time independent non-Newtonian liquids in smooth circular pipes, Dodge and Metzner[3] have suggested the following equation:

$$f = \frac{a}{N_{Re}^b} \qquad (3-68)$$

where a and b are functions of n' which is defined in Equation (3–21). The Reynolds number N_{Re} in Equation (3–68) is

$$N_{Re} = \frac{\rho u d_i}{K_p'(8u/d_i)^{n'-1}} \qquad (3\text{-}56)$$

Values of a and b for various values of n' are listed in Table 3–2.[14] These enable the Fanning friction factor f to be calculated if point values of K_p' and n' are known. The pressure drop is then obtained from Equation (3–65).

TABLE 3-2. Solution for Equation (3-68)[14]

n'	a	b
0.2	0.0646	0.349
0.3	0.0685	0.325
0.4	0.0712	0.307
0.6	0.0740	0.281
0.8	0.0761	0.263
1.0	0.0779	0.250
1.4	0.0804	0.231
2.0	0.0826	0.213

An alternative to the Blasius equation for the turbulent flow of Newtonian liquids in smooth circular pipes is the von Karman equation[2] which is normally written in the form

$$\frac{1}{f^{1/2}} = 4.0 \log_{10}(N_{Re}f^{1/2}) - 0.4 \qquad (3\text{-}69)$$

where f is the Fanning friction factor.

For the turbulent flow of time independent non-Newtonian liquids in smooth circular pipes, Dodge and Metzner[3] have written the von Karman equation in a general form as follows:

$$\frac{1}{f^{1/2}} = \left[\frac{4.0}{(n')^{0.75}}\right] \log_{10}\left\{N_{Re}f^{[1-(n'/2)]}\right\} - \frac{0.4}{(n')^{1.2}} \qquad (3\text{-}70)$$

Equation (3–70) reduces to Equation (3–69) when n' defined in Equation (3–21) is unity.

A plot of $\Delta P/(4\ell/d_i)$ vs $(8u/d_i)$ for the laminar flow of a non-Newtonian liquid in a pipe gives a single line independent of pipe size. In contrast, a plot of $\Delta P/(4\ell/d_i)$ vs $(8u/d_i)$ for the turbulent flow of a non-Newtonian

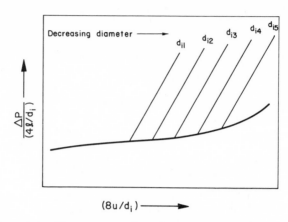

Figure 3–4.   Shear stress at the wall vs flow characteristic for a
non-Newtonian liquid flowing in a pipe.

liquid in a pipe gives a separate line for each pipe size. The effect of pipe
size on the $\Delta P/(4\ell/d_i)$ vs $(8u/d_i)$ plot in the turbulent region is illustrated
in Figure 3–4. The ordinate $\Delta P/(4\ell/d_i)$ in Figure 3–4 is the shear stress R
at the wall. The onset of turbulence in pipeline flow is accompanied by a
sharp increase in the shear stress R. This is shown in Figure 3–4 as a
sudden increase in slope of the $\Delta P/(4\ell/d_i)$ vs $(8u/d_i)$ plot. It is clearly seen
from Figure 3–4 that the onset of turbulence for a non-Newtonian liquid
flowing in a pipe occurs at different values of the flow characteristic
$(8u/d_i)$ for different pipe sizes.

For Newtonian liquid flow in pipes, the onset of turbulent flow occurs
at a Reynolds number N_{Re} of approximately 2100. Dodge and Metzner[3]
showed that for pseudoplastic liquids obeying the power law, the end of
the laminar flow region in pipes occurred at a Reynolds number which
increased as the power law index n decreased.

Savins[10] has described how the addition of certain organic gelling
agents enables gasoline to be pumped through pipelines at a lower pressure
drop and, hence, lower power consumption for the same flow rate. He
states that this is not necessarily due to the suppression of the onset of
turbulence. For example, it is possible with a particular combination of
Reynolds number, pipe size and rheological properties for an aqueous non-
Newtonian liquid to have a lower friction factor than water for the same
pipe size and liquid flow rate. In addition, certain non-Newtonian liquids
exhibit a pronounced diameter effect in the turbulent flow region. For
these liquids, the friction factors were found to decrease with pipe size.[10]

Turbulent Flow Velocity Distribution in a Pipe for Power Law Liquids

Dodge and Metzner[3] have given equations for the turbulent flow velocity profile of power law liquids in pipes. For the central flow region, the appropriate equation is

$$v^+ = \frac{5.66}{(n)^{0.75}} \log_{10} z^+ - \frac{0.40}{(n)^{1.2}} + \frac{2.458}{(n)^{0.75}} \left\{ 1.960 + 1.255n \right.$$
$$\left. - 1.628n \log_{10} [3 + (1/n)] \right\} \qquad (3\text{-}71)$$

For Newtonian liquids where $n = 1$, Equation (3-71) reduces to

$$v^+ = 5.66 \log_{10} z^+ + 5.1 \qquad (3\text{-}72)$$

which does not differ significantly from Equation (2-31), which can also be written as:

$$v^+ = 5.75 \log_{10} z^+ + 5.5$$

since $2.5 \log_e z^+ = 5.75 \log_{10} z^+$.

In Equation (3-71), v^+ and z^+ are a dimensionless velocity and a dimensionless distance, respectively, defined as follows:

$$v^+ = \frac{v}{\sqrt{R/\rho}} \qquad (3\text{-}73)$$

and

$$z^+ = \frac{\rho z^n (R/\rho)^{1-(n/2)}}{K_p} \qquad (3\text{-}74)$$

In Chapter 2, v^+ and z^+ were defined for Newtonian liquids. Equation (3-73) is identical with the definition in Chapter 2. For a power law index $n = 1$, Equation (3-74) reduces to the definition given in Chapter 2 for Newtonian liquids.

It was shown in Chapter 2 that for Newtonian liquids in the laminar sublayer adjacent to the pipe wall,

$$v^+ = z^+$$

The corresponding equation for power law liquids is:[3]

$$v^+ = (z^+)^{1/n}$$

Expansion and Contraction Losses for Power Law Liquids

Wilkinson[15] has shown that for power law liquids, the loss in head due to sudden expansion is:

$$h_e = \frac{1}{g}\left(\frac{Q}{A_1}\right)^2\left(\frac{3n+1}{2n+1}\right)\left[\frac{n+3}{2(5n+3)}\left(\frac{A_1}{A_2}\right)^2 - \left(\frac{A_1}{A_2}\right)\right.$$
$$\left. + \frac{3(3n+1)}{2(5n+3)}\right] \quad (3\text{-}75)$$

where Q is the volumetric flow rate, g is the gravitational acceleration, n the power law index of the liquid and A_1 and A_2 are the cross-sectional flow areas in the smaller and larger pipes, respectively.

When $n = 0$, Equation (3-75) reduces to:

$$h_e = \frac{u_1^2}{2g}\left(1 - \frac{A_1}{A_2}\right)^2 \quad (3\text{-}76)$$

where u_1 is the mean linear velocity in the smaller pipe. Equation (3-76) is the same as the approximate expression for the turbulent flow of a Newtonian liquid when the velocity profile is assumed to be flat. This can also be written in terms of the inside pipe diameters as

$$h_e = \frac{u_1^2}{2g}\left(1 - \frac{d_{i1}^2}{d_{i2}^2}\right)^2 \quad (3\text{-}77)$$

Equation (3-77) is given in Figure 2-6.

At the present time, there is no reliable expression for the head loss due to contraction for any kind of non-Newtonian liquid.

NOMENCLATURE

A	cross-sectional flow area in a pipe
a	proportionality factor in Equation (3-68)
b	exponent in Equation (3-68)
d_i	inside pipe diameter
f	Fanning friction factor (dimensionless) $= 2R/\rho u^2$
g	gravitational acceleration
h_e	head loss due to sudden expansion
j_t	basic friction factor (dimensionless) $= R/\rho u^2$
K	consistency coefficient
ℓ	pipe length
n	power law index (dimensionless)

N_{He}	Hedstrom number (dimensionless)
N_{Re}	Reynolds number (dimensionless)
P	pressure
Q	volumetric flow rate
r	radial distance from the center of a pipe
R	shear stress
u	mean linear velocity of liquid inside a pipe
v	linear velocity of liquid at a point in a pipe
Y	yield number for Bingham plastics (dimensionless)
z	distance from pipe wall in a radial direction
$\dot{\gamma}$	shear rate
μ	viscosity of liquid
ρ	density of liquid

REFERENCES

1. Alves, G. E., Boucher, D. F., and Pigford, R. L., *Chem. Eng. Progr.*, **48**, 385 (1952).
2. Bennett, C. O., and Myers, J. E., "Momentum, Heat and Mass Transfer," p. 138, New York, McGraw-Hill Book Co. Inc., 1962.
3. Dodge, D. W., and Metzner, A. B., *A.I.Ch.E. J.*, **5**, 189 (1959).
4. Eirich, F. E., "Rheology," Vol. 3, p. 205, New York, Academic Press, 1960.
5. Govier, G. W., *Chem. Eng.*, **66**, No. 17 (1959).
6. Hedstrom, B. O. A., *Ind. Eng. Chem.*, **44**, 651 (1952).
7. Metzner, A. B., and Reed, J. C., *A.I.Ch.E. J.*, **1**, 434 (1955).
8. Potts, W. E., Brinkerhoff, R., Chapman, F. S., and Holland, F. A., *Chem. Eng.*, **72**, No. 6 (1965).
9. Rabinowitsch, B. Z., *Phys. Chem.*, **145A**, 1 (1929).
10. Savins, J. G., *J. Inst. Petrol*, **47**, 454 (1961).
11. Wilkinson, W. L., "Non-Newtonian Fluids," p. 6, London, Pergamon Press, 1960.
12. *Ibid.*, p. 56.
13. *Ibid.*, p. 58.
14. *Ibid.*, p. 68.
15. *Ibid.*, p. 76.

CHAPTER 4

Valves

The discussion of valves in this chapter is limited to those which regulate the flow of liquids in pipelines.

CLASSIFICATION OF VALVE TYPES

Valves can be classified into functional groups as follows: (1) on-off service, (2) throttling or metering service, (3) prevention of back flow, and (4) pressure and/or temperature control. The latter will not be discussed in this chapter. Pressure relief and safety valves are treated in connection with positive displacement pumps in Chapter 5.

Valves for On-off Service

Since in the fully open position, a relatively straight unrestricted passage is available to the flowing liquid, pressure drop through these valves is low (see Table 4–1). The flow control element in on-off valves functions by sliding over an orifice in the valve body. Sealing or seating surfaces at the orifice prevent leakage past the flow control element. The flow control element may be flat, cylindrical or spherical. The common valves in this group are: gate, plug, ball and slide valves.

Gate Valves. These are by far the most common. They account for nearly 30 per cent of the total number of valves used in the processing industries.[1] Figure 4–1 shows a typical gate valve. The components related to flow control are (1) the wedge or disk, and (2) the valve stem.

(1) The wedge or disk is a flat flow control element peculiar to gate valves. When raised to the fully open position, the wedge completely clears the liquid stream. The unrestricted flow path reduces the pressure drop to a minimum. Various designs of wedges are used, but the solid wedge (Figure 4–1) is the most common. It has the advantage of simplicity and positive contact with the wedge guides. This reduces chatter when the valve is in a partially closed position.

TABLE 4-1. Equivalent Lengths of Valves and Fittings

Equivalent Length of Smooth Schedule 40 Steel Pipe (ft)

Nominal diameter of Schedule 40 steel pipe, inches →	½	¾	1	1¼	1½	2	2½	3	4	5	6	8	10	12	14	16
VALVES[a]																
Gate	0.56	0.70	0.85	1.10	1.20	1.50	1.70	1.80	2.30	2.70	3.40	4.80	5.90	7.80	8.50	10.1
Globe:																
bevel seat or composition disk	11.3	16.1	22.2	31.5	38.4	54.0	65.0	85.0	119	156	194	272	337	443	483	578
plug disk	14.4	20.6	28.5	40.2	49.0	66.8	83.1	109	152	—	—	—	—	—	—	—
Angle	4.30	6.10	8.40	11.9	14.5	19.8	24.6	32.2	45.0	59.4	73.6	103	128	168	183	219
Check:																
flapper, Y pattern	2.40	3.40	4.70	6.70	8.10	11.1	13.8	18.0	25.2	33.2	41.1	57.5	71.3	93.9	102	123
lift, plug, globe pattern	16.4	23.5	32.5	46.0	56.0	76.3	94.8	124	173	228	283	396	492	647	706	843
lift, ball, globe pattern	111	159	219	310	378	515	640	—	—	—	—	—	—	—	—	—
Foot, bottom strainer	24.7	35.3	48.7	68.9	83.9	114	142	186	260	343	425	594	738	970	1060	1270
FITTINGS[a]																
Elbows:[b]																
90°, standard	3.60	4.40	5.30	6.80	7.80	8.50	9.10	11.0	13.8	17.6	21.5	29.7	36.9	48.5	53.0	63.3
90°, long radius	0.66	0.94	1.30	1.80	2.20	3.10	3.80	5.00	6.90	9.10	11.3	15.9	19.7	25.9	28.2	33.7
45°, standard	0.59	0.85	1.20	1.70	2.00	2.80	3.40	4.50	6.20	8.20	10.2	14.3	17.7	23.3	25.4	30.4
Close return bend, 180°	2.40	3.50	4.80	6.80	8.30	11.3	14.0	18.3	25.6	33.7	41.8	58.5	72.6	95.5	104	125
Tees:																
line flow	0.66	0.94	1.30	1.80	2.20	3.10	3.80	5.00	6.90	9.10	11.3	15.9	19.7	25.9	28.2	33.7
branch flow to line	2.50	3.60	5.00	7.10	8.60	11.7	14.6	19.1	26.6	35.1	43.5	60.9	75.5	99.5	108	130
line flow to branch	1.80	2.50	3.50	5.00	6.00	8.20	10.2	13.4	18.7	24.6	30.6	42.7	52.9	69.7	76.1	91.0
Unions and Couplings	0.21	0.24	0.31	0.38	0.42	0.50	0.55	0.53	0.66	—	—	—	—	—	—	—

[a] Values given for screwed connections.

[b] For equivalent lengths of flanged fittings use the following factors: reg. 90° elbow × 0.34, long rad. 90° elbow × 0.46, reg. 45° elbow × 0.53, close rtn. bend × 0.24.

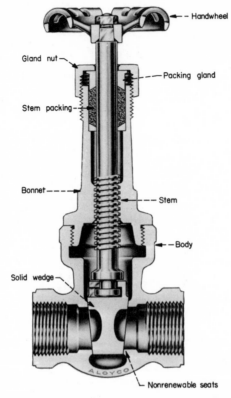

Handwheel

Gland nut

Packing gland

Stem packing

Bonnet

Stem

Body

Solid wedge

Nonrenewable seats

Figure 4-1. Rising-stem, solid wedge gate valve. (*Courtesy Alloy Steel Products Co.*)

Solid wedges have the following disadvantages: a tendency to gall the sealing surfaces when slight misalignments occur, and a tendency to jam at high temperatures due to thermal expansion.

To avoid these disadvantages, split wedges are often used. Since split wedges are relatively flexible, they compensate for thermal expansion at high temperatures and show less tendency to gall. Extremely tight seals are possible with split wedges. In both solid and split wedge gate valves, the liquid pressure forces the wedge face against the inclined seating surfaces.

A third type of wedge is also used; this type of valve does not rely on the liquid pressure to form a leak-tight seal. Known as a double disk parallel seat gate valve, it has two disks separated by a spreader device. When the valve is being closed, the two disks are forced against their respective seats by the positive action of the intermediate wedge or spreader.

A fourth type has two separate disks joined by a ball and socket connection. These are extremely flexible and are self-aligning to each of the inclined seating faces.

Regardless of the wedge design used, the faces contacting the seating surfaces should be highly polished. This insures a tight seal and prevents unnecessary wear at the points of sliding contact, especially in metal-to-metal sealing surfaces. The ball and socket wedge is shown in Figure 4–2, which illustrates a special purpose gate valve designed to handle cryogenic liquids at very low temperatures.

(2) The valve stem is a shaft used to control the position of the wedge. It is connected to the wedge by either a trunion joint or a thread, and it passes through the valve body to its exterior, at which point a handwheel or other turning device is attached. On the basis of stem movement, gate valves may be classified into three additional types: rising-stem (inside thread), rising-stem (outside thread), and nonrising-stem.

Rising-stem valves (Figure 4–1) have a male threaded stem which engages a female threaded portion of the valve bonnet. As the hand-wheel

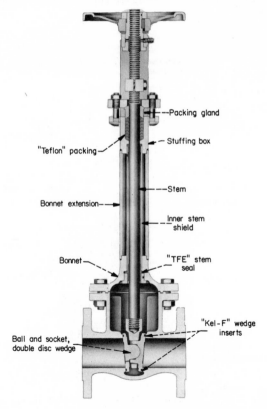

Figure 4-2.   Double disk, OS & Y cryogenic gate valve. (*Courtesy Alloy Steel Products Co.*)

is turned in a clockwise direction, the stem moves upward along the threaded section. Thus the wedge rises and allows liquid to flow. Rising-stem gate valves may have either an inside threaded or an outside threaded stem. The outside threaded, rising-stem valve (Figure 4–3) is also called an outside screw and yoke (OS & Y) valve.

Rising-stem valves have the advantage that the wedge position is indicated by the extent of the stem rise. Furthermore, outside screw valves are easily lubricated, since the threaded portion of the stem is exposed.

Since this is sealed from the process liquid by the packing gland, the threads are protected from corrosive or abrasive liquids. Disadvantages are: (a) adequate headroom is required to allow for the rise of the stem when the valve is in the fully open position, (b) the exposed stem in the raised position is prone to damage from mechanical abuse and corrosive atmospheres, and (c) the threads of inside threaded stems come into contact with the process liquid and are therefore subject to erosion and corrosion.

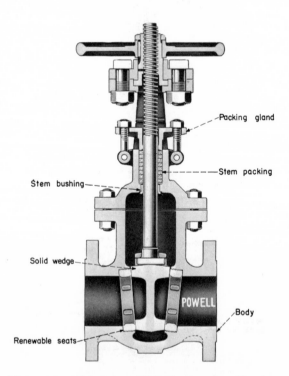

Figure 4-3.   Rising-stem, OS & Y gate valve. (*Courtesy The Wm. Powell Co.*)

The rising-stem gate valves considered so far are not quick acting since they require turning to raise the control element. Figure 4–4(A) shows a valve which does not require turning. In this valve, the stem slides up or down through the action of a mechanical lever. Quick-acting valves are commonly used in lines carrying extremely flammable or hazardous liquids. They can be equipped with a self-acting weighted lever and a fusible linkage. In case of fire, the linkage melts and the weighted handle automatically swings to the off position. Pressure sensing actuators can be used to close these valves if a downstream pipe bursts. Single or double seats are used to provide pressure control in one or both directions, respectively. The control lever may be connected either directly to the sliding stem or

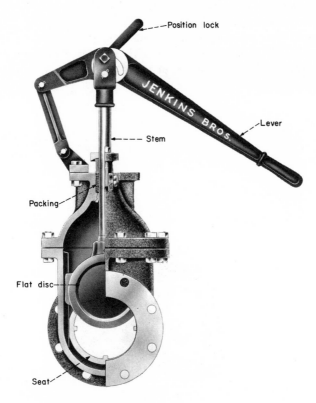

(A) Vertical sliding stem gate valve.

Figure 4-4.   Quick-opening gate valves.
(*Courtesy Jenkins Bros.*)

through worms or other torque multipliers. The latter units are common in high pressure service.

Figure 4–4(B) shows another type of quick-acting gate valve. This has a cam actuated rotating disk in place of a sliding stem. A lever moves the wedge which travels in an arc across the seating surfaces.

Nonrising-stem gate valves have a male threaded stem meshing with a female threaded wedge (Figure 4–5). As the stem is turned, the wedge travels up the threaded engagement while the stem remains in a fixed position. Since nonrising-stem gate valves require thread contact between the stem and the wedge, only inside threaded types are available.

The advantages of this design are: (a) less headroom is required than with rising-stem valves, (b) the stem is not subject to damage from mechanical abuse, and (c) the absence of axial stem movement provides a tighter stem packing seal. The packing in rising-stem valves must withstand both turning and axial motion.

The primary disadvantage of nonrising-stem gate valves is the rapid wear of the stem threads when used with slurries. Corrosion is also a problem, since the threaded section of the stem is exposed to the process liquid.

(B) Parallel rotating shaft gate valve.

Figure 4-4. *Cont'd*

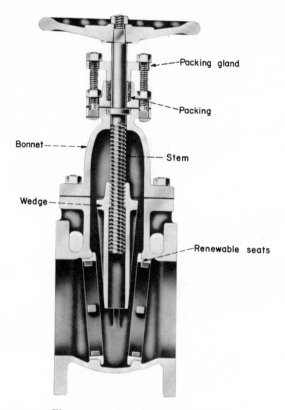

Figure 4-5.   Nonrising-stem gate valve.
(*Courtesy Jenkins Bros.*)

Gate valves should never be used for throttling or controlling liquid streams. The reasons are: (a) when the wedge is in an intermediate position, the high velocity liquid streams cause rapid erosion of the wedge and distortion of the lower seating surface; (b) the flow control profile is not linear, since most of the shut-off takes place when the valve is almost closed. The latter characteristic is undesirable if accurate control of flow rates is required. The valve shown in Figure 4–6 employs a raisable, nonrotating, tapered plug in place of the usual flat wedge. This provides good throttling characteristics in addition to the general straight through flow of gate valves.

Gate valves are widely available in the size range ⅛ to 48 inches NPS for use at temperatures up to 1200° F and pressures up to 2500 psi. Specially designed valves can be obtained for higher pressures and temperatures. Line connections may be flanged, inside screw, outside screw or brazed.

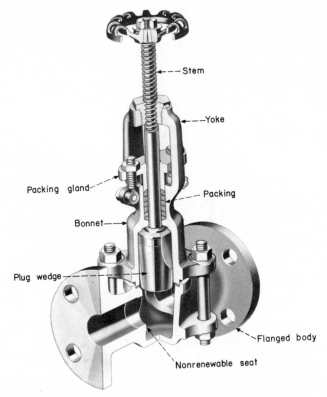

Figure 4-6.   Plug wedge, rising-stem gate valve.
(*Courtesy Crane Co.*)

Valve seats are especially prone to rapid wear in slurry or abrasive service.[1,5,6] For this case, easily installed renewable surfaces are available. These are shown in Figures 4–3 and 4–5.

Seats, wedges and other valve parts are available in a wide variety of materials, ranging from cast iron to titanium. Frequently, the wedge is equipped with a facing or circular insert of a pliable material such as "Teflon" or "Kel-F". This provides a tighter seal than that obtained with metal-to-metal contact. Figure 4–2 shows a valve with "Kel-F" insert rings on a double disk wedge. A stem seal and extended bonnet house a tubular stem shield which protects the packing and upper valve parts from extreme cold. Completely lined valves are also available for use at moderate pressures and temperatures in place of the high cost alloyed valves used for severe duty. Valves are lined with materials such as rubber, "Teflon," "Penton," and graphite.

Plug Valves. Like gate valves, plug valves are essentially intended for on-off service. The disadvantages of using these valves for throttling service are: (a) the internal parts wear rapidly, and (b) the flow is not a linear function of the degree of closure. The only primary moving part in a typical plug valve is the tapered or cylindrical plug. This is transversely pierced to allow liquid to flow when the pierced section is exposed to the valve port. In simple, single-port, plug valves, flow is controlled by turning the plug 90°.

Plug valves can be classified as lubricated and nonlubricated. Both types are identical in operation, but differ in plug and seat design. Common lubricated plugs [Figures 4–7(B) and 4–7(C)] are equipped with peripheral lubrication channels which ride against a metallic valve seat. The lubricant is forced, under pressure, through these channels to provide a thin film between the plug surface and the seat wall. The lubricant is kept within the valve by a ball check valve in the stem. The lubricant reduces wear between the two surfaces and reduces friction and, hence, the tendency to jam. Nonlubricated plug valves must be used when it is necessary to avoid contamination of the process liquid. Either of two methods is

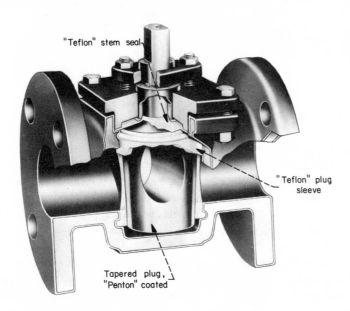

"Teflon" stem seal

"Teflon" plug sleeve

Tapered plug, "Penton" coated

(A) Nonlubricated, tapered plug, fully "Penton" coated plug valve.

Figure 4-7.   Plug valves. (*Courtesy A-Duriron Co.; B&C-WKM Div., ACF Industries*)

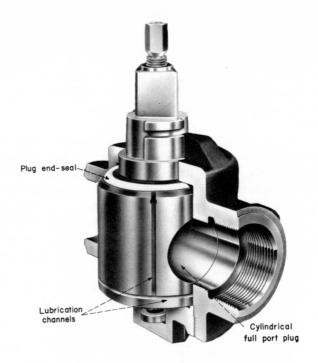

Plug end-seal

Lubrication
channels

Cylindrical
full port plug

(B) Lubricated, cylindrical, full port plug valve.

Figure 4-7. *Cont'd*

employed to prevent leakage and provide smooth operation: an elastomeric
or polymeric sleeve surrounding the plug or an elastomeric or polymeric
coating on the plug itself. Materials having self-lubricating properties,
such as "Teflon," "Penton," nylon, etc., are used.

Figure 4–7(A) illustrates a nonlubricated, tapered plug valve in which a
"Teflon" plug collar, or sleeve, acts as the sealing surface. A gasket is
required above the plug to act as a stem seal. Since no other packing is
required, a stuffing box is not necessary. This valve is intended for service
with highly corrosive materials. Both the interior and the exterior surfaces
are coated with "Penton," a very inert polymer. A second type of nonlubricated plug valve incorporates a split plug and expander.[5] When the
plug is in the desired position, the expander wedge forces it against the

Tapered plug

Rectangular port

(C) Lubricated, tapered plug valve.

Figure 4-7. *Cont'd*

sleeve to form a tight seal. In operation, the expander lifts slightly, allowing the plug to turn freely; the only friction is at the stem packing.

The valves shown in Figures 4–7(A), 4–7(B) and 4–7(C) require only a single lever to control the plug. Others have two levers: one to "break" or reseal the plug-to-sleeve joint, and the second to turn the plug to any desired position.

Plug valves have the advantages of simple construction and compactness. Their simple seals are suitable for multi-port service. These can handle three to four separate streams. The most common valves are three- and four-port units handling two and three and four streams, respectively. A single four-way plug valve can take the place of four straight flow valves. This also reduces the piping and the number of fittings needed.

Multi-port plugs, however, are more complex than single-port units. Although in single-port plugs, the valve can be opened or closed by a 90° turn, the multi-port units require intermediate positions for each stream. Suitable stop-tabs are normally supplied, but inexperienced operators can easily make mistakes.

Lubricated plug valves are available in sizes ranging from $\frac{1}{4}$ to 30 inches NPS. These normally operate at pressures up to 5500 psi and temperatures up to 600°F. Nonlubricated plugs, particularly those using "Teflon" sleeves, are commonly found in sizes ranging from $\frac{1}{4}$ to 16 inches NPS. Since "Teflon" deforms under extreme temperature and pressure conditions, these valves are limited to 425°F and 750 psi, respectively.[1]

Ball Valves. A modification of the plug valve is the ball valve in which the cylindrical or tapered plug is replaced by a spherical plug. Although ball valves are not a new innovation, it is only since the advent of modern elastomeric and polymeric materials such as "Teflon" that they have been used with any degree of success. Prior to this, ball valves had a tendency to leak. For this reason, they could not be used for handling flammable materials.

Various ball valve designs are available, such as the full-flow, venturi or reduced-flow units. All operate, however, on the quarter-turn principle, for on or off service. Like plug valves, they are compact with few components. Figure 4–8 illustrates the construction of a typical ball valve from uncommon materials. The ball valve shown in Figure 4–8(A) is a full-flow unit, since the ball portings are the same diameter as the main body channel. The unobstructed path through the valve results in a minimum pressure drop. The inert lining and covering materials make this valve suitable for severe duty. Liquids such as hydrochloric, sulfuric and hydrofluoric acid, at all concentrations, may be handled with no damage to internal parts.

The tongue and groove attachment of liner to body and coating to ball prevents lining separation when the valve is used under vacuum. This problem is common to all types of lined or coated valves. In the venturi type of porting [Figure 4–8(B)], the body channel slopes gently from the pipe diameter to a smaller ball port diameter. This valve is also intended for severe service.

In the valve shown in Figure 4–8(B), both ball and lining are composed of impervious graphite, which is inert to most acids and other corrosives. The "Impervite" is also immune to thermal shock which may arise from rapid temperature changes. This, together with the "Teflon" seats, provides a valve requiring no lubrication and having excellent sealing characteristics.

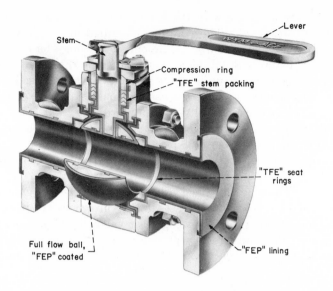

(A) Full flow, completely lined ball valve.

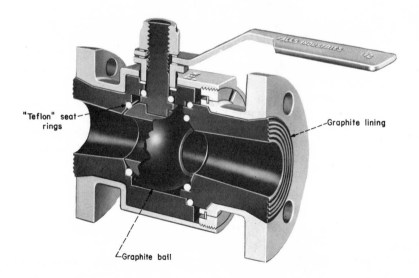

(B) Venturi flow, graphite ball and liner ball valve.

Figure 4-8.   Ball valves. (*Courtesy A-WKM Div., ACF Industries;*
B-Falls Industries, Inc.)

Ball valves are available with the common valve-to-pipe connections: flanges, screw threads, etc. They are manufactured in a wide variety of materials, ranging from cast iron to zirconium and may be coated with inert polymers [Figure 4–8(A)]. Line sizes range from $\frac{1}{4}$ to 36 inches NPS. The upper temperature limit is about 575°F. Temperature limits for polymeric lined or coated valves are usually considerably lower than for all metal construction. Since ball valves produce very tight seals with an almost even pressure distribution on the spherical sealing surface, they can be used at pressures up to 7000 psi.

Like gate and plug valves, ball valves are not recommended for throttling service.[1,5,6]

Slide Valves. These are modified solid wedge, rising-stem gate valves. A flat gate slides between parallel seats in the valve body. In place of the mechanical force used in the split wedge gate valve, liquid pressure pushes the gate against the downstream seat to form an effective seal. A typical slide valve is shown in Figure 4–9. This particular valve has an outside

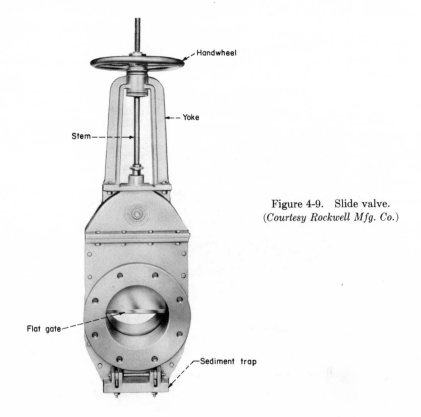

Figure 4-9.   Slide valve.
(*Courtesy Rockwell Mfg. Co.*)

screw and yoke mechanism, although other types are available such as a quick-acting vertical slide. Slide valves are used at pressures up to 400 psi and temperatures up to 1200°F. They give excellent service when tight seals are not required. The high upper temperature limit is made possible by the relatively large clearances at the seating areas. These valves have a tendency to clog at the seats when used with slurries. To avoid this, valves are available with sedimentation chambers below the bottom of the seating surfaces. The flat gate pushes any foreign materials out of the seating groove and into this chamber. The latter may be cleaned out without disturbing the piping connections. Slide valves are available in line sizes ranging from 2 to 72 inches NPS. Materials of construction vary, according to the service, although materials such as cast iron and steel are most common.

Throttling and Control Valves

These are used to control liquid flow through a pipeline at some rate less than the maximum. The valves discussed so far cannot provide this type of flow control, since the greater portion of their shut-off occurs immediately prior to complete closure of the orifice. With gate valves, for example, only minor changes in flow rate occur until the wedge is nearly seated and the cross-sectional flow area is reduced to a small crescent-shaped element.

Accurate flow control under these conditions is difficult. Reproducibility is even more difficult, since the internal parts are subject to wear.

Throttling valves are designed to exhibit an essentially linear flow response as a function of orifice closure. This is accomplished by uniformly varying the cross-sectional area through which liquid must flow.

In most throttling valves, the flow is directed along an axis parallel to that of the closure component, in contrast to on-off valves where the liquid stream flows perpendicular to the axis of the flow control element. The following valves exhibit linear flow control characteristics and can therefore be used for throttling: globe, angle and "Y," pinch, diaphragm and butterfly valves. These are called throttling valves if operated manually and control valves if actuated automatically by a sensing device.

Manually operated throttling valves are discussed in this section. Control valves are treated in a later section.

Globe Valves. These are the most widely used throttling valves, accounting for about 10 per cent of the total valve market and some 50 per cent of all throttling valves.[1] Flow is controlled by a tapered plug or disk which closes onto a seating surface.

Whereas gate valves can have rising or nonrising stems, the disk in globe valves is always controlled by a rising stem. In gate valves, the seating surfaces are in a plane perpendicular to the flow; this provides an unrestricted flow passage when the gate or wedge is in the fully raised position. In contrast, the seating surfaces in a globe valve are in a plane parallel to that of the flow. The disk travels vertically, perpendicular to the seating surface. This action provides the necessary linear flow response.

Figure 4–10 shows a typical globe valve. The liquid flowing through the valve makes two right angle turns. Liquid enters parallel to the seat, along the horizontal axis of the pipeline and valve.   A stationary partition causes a 90° turn in flow, directing the liquid axially up into the face of the disk. After passing around the disk, the liquid again flows along the pipe axis. Because of this circuitous liquid path, the pressure drop through a globe valve is much higher than in a gate valve.

Globe valves differ primarily in their disk and seat designs. The three basic types available are: flat metal disk, metal tapered plug disk, and composition disk.

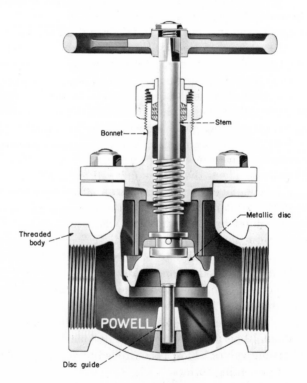

Figure 4-10.   Metal disk, rising-stem globe valve.
(*Courtesy The Wm. Powell Co.*)

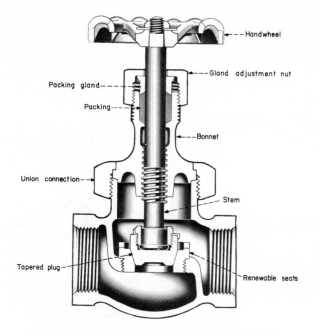

Figure 4-11.   Tapered plug, rising-stem globe valve.
(*Courtesy Crane Co.*)

The globe valve shown in Figure 4–10 has a flat metal disk. Contact between disk and seat is a single line around the circumference of the disk. This does not always give leakproof sealing at shut-off, since foreign particles may become wedged between the disk and seat.

Figure 4–11 shows a tapered plug disk. This is tapered at the same angle as the seating surface. In the fully off position, contact is made over the entire side surface area of the plug to form a leak-tight seal. Compared with a flat disk, the tapered plug has a relatively high resistance to erosion and seat deformation and less chance of galling.

A composition disk globe valve is shown in Figure 4–12. It has a metallic disk holder and an annular disk insert. The disk, or ring, is composed of materials such as "Teflon," "Kel-F" or other resilient polymers. This particular valve is a quick opening unit and is equipped with a self-returning, spring actuated disk. The valve is opened with a hand lever. A ball check valve within the disk holder provides some protection against waterhammer by retarding the shut-off time. Waterhammer or shock waves within the system are caused when any valve is closed too rapidly. Waterhammer is discussed in Chapter 10. Tight seals are formed, since the

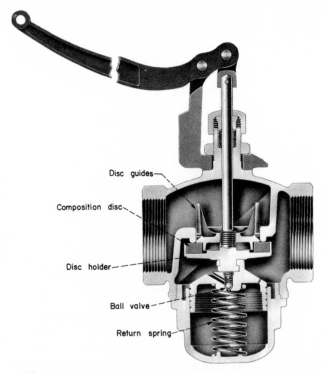

Disc guides

Composition disc

Disc holder

Ball valve

Return spring

Figure 4-12.   Quick-opening, self-closing, composition disk
globe valve. (*Courtesy Jenkins Bros.*)

metallic seal can be firmly imbedded against the softer disk without galling
or other damage. Any small particles caught between the seat and insert
are depressed below the area of surface contact.

Composition disk globe valves are, however, less effective as throttling
devices, since the disk insert is prone to erosion by the high velocity
liquid streams produced when the valve is in the near closed position.[1]

The stainless steel globe valve shown in Figure 4–13 is fully jacketed to
allow heating or cooling. Jacketed valves and fittings are discussed in
Chapters 9 and 10.

Globe valves are available in sizes ranging from $\frac{1}{8}$ to 30 inches. They
can be used at pressures and temperatures up to 2500 psi and 1000°F.
respectively. Materials of construction vary widely. Seat and disk material
combinations run from metal on metal to "Teflon" on metal. A wide
range of polymeric materials is in common use.

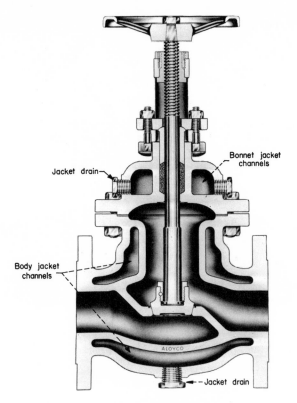

Figure 4-13.   Jacketed, OS & Y globe valve.
(*Courtesy Alloy Steel Products Co.*)

Angle and "Y" Valves

The main disadvantage of globe valves is their high pressure drop (see Table 4–1). Other valves are available which retain the desired throttling characteristics of globe valves but have a reduced pressure drop across the disk and seats. This is accomplished by decreasing either the number or the severity of the bends within the valve.

In "Y" valves (Figure 4–14), the seat is at a 45° angle to the horizontal. This gives a relatively unrestricted flow path. Flow through a "Y" valve is nearly as free as in gate valves. Stem, disk and seating arrangements are the same as for globe, gate and other valves discussed so far.

The "Y" valve shown in Figure 4–14(A) is an OS & Y unit. Figure 4–14(B) shows a "Y" valve with a porcelain lining and a solid porcelain piston-type plug. This can be used even with hot concentrated acids.

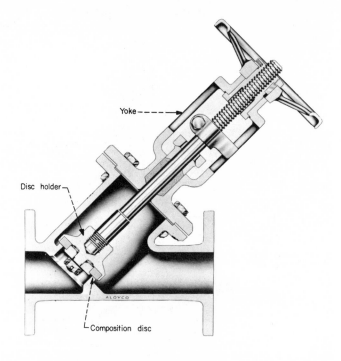

Yoke

Disc holder

Composition disc

(A) O S & Y, composition disc Y valve.

Figure 4-14. Y valves. (*Courtesy A-Alloy Steel Products Co.;*
B-Lapp Insulator Co.)

However, hydrofluoric acid and other fluorine compounds attack porcelain. Many other valve types are available with porcelain interiors.

For low to moderate temperatures, "Y" valves should be installed with the inlet liquid impinging on to the face of the disk or plug. The liquid pressure tends to push the plug out of the seat and to promote easier operation of the valve. This also keeps erosion of the seat and the disk to a minimum. For high temperatures, the liquid pressure should be applied above the disk. Otherwise the stem will be at a lower temperature than the disk and seat, and contraction of the stem may raise the disk from its seat. The resultant leakage accelerates erosion and wiredrawing of the disk and seats. This high temperature rule for reversed installations applies also to globe and angle valves.

Angle valves are also modified globe valves. The liquid flow takes one 90° turn (Figure 4–15) as opposed to two such turns in the globe type.

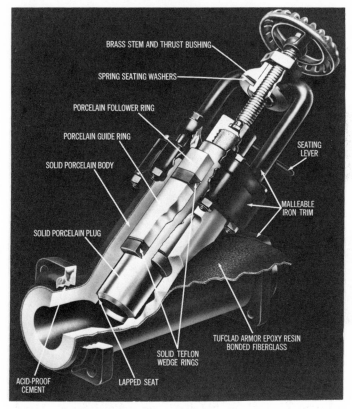

BRASS STEM AND THRUST BUSHING

SPRING SEATING WASHERS

PORCELAIN FOLLOWER RING

PORCELAIN GUIDE RING

SOLID PORCELAIN BODY

SEATING
LEVER

SOLID PORCELAIN PLUG

MALLEABLE
IRON TRIM

TUFCLAD ARMOR EPOXY RESIN
BONDED FIBERGLASS

SOLID TEFLON
WEDGE RINGS

ACID-PROOF
CEMENT

LAPPED SEAT

(B) OS & Y porcelain plug and liner Y valve.

Figure 4-14. *Cont'd*

Angle valves are usually constructed with a unitized body, although special designs are available having a split body construction.[1] The latter facilitates replacement or regrinding of the seating surfaces which are inaccessible in a one-piece body.

Another type of angle valve, which does not require any seating surfaces, has a piston or plunger that extends past the entrance port when in the shut-off position. The plunger is equipped with packing rings above and below the inlet port to prevent leakage.

Needle Valves. These are equipped with a long-taper or needle-like plug that accurately fits into the valve seat. The stem threads are very fine, allowing close control of flow through the valve. Needle valves are available in the globe, angle and "Y" configurations. They are of the inside thread, rising-stem design and can be used for pressures up to 10,000 psi.

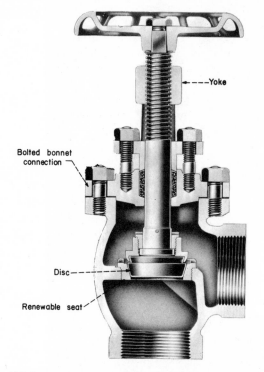

Figure 4-15. OS & Y angle valve. (*Courtesy Jenkins Bros.*)

High pressure needle valves are commonly fabricated from solid bar stock in materials such as "Monel" and stainless steel. Metal-to-metal seals are preferred at the higher pressures. These valves should not be used at temperatures below −100° F or above 500° F. Usually intended for small flows, they range in size from ⅛ to 1 inch NPS.

Pinch Valves. These consist of two primary components: a flexible tube and a set of pinch bars, one movable and the other stationary. The flexible tube is positioned between the two pinching bars (Figure 4–16). Flow is controlled by pinching the flexible tube between the upper and lower bars to reduce the cross-sectional flow area inside the tube. These valves may be used for throttling, since the change in area, as the tube is pinched, is a substantially linear response. In the fully open position, an unrestricted path is available; hence, pressure drop is relatively low and is comparable to that in gate and slide valves. The low pressure drop and obstruction-free path are an advantage when these valves are used in slurry and paste handling.

Other advantages are the simple design and the absence of contact between the metallic moving parts and the process liquid. This avoids

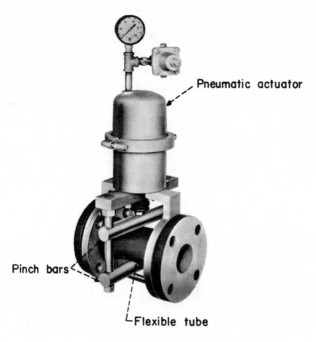

Figure 4-16.   Pneumatically actuated pinch valve. (*Courtesy RKL Controls, Inc.*)

product contamination and corrosion. The only component in contact with the liquid is the flexible tube (see Figure 4–16).

The pressure and temperature ranges of these valves are determined by the tube material. Since the tube must be deformed to a considerable extent, noncracking materials such as natural rubber, buna and neoprene must be used. The tube material is often reinforced and covered with a fabric shield or sleeve. Even so, pinch valves are normally limited to pressures up to 350 psi and temperatures ranging from -100 to $500°F$. Vacuum service is not recommended as the tube tends to collapse.

The pinch bar is controlled by devices such as handwheels, pneumatic and hydraulic cylinders (Figure 4–16), and electrically power driven mechanisms. Tube diameters range from 1 to 18 inches NPS.

In a modified version of the pinch valve, a flexible tube is enclosed within an airtight jacket. Air or hydraulic fluid surrounds the tube. As the pressure in the jacket is increased, the tube is depressed, causing a decrease in flow. This valve is extremely reliable, since no moving parts are used. Failure of the flexible tube or pressure supply is the only area where trouble can normally occur. Valves with this method of closure are used in the same areas as the ordinary pinch type, e.g., slurries, abrasives, etc.

Diaphragm Valves. In these valves, the process liquid is isolated from the stem and stem collar by a flexible diaphragm. Two general methods of sealing are in common use. These are illustrated in Figures 4–17 and 4–18, respectively. In the valve shown in Figure 4–17, both the compression head and the stem mechanism are completely isolated from the process liquid. The valve is closed by forcing the diaphragm into a partition or weir, which mates with the compression head. In the fully open position, the flow is only mildly restricted.

This type of valve is also available without the weir. Although this gives straight through flow, the increased diaphragm deformation at, or near, shut-off contributes to rapid wear and diaphragm failure. Since the weir-type diaphragm valve requires a shorter closure stroke than does the full-flow valve, semiflexible materials such as "Teflon" and "Kel-F" may be used. These provide excellent resistance to corrosive liquids. Full-flow valves, however, require highly flexible diaphragm materials such as the natural and synthetic rubbers; these are subject to abrasion and cannot be used with liquids which are rubber solvents. Both types of valves are available completely lined. Figure 4–17 shows a rubber lined weir-type diaphragm valve.

In the valve shown in Figure 4–18, the flexible diaphragm acts only as a stem seal. The valve is closed by a disk which seats on the liquid side of

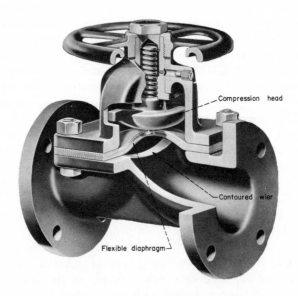

Figure 4-17. Weir-type diaphragm valve.
(*Courtesy Hills-McCanna Co.*)

the diaphragm. In unlined valves, an annular insert in the disk provides a tight seal against the seat. In the lined valve in Figure 4–18, the disk is completely covered with lining material.

Stem mechanisms in diaphragm valves may be rising, nonrising or sliding. Throttling characteristics are good. An exception is the weir-type at low flows. This can be corrected by using a composite compression head which opens the center section of the valve before the entire diaphragm lifts off the weir.[1,6]

Diaphragm valves do not tend to clog and can therefore be used with slurries of high solids content. They are also used with viscous liquids. Diaphragm valves are available in a variety of body and lining materials. Sizes range from $\frac{1}{8}$ to 30 inches NPS. Diaphragm valves are commonly used in the temperature range -60 to $500°F$ and at pressures up to 350 psi. The limiting factor is usually the diaphragm material. Since this is affected by the combination of temperature and pressure, higher pressures can be used at lower temperatures. Conversely, higher temperatures can be used at lower pressures.

Butterfly Valves. These valves have a single primary moving part which is a disk or vane. This disk is pivoted on either a horizontal or a vertical axis within the valve body as shown in Figure 4–19. In the fully open position, the disk is in a plane parallel to that of the flowing liquid. Butterfly valve disks are made as thin as possible and the disk edges are tapered. Since the flow restriction is small, butterfly valves have a low pressure drop. The valve shown in Figure 4–19 has a mechanical disk-positioning control. Handwheel, ratchet, hydraulic and electric controls are also commonly used.

Butterfly valves have the following advantages: (1) compactness and simplicity, (2) low pressure drop, (3) good for slurries since they are self-cleaning, and (4) satisfactory throttling characteristics over most of the range.

Disadvantages are: (1) the unbalanced torque on the disk (except when the valve is fully open or closed) tends to close the valve, (2) large valves require a large amount of force to operate the disk, and (3) throttling characteristics are poor when the disk is less than 15° from the fully closed position.

A number of different methods are used to seal the disk in butterfly valves. In light duty valves, the disk seats directly on the body wall, making a metal-to-metal contact. This does not normally give a bubble-tight seal. For high pressure service or where really tight seals are required, the disk can be equipped with a resilient lip on its periphery. Alternatively, seal rings can be incorporated into the valve wall as shown in Figure 4–19.

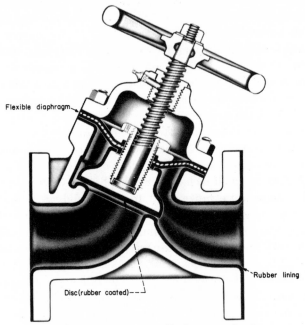

Flexible diaphragm

Rubber lining

Disc(rubber coated)

Figure 4-18.   Y pattern, diaphragm seal valve.
(Courtesy Crane Co.)

Butterfly valves are available in diameters from 1 inch to specially made units as large as 10 feet. The disk-to-wall seal is the limiting factor for temperature and pressure. Valves with metal-to-metal seals are generally able to withstand higher temperatures than those with resilient seating materials such as "Teflon," rubber or "Hypalon." Valves with seal ring inserts have been used successfully at pressures up to 3000 psi.

Valves Preventing Back Flow

These are known as one-way or check valves and are used to insure that flow takes place in only one direction. Check valves are of simple construction and usually have only one moving part. They are classified on the basis of the shape and motion of the flow control element.

Ball or piston lift, disk lift, tilting disk, flapper or swinging disk check valves shown in Figure 4–20 are all in common use. They all operate on the same principle. The force or pressure of the flowing liquid raises the control element from its seat. When flow stops, the control element is returned to the seating surface by its own weight. When back pressure develops in the line, the control element is forced against the seat and flow in the reverse direction is prevented.

Ball Check Valves. These are the simplest type of check valve. The control element is a freely moving solid ball which fits snugly into a seat to form a tight seal. The straight through ball valve illustrated in Figure 4–20(A) is used in vertical lines. Globe-type ball valves are used in horizontal lines. Pressure drop through both types is moderately high, since the ball is usually directly in the path of the flowing liquid. Slurries cause ball check valves to clog and to wear rapidly. The valve shown in Chapter 5 (Figure 5–16) is designed to allow easy access to the ball and seats by means of a quick-opening cover. The seats and ball in this valve can be replaced without removing the valve body from the pipeline.

Since in ball valves the ball is free to rotate within its guides, wear is not localized, as the ball will usually seat in a different position each time the valve closes. Most types have a metallic ball sealing against metallic seats. Commonly used materials are: cast iron, steel, bronze and stainless steel. Completely lined valves with a coated ball are sometimes used for slurries. Lining materials used include "Hypalon," "Nordel" and neoprene.

Figure 4-19. Mechanically actuated, vertical axis butterfly valve. (*Courtesy Rockwell Mfg. Co.*)

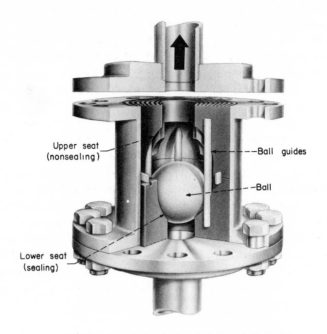

(A) Ball-lift check valve (straight through design)

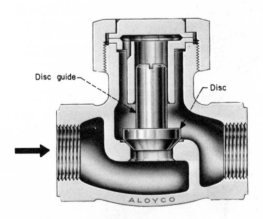

(B) Disc lift check (globe design).

Figure 4-20.   Check valves. (*Courtesy A-Appcor Application Corp.; B&D-Alloy Steel Products Co.; C-Chapman Div., Crane Co., E-Crane Co.*)

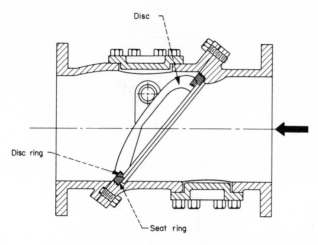

(C) Tilting disc check valve.

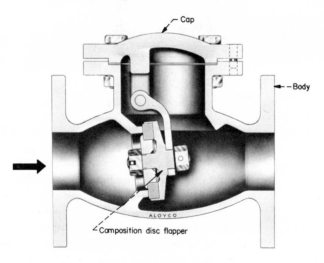

(D) Flapper check valve.

Figure 4-20. *Cont'd*

Line sizes are available for ⅛ to 24 inches NPS in screwed, flanged and welded connections.

Disk Lift and Piston Lift Check Valves. These are globe-type valves. Closure is accomplished through a disk or plug which travels along a vertical axis. Disk or plug guides are necessary to provide alignment with the valve seat. Disk lift valves operate immediately if the liquid flow ceases

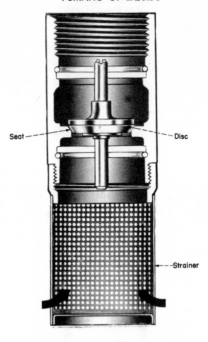

(E) Foot valve.

Figure 4-20. *Cont'd*

or back pressure develops. Piston lift types are equipped with a dash pot to retard the valve action and smooth out rapid fluctuations. In both valves, provisions are made to allow easy access to the seats and disk or piston—usually by removing a screwed or bolted cap. When the cap is removed, the moving parts may be lifted out of the valve body and the seats cleaned, reground or replaced. Liquids which solidify easily upon cooling can be a problem in check valves. For this reason, jacketed check valves are available. Pressure drop in disk lift and piston lift check valves is less than with regular globe valves, since the bends taken by the liquid are less than 90°.

Flapper or Swing Check Valves. These produce less pressure drop and turbulence than other check valves. The control element is a hinged disk and arm which is pivoted at a point above the main flow path. The disk swings away from the seats when liquid flows in the desired direction. Reversed flow is quickly checked since the disk is forced back to the closed position. Figure 4–20(D) shows a straight through swing check valve in which the seat is perpendicular to the direction of flow. Swing check valves are also available in the "Y" configuration with seats at 45° to the horizontal. Straight through valves create slightly less pressure drop and turbulence than "Y" units. The swinging disks are made of the same materials as the disks in globe valves. They may be either coated or solid metal.

Tilting Disk Check Valves. This valve [Figure 4–20(C)] is a modification of the standard swing check valve. The pivot point of the disk provides a very rapid closing action with a shorter travel distance than swing checks. When fully open, the disk hangs parallel to the axis of flow. Since the disk presents little resistance to flow, the pressure drop is low. Tilting disk valves do not chatter or flutter like swing and ball checks.

Foot Valves. These are used to maintain a centrifugal pump's prime. They are installed at the foot or end of the pump's suction line. Figure 4–20(E) shows a disk lift foot valve. Once the pump is primed, the foot valve prevents liquid from leaving the suction line when the pump is not operating. Furthermore, without a foot valve, a cavitating pump may lose its prime. Self-priming centrifugal pumps have a foot valve in the suction line and an additional check valve in the priming chamber.

Control Valves

Control valves provide automatic flow control. The control system consists of three basic elements: (1) the valve itself, (2) a valve actuator and (3) a sensing device or controller. The combination of the valve and actuator is normally referred to as the control valve.

The control element inside the valve is automatically adjusted by the actuator to the desired flow rate. The actuator, in turn, is controlled through signals sent from the sensing element or controller. Three types of controllers and actuators are commonly used: electronic, hydraulic or pneumatic. Normally, the same mode of operation is maintained throughout a control system, e.g., pneumatic controllers are linked to pneumatic actuators. Pneumatic systems are widely used in chemical processing.[7]

Controller Operation. Pneumatic controllers usually provide output air in the pressure range 3 to 15 psi. The actuator changes the position of the control element inside the valve on the basis of air pressure fluctuations. Numerous controller designs are available; the simplest provides only on-off valve control. However, the basic operating principle of all pneumatic controllers is the same.[7] This is illustrated in Figure 4–21. Air supplied at a constant pressure divides into two paths as shown in Figure 4–21. One leads to the actuator, the other through a nozzle to a flapper. The proximity of the flapper to the nozzle determines the back pressure in the system. The back pressure is high when the flapper is close. This increases the flow of air to the actuator. As the flapper moves away from the nozzle,

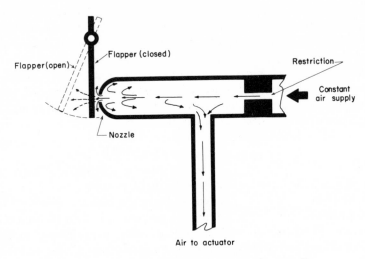

Figure 4-21. Operation of a simple pneumatic controller.

the air flow through the nozzle increases. This decreases the air flow to the actuator.

Actuator Operation. Simple pueumatic actuators consist of a flexible diaphragm and a single or double helical spring. Figure 4–22 shows both the air-to-open and air-to-close type of actuator. In the former, the spring applies a force which tends to open the valve. The air pressure from the controller exerts a force against the spring. The valve closes when this force exceeds the spring force. This valve opens when the air supply fails. In air-to-close valves, the spring applies a force which tends to close the valve. The valve opens when the air pressure exceeds the spring force. This valve closes when the air supply fails.

Springless actuators are also used, although less so than diaphragm spring units. Two common springless designs are the pressure balanced diaphragm and the pressure balanced piston. In the diaphragm type shown in Figure 4–23, the helical spring is replaced by a constant supply of high pressure air. For this type of actuator, a valve positioner is usually required.[3,7] The positioner is an auxiliary device which provides the constant high pressure air supply in addition to the variable pressure actuating air. The positioner is a closed loop controller. It receives signals from the network's sensing controller and adjusts the actuating air pressure accordingly. The difference between the actuating and supply air pressure determines the position of the diaphragm. This, in turn, positions the control element inside the valve which regulates the liquid flow rate. The pressure balanced piston actuator also requires a valve positioner. Operation is similar to the pressure balanced diaphragm unit. However, a freely moving piston is used in place of a flexible diaphragm.

The main advantage of springless actuators is that they have more power than spring units. This makes them useful on large valves or in high pressure service. Since they depend entirely on air, they do not fail safe in either the closed or the open position. This is a disadvantage compared to spring diaphragm units.

Flow Characteristics. Various valve types such as a single- and double-port globe, angle, butterfly, "Saunders" (diaphragm), needle and three-way diverting valves are used in control systems.

The single- and double-port globe valves shown in Figures 4–24(A) and 4–24(B), respectively, are two of the most widely used control valves.

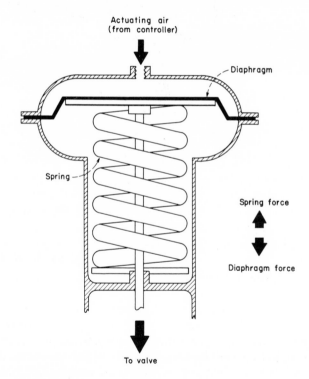

(A) Fail open or air to close pneumatic actuator.

Figure 4-22.   Pneumatic control valve actuators.

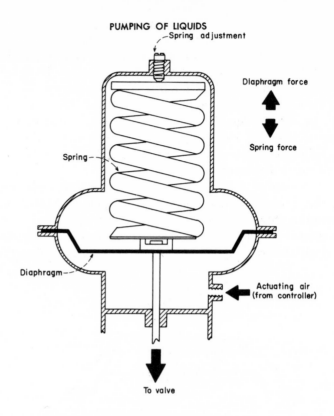

(B) Fail closed or air to open pneumatic actuator.

Figure 4-22. *Cont'd*

They are more prone to seat and plug erosion than angle valves. Single-port valves are leak-tight when closed, but are hydraulically unbalanced since flow through a single port produces a force in only one direction. Double-port valves are almost balanced, since one plug is pushed upward and the other downward. However, they are not usually leak-tight when closed.

Butterfly valves are used in slurry service or in large diameter lines. Because of their simple construction, they are less expensive than globe or angle valves. "Saunders" (diaphragm) valves are also used with slurries. The latter tend to clog globe and other plug and seat valves. Needle valves are used to control small flows. Diverter valves are used in branched line systems.

The flow characteristic of a control valve is the relationship between the degree of closure and the flow rate. When liquid flows through a valve, it exerts a thrust on the plug or valve control element which is a function

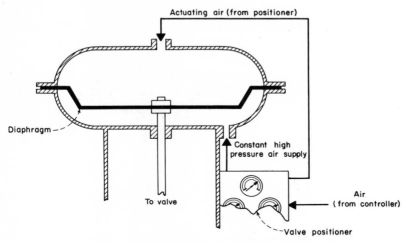

Figure 4-23. Springless control valve actuators.

of the pressure drop through the valve. All control valves operate by balancing the thrust on the plug against the thrust of the actuator. The actuating force is the product of the control air pressure and the area of the diaphragm or piston. The actuator positions the plug to give the desired rate of flow through the valve. This flow is a function of the vertical plug movement (plug travel). It is proportional to the cross-sectional area of the orifice and the square root of the pressure drop. Thus the flow characteristic of a valve at a constant pressure drop is a function of a single variable: the orifice area. The latter is determined by the shape of the plug and seat. Control valves are generally classified into three basic flow characteristic groups: linear, equal percentage and quick-opening.[2,3]

In the first group, the rate is proportional to the degree of plug lift from the seat. In the equal percentage group, the percentage change in flow rate is linearly related to the percentage change in plug lift. For example, consider a valve at a plug lift of 20 per cent of maximum and a flow rate of 100 gpm. Let the opening increase by an increment of 10 per cent to a plug lift of 30 per cent of maximum to give a percentage increase in flow rate of 25 per cent to 125 gpm. Let the opening increase by an additional increment of 10 per cent to a plug lift of 40 per cent of maximum. In an equal percentage valve, this change would increase the flow rate by an additional 25 per cent to 125 gpm × 1.25 = 156.3 gpm.

In a linear valve, an increase of 10 per cent in the plug lift from 20 to 30 per cent of maximum would increase the flow rate by 10 per cent from

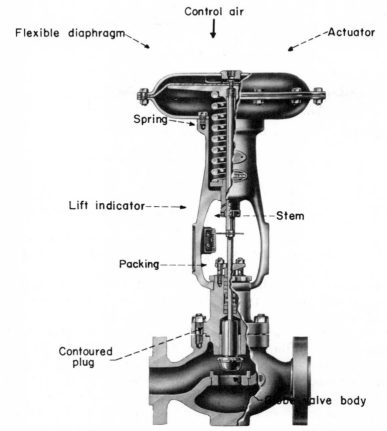

Control air

Flexible diaphragm

Actuator

Spring

Lift indicator

Stem

Packing

Contoured
plug

Globe valve body

(A) Single port, air to close, diaphragm and spring control valve.

Figure 4-24.   Globe-type control valves. (*Courtesy Mason-Neilan Div.,
Worthington Corp.*)

100 to 110 gpm. A further increase of 10 per cent in the plug lift from 30
to 40 per cent of maximum would increase the flow rate by an additional
10 per cent from 110 to $110 \times 1.10 = 121$ gpm.

Plugs providing equal percentage flow characteristics may be either
the percentage ported or the percentage contour type. The characteristic
curves of these, together with linear and quick-opening types, are shown
in Figure 4–25.

In the quick-opening group, a large increase in flow results from a small
change in plug lift. Nearly full flow is obtained when the plug travel is

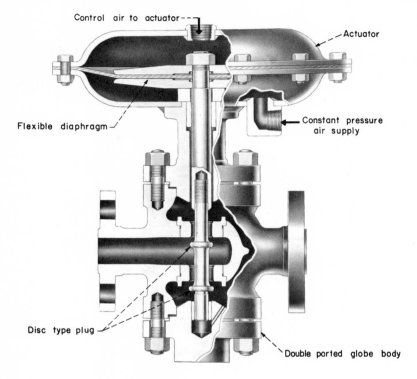

Control air to actuator

Actuator

Flexible diaphragm

Constant pressure
air supply

Disc type plug

Double ported globe body

(B) Double port, quick opening, springless control valve.

Figure 4-24. *Cont'd*

approximately 50 per cent of maximum.[3,4,5] Disk-type plugs are used in quick-opening valves. Figure 4–24(B) illustrates a springless diaphragm, disk-type, double-port control valve.

DESIGN CONSIDERATIONS

Equivalent Lengths of Valves and Fittings

The pressure drop ΔP or frictional head loss h_f given by Equations (2–35) and (2–38), respectively, is directly proportional to the length to diameter ratio ℓ/d_i of the pipeline. Thus the ℓ/d_i ratio is a measure of pipeline resistance to flow.

When a valve or fitting is present in a pipeline, the overall resistance to flow is increased, The ℓ/d_i ratio used in pressure drop calculations must represent the overall resistance and not just that due to the pipe. The

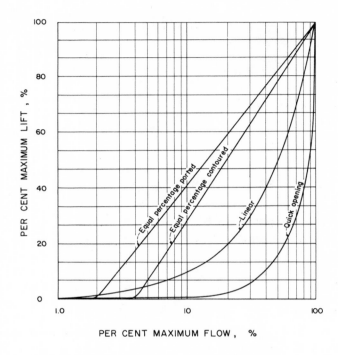

Figure 4-25.   Control valve flow characteristics.

resistance to flow created by valves and fittings is accounted for by using
an equivalent length ℓ_e of pipe. This length is added to the pipe length
to give the overall ℓ_e/d_i ratio.

The exact resistance of a particular valve or fitting cannot be calculated
theoretically. Pressure drop is a function of the path taken through the
valve or fitting. Figure 4–26 shows the flow paths through some common
valves. The equivalent lengths of common valves and fittings have been
determined experimentally. The results are shown in Table 4–1[8] (page 79).

EXAMPLE

Determine the ℓ_e/d_i ratio of a straight run of 4 inch NPS, schedule 40 steel pipe
having one composition disk globe valve, one "Y" type flapper check valve and
one angle valve. All fittings have screwed connections and the pipe is 100 ft in
length, excluding the length of the fittings.

(1) Calculate the total equivalent length of the system where

$$\ell_{e(total)} = \ell_{(pipe)} + \ell_{e(fittings)}$$

From Table 4–1,

$$\ell_{e(\text{fittings})} = \ell_{e(\text{globe valve})} + \ell_{e(\text{check valve})} + \ell_{e(\text{angle valve})}$$

$$= 119 \qquad + \qquad 25.2 \qquad + \qquad 45$$

$$= 189.2 \text{ ft}$$

Therefore,

$$\ell_{e(\text{total})} = 100 \text{ ft} + 189.2 \text{ ft} = 289.2 \text{ ft}$$

(2) Read the inside diameter d_i of 4 inch schedule 40 steel pipe from Table 10–1 to be 4.026 inches = 0.334 ft. Therefore,

$$\ell_e/d_i = \frac{289.2 \text{ ft}}{0.334 \text{ ft}} = 865$$

Control Valve Specification

The factors to consider in sizing control valves are pressure drop, liquid viscosity, density and flow rate, temperature and the valve characteristics.[3]

Valve Rangeability. This is the ratio of the maximum to the controllable minimum flow through a valve. If the smallest controllable flow is 2 per cent and the maximum 100 per cent, the rangeability, at a constant ΔP, is $100/2 = 50$. Holzbock states that it is good practice to expect an average rangeability of 8, approaching 15 on larger valves.[3] Manufacturers supply rangeability factors for their own control valves.

Pressure drop is related to the required valve rangeability R by the equation:

$$R = \frac{Q_1}{Q_2} \left(\frac{\Delta P_1}{\Delta P_2}\right)^{0.50} \qquad (4\text{–}1)$$

where Q_1 is the maximum flow with its pressure differential ΔP_1 and Q_2 is the minimum controllable flow with its pressure differential ΔP_2.

Flow Coefficient. This is a useful concept which simplifies valve sizing. The flow coefficient C_v is defined as "the number of U.S. gallons per minute of water which pass through a fully open valve with a pressure drop of 1 psi."[2,4,5]

The flow coefficient C_v is given by the equation

$$C_v = Q \sqrt{\frac{sp\ gr}{\Delta P}} \qquad (4\text{–}2)$$

where Q is the volumetric flow rate in U.S. gpm, ΔP is the pressure drop in psi across the fully open valve, and $sp\ gr$ is specific gravity of the liquid.

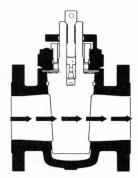

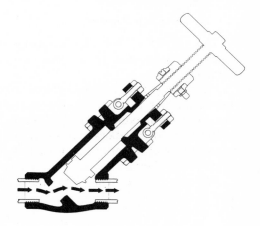

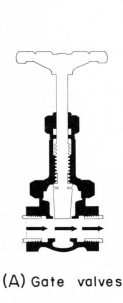

(B) Plug and ball valves—
full flow designs

(A) Gate valves

(C) Y valves

Figure 4-26.   Flow characteristics of common valves in order of increasing pressure
drop. (*Courtesy The Wm. Powell Co.*)

EXAMPLE

An equal percentage ported valve will be used to control a process flow of 1000
U.S. gpm with a pressure drop of 80 psi. This process liquid has a specific gravity
of 0.80 at 60°F. Determine the flow coefficient and size a valve based on this value.

(1) The flow coefficient

$$C_v = Q\sqrt{\frac{sp\ gr}{\Delta P}}$$

$$= 1000\sqrt{\frac{0.80}{80}} = 100$$

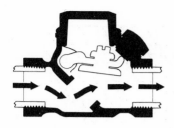

(D) Y swing-check valves

(E) Globe lift-check valves

(F) Angle valves

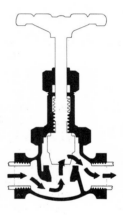

(G) Globe valves

Figure 4-26. *Cont'd*

(2) Inspect Figure 4–27, which is a typical manufacturer's curve for C_v vs plug lift to find the required valve size. It is seen that a number of valves have a flow coefficient $C_v = 100$ from a 3 inch valve at 100 per cent maximum lift to a 14 inch valve at 23 per cent lift. Control valves, however, are best operated at 70 per cent of their maximum rated flow.[5] From Figure 4–25, read 91 per cent of maximum lift corresponding to 70 per cent of maximum flow for the equal percentage ported valve. Locate the point on Figure 4–27 corresponding to 91 per cent of maximum lift and a flow coefficient $C_v = 100$. Select a 4 inch valve.

For more sophisticated calculations involving viscosity correction, etc., manufacturers' bulletins should be consulted.

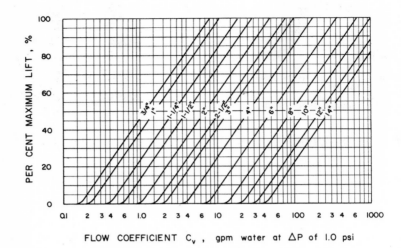

Figure 4-27. Flow coefficients for a typical equal-percentage, ported control valve.
(*Courtesy Mason-Neilan Div., Worthington Corp.*)

NOMENCLATURE

C_v	flow coefficient in Equation (4–2)
d_i	inside pipe diameter, ft
ℓ	pipe length, ft
ℓ_e	equivalent length, ft
P	pressure, psi
Q	volumetric flow rate, gpm
R	rangeability factor in Equation (4–1)
sp gr	specific gravity

REFERENCES

1. Ciancia, J., and Steymann, E. H., *Chem. Eng.*, **72**, No. 18 (1965).
2. "Control Valves," Mason-Neilan Div., Worthington Corp., Norwood, Mass.
3. Holzbock, W. T., *Chem. Eng.*, **66**, No. 5 (1959).
4. "Honeywell Process Control Valves," Honeywell Inc., Philadelphia, Pa.
5. Kropholler, H. W., and Spikins, D. J., *Chem. & Process Eng.*, **44**, No. 12 (1963).
6. Pearson, G. H., *Chem. & Process Eng.*, **44**, No. 1 (1963).
7. Perry, R. H., Chilton, C. H., and Kirkpatrick, S.D., "Chemical Engineers' Handbook," Fourth ed., Sect. 22–85, New York, McGraw-Hill Book Co. Inc., 1963.
8. "Resistance of Fittings," Standard Pump Div., Worthington Corp., Norwood, Mass.

CHAPTER 5

Liquid Transport With Positive Displacement Pumps

Pumps are devices for supplying head to a flowing liquid in order to overcome head losses due to friction and also, if necessary, to raise the liquid to a higher level. Positive displacement pumps are normally used for high head applications. Consider the different heads involved in a flowing liquid in the light of the Bernoulli equation.

The Bernoulli Equation

Consider a liquid of density ρ lb/cu ft flowing at a mean linear velocity of u ft/sec in a circular pipe of inside diameter d_i as shown in Figure 5–1. Consider two points 1 and 2 in the pipe at a distance ℓ ft apart.

The head of the liquid at any point is made up of the following three components:

(1) The static head or head of position z measured in ft above an arbitrarily chosen base line.

(2) The pressure head which is given by a pressure gauge placed at the point. If the reading of the pressure gauge is P in psi, the pressure head is $(144P/\rho)(g_c/g)$ ft. If the pressure P were in poundals/sq in., the pressure head would be $144P/\rho g$ ft. Since $g_c = 32.174$ ft $\mathrm{lb_m}/\mathrm{lb_f}$ sec^2, the ratio g_c/g will be taken as unity for the remainder of the text.

(3) The velocity head $u^2/2g\alpha$ which is in ft if u is in ft/sec and g the gravitational acceleration is in ft/sec^2. α is a dimensionless factor which for fluid flow in a circular pipe can be shown to be ½ for laminar flow and approximately 1 for turbulent flow.[2] α is a correction factor which accounts for the velocity distribution across the pipe.

The head h in ft at any point can thus be written as:

$$h = z + \frac{144P}{\rho} + \frac{u^2}{2g\alpha} \qquad (5\text{–}1)$$

At point 1, the head is

$$h_1 = z_1 + \frac{144P_1}{\rho} + \frac{u_1^2}{2g\alpha} \qquad (5\text{-}2)$$

At point 2, the head is

$$h_2 = z_2 + \frac{144P_2}{\rho} + \frac{u_2^2}{2g\alpha} \qquad (5\text{-}3)$$

For a constant pipe diameter, $u_1 = u_2$, and the velocity head remains constant as the liquid flows from point 1 to point 2. The change of static head and pressure head with position in the pipe is illustrated in Figure 5-1.

The head h_2 at point 2 is less than the head h_1 at point 1 by the head loss h_f due to friction, where

$$h_f = 8\left(\frac{R}{\rho u^2}\right)\left(\frac{\ell}{d_i}\right)\left(\frac{u^2}{2g}\right) \qquad (2\text{-}38)$$

$R/\rho u^2$ is the dimensionless basic friction factor which is obtained from a plot of $R/\rho u^2$ vs the dimensionless Reynolds number $N_{Re} = \rho u d_i/\mu$ as shown in Figure 2-4.

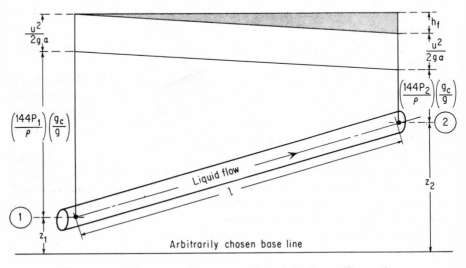

Figure 5-1.   Diagrammatic representation of the Bernoulli equation.

Alternatively, the head loss due to friction h_f is given by the equation:

$$h_f = 4f\left(\frac{\ell}{d_i}\right)\left(\frac{u^2}{2g}\right) \tag{2-45}$$

where f is the Fanning friction factor. The ℓ/d_i ratio in Equations (2–38) and (2–45) is a dimensionless shape factor defined as the length to diameter ratio of the pipe section considered.

μ is the viscosity of the liquid in appropriate units, in this case lb/ft sec where 1 cp = 0.000672 lb/ft sec.

Clearly a pump is required to supply head in order to make good the head loss h_f due to friction.

Equating heads using the Bernoulli equation is equivalent to making an energy balance on 1 lb of material.

System Heads

The following definitions are given in reference to the typical pumping system shown in Figure 5–2 where the arbitrarily chosen base line is the centerline of the pump.

Suction head:

$$h_s = z_s + \frac{144P_s}{\rho} - h_{fs} \text{ in ft} \tag{5-4}$$

Discharge head:

$$h_d = z_d + \frac{144P_d}{\rho} + h_{fd} \text{ in ft} \tag{5-5}$$

where h_{fs} and h_{fd} are the head losses due to friction in the suction and discharge lines, respectively; z_s and z_d are the static heads on the suction and discharge sides of the pump, respectively, measured above the centerline of the pump.

If the liquid level on the suction side is below the centerline of the pump, z_s is negative. P_s is the gas pressure in psi above the liquid on the suction side of the pump and P_d is the gas pressure in psi at the end of the discharge line.

The head which the pump is required to impart is called the total head and is the difference between the discharge and the suction heads.

Total head:

$$h_d - h_s = (z_d - z_s) + \left[\frac{144(P_d - P_s)}{\rho}\right] + (h_{fd} + h_{fs}) \text{ in ft} \tag{5-6}$$

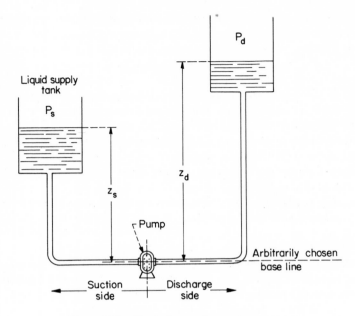

Figure 5-2. Typical pumping system.

The pressures P_d and P_s can either be gauge or absolute pressures, but they must be consistent with each other.

The suction head decreases and the discharge head increases with increasing liquid velocity because of the increasing value of the frictional head loss terms h_{fs} and h_{fd}. Thus the total head increases with pumping rate.

The head available to get the liquid through the suction piping is called the net positive suction head usually abbreviated to $NPSH$. The available $NPSH$ in a system is defined as:

$$NPSH = z_s + \left[\frac{144(P_s - P_{vp})}{\rho} \right] - h_{fs} \qquad (5\text{--}7)$$

where P_{vp} is the vapor pressure in psi of the liquid being pumped at the particular temperature in question.

$NPSH$ is seen to be the suction head minus the vapor pressure in ft of liquid. Since P_{vp} would normally be in psia units, the gas pressure P_s above the suction side liquid should in this case also be written in psia units. The available $NPSH$ in a system should always be positive, i.e., the suction head must always be capable of overcoming the vapor pressure.

Since the frictional head loss h_{fs} increases with increasing liquid flow, the available $NPSH$ decreases with increasing flow rate. When the liquid is at its boiling temperature, P_s and P_{vp} are equal and the available $NPSH$ becomes $z_s - h_{fs}$. In this case z_s must be positive and no suction lift is possible. Normally liquid can be lifted from below the centerline of the pump, i.e., z_s negative, provided the term $(P_s - P_{vp})$ is sufficiently large.

Classification of Positive Displacement Pumps

Positive displacement pumps can be classified as: rotary pumps, reciprocating pumps and miscellaneous pumps.

Rotary pumps forcibly transfer liquid from suction to discharge through the action of rotating gears, lobes, vanes, screws, etc., operating inside a rigid container. Rotary pumps do not require valves. Normally, pumping rates are varied by changing the speed of the rotor. Rotary pumps may be classified as: external gear, internal gear, lobe, vane, screw or flexible impeller.

Reciprocating pumps forcibly discharge liquid against a pressure by changing the internal volume of the pump. Reciprocating pumps require valves on both the suction and the discharge sides of the pump. Pumping rates are varied by changing either the frequency or the stroke length. Reciprocating pumps may be classified as piston or diaphragm.

A number of miscellaneous positive displacement pumps exist which have some of the characteristics of both rotary and reciprocating pumps. Positive displacement pumps are self-priming. This is a great advantage in many applications.

OPERATING PRINCIPLES OF ROTARY PUMPS

External Gear Pumps

Figure 5–3 shows a typical external gear pump. The fixed casing contains two meshing gears of equal size. One of the gears is coupled to the drive shaft which transmits the power from the motor. Usually the other gear runs free, i.e., it is an idler gear. For severe service, both pumping gears are driven by timing gears, as shown in Figure 5–5 for a double helical gear pump. A partial vacuum is formed by the unmeshing of the rotating gears. This causes liquid to flow into the pump. Liquid is then carried to the other side of the pump between the rotating gear teeth and the fixed casing. At this point the meshing of the rotating gears generates an increase in pressure which forces the liquid into the outlet line.

The direction of the gear rotation determines which is the discharge side of the pump. A basic external gear pump can discharge liquid either way,

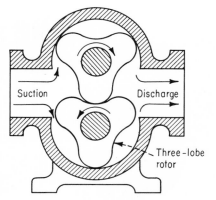

Figure 5-7.   Pumping action of a three lobe pump.

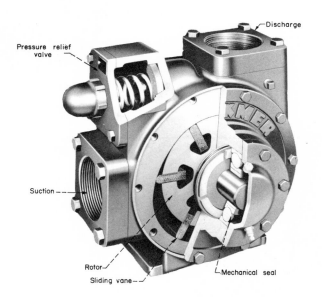

Figure 5-8.   Sliding vane pump.
(*Courtesy Blackmer Pump Co.*)

liquid. This is carried to the other side of the pump in the space between the rotor and the fixed casing. At the discharge side of the pump, the eccentricity of the revolving rotor generates an increase in pressure which forces the liquid into the outlet line.

Normally pumping rates of rotary pumps are varied by changing the speed of the rotor. In a vane pump, the pumping rate can also be varied by changing the degree of eccentricity of the rotor since this determines the amount of liquid carried through per cycle. This is usually done by turning a graduated dial which operates a rack and pinion. This in turn rotates an eccentric cylindrical liner in the fixed casing. This arrangement lends itself well to automatic control.[7]

Other types of vane pumps are the swinging vane pump shown in Figure 5–9 and the shuttle block pump.

Screw Pumps

Figure 5–10 shows a typical single screw pump. A helical screw rotor revolves in a fixed casing. The latter is shaped such that cavities formed at the suction progress toward the discharge side of the pump as the helical screw rotates. The creation of a cavity produces a partial vacuum which causes liquid to flow into the pump. Liquid is then carried to the other side of the pump inside the progressing cavity. At the discharge side of the

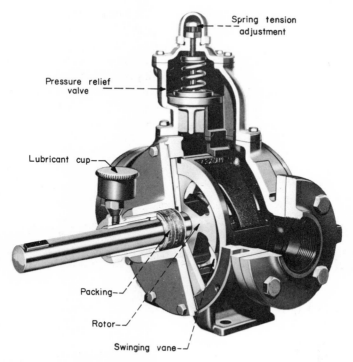

Figure 5-9.   Swinging vane pump. (*Courtesy Blackmer Pump Co.*)

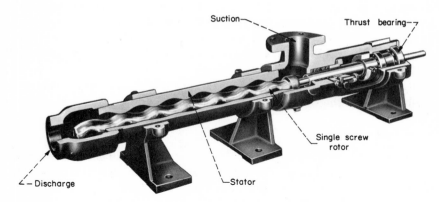

Figure 5-10.   Single screw "Moyno" pump. (*Courtesy Robbins and Myers, Inc.*)

pump, the shape of the fixed casing causes the cavity to close. This generates an increase in pressure which forces the liquid into the outlet line. The discharge pressure required determines the length and the pitch of the helical screw rotor.

Another screw pump illustrated in Figure 5–11 employs twin screws with helicoid surfaces in place of a single helical screw rotor. On entering the suction chamber, liquid is divided and flows to opposite ends of the pump body. At these points liquid enters the twin rotors and is conveyed to the center of the pump where it is discharged into the outlet line. Timing gears, lubricated by the liquid pumped, prevent contact between the twin screw rotors.

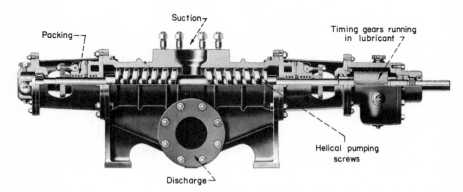

Figure 5-11.   Twin screw pump. (*Courtesy Warren Pumps, Inc.*)

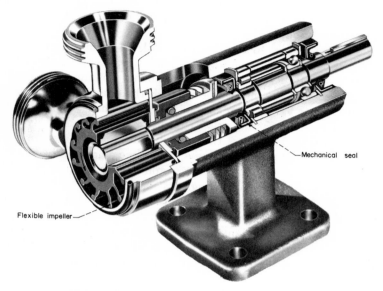

Figure 5-12.   Flexible impeller pump. (*Courtesy Jabsco Pump Co.*)

Although screws will convey liquid either way depending on the direction of rotation, the screw pumps shown in Figures 5–10 and 5–11 are designed to operate in one direction only.

Flexible Impeller Pumps

These are eccentric rotor pumps. The rotor consists of an impeller with flexible blades. The pump and action are illustrated in Figure 5–12. The impeller blades unfold as they pass the suction port. This unfolding creates a partial vacuum which draws in liquid. As the impeller rotates, each successive blade draws in liquid and carries it from the suction to the discharge port. The eccentricity of the impeller causes the flexible impeller blades to bend against the fixed casing at the discharge port. This results in a squeezing action on the liquid which is forced into the outlet line.

OPERATING PRINCIPLES OF RECIPROCATING PUMPS

Piston Pumps

In piston pumps the pumping action is effected by a piston which is free to move, in a reciprocating cycle, along a cylinder. The piston is attached

OPERATING PRINCIPLES OF MISCELLANEOUS PUMPS

Eccentric Cam Pumps

These pumps are sometimes called rotating piston or plunger pumps. In a true rotary pump, the liquid being pumped is in direct contact with a rotating surface. In addition, the total volume available in the pump for liquid remains constant. Eccentric cam pumps can be divided into those which maintain a constant volume of liquid in the pump and those which have a variable liquid volume in the pump.

Constant Volume Eccentric Cam Pumps. These resemble true rotary pumps in operating with a constant volume of liquid in the pump but differ from true rotary pumps in not having a rotating surface in contact with the pumped liquid. A typical constant volume eccentric cam pump is illustrated in Figure 5–17. The rotating eccentric cam, moving inside a cylindrical plunger which is in direct contact with the pumped liquid, creates a cavity at the suction side of the pump. This progressively increases as the cam rotates. The partial vacuum created draws in liquid which fills the pump. At the end of the cam cycle, the liquid in the pump is open to the discharge side and sealed from the suction side of the pump. During the cam cycle the volume available for this liquid progressively decreases. Thus the pressure is increased and the liquid is forced into the outlet line.

These pumps require no check valves. A loose septum fitting prevents back flow from the discharge to the suction side of the pump. This fitting also prevents the cylindrical plunger from rotating. The only rotating component of the pump is the eccentric cam which rotates within a circular housing inside the cylindrical plunger. This in turn causes the cylindrical

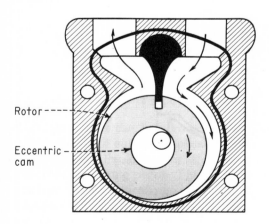

Rotor

Eccentric cam

Figure 5-17. Eccentric cam pump. (*Courtesy Eco Engineering Co.*)

plunger to change position relative to the fixed casing. The slightly different pumping action of a rotary plunger pump is shown in Figure 5–18.

Another type of constant volume eccentric cam pump is the flexible liner pump shown in Figure 5–19. The eccentric cam rotates within a flexible liner. A progressive squeegee action is exerted on the liquid trapped between the flexible liner and the fixed casing. No packing seals are required since the flexible liner isolates the process liquid from direct contact with any primary moving parts. The pumping action is analogous to the squeezing of a soft tube containing liquid.

A third type of constant volume eccentric cam pump is the eccentric cam diaphragm pump. The eccentric cam rotates within a circular housing inside the circular diaphragm. This rotation causes the circular diaphragm to change position relative to the fixed casing. The movement produces a cavity adjacent to the suction port. This draws liquid in. Further movement of the diaphragm forces liquid through the pump and out through the discharge port.

Variable Volume Eccentric Cam Pumps. These resemble true rotary pumps in having a rotating surface in direct contact with the pumped liquid. They differ from true rotary pumps in not maintaining a constant volume of liquid throughout the pumping cycle.

Three eccentric cams fit closely into shoes. A single cam and shoe is shown in Figure 5–20. As the eccentric cam rotates, the volume available for liquid inside the shoe successively increases and decreases. The eccentric cam produces an up and down movement of the shoe. This alternatively

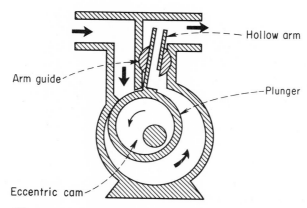

Figure 5-18.   Pumping action of a rotary plunger pump.

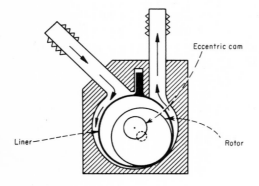

Figure 5-19. Flexible liner eccentric cam pump. (*Courtesy Vanton Pump and Equipment Corp.*)

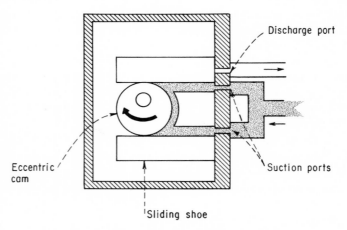

Figure 5-20.   Pumping action of sliding shoe pump.

connects the interior of the shoe to the suction and the discharge side of the pump. Since the available volume in the shoe is increasing when the suction side is connected, and decreasing when the discharge side is connected, a liquid pumping action results. The three eccentric cam shoe systems provide a more uniform pumping rate than a single system. These pumps are known as sliding shoe pumps.

Peristaltic Pumps

A typical peristaltic pump is shown in Figure 5–21. At each end of the rotor there is located a roller which is free to revolve. A flexible tube passes through the fixed casing of the pump. As the rotor moves, the rollers press and revolve against the flexible tube. This exerts a squeegee action on the

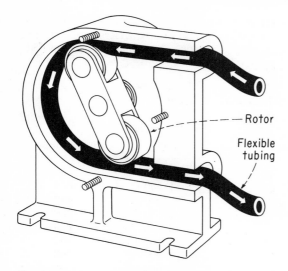

Rotor

Flexible
tubing

Figure 5-21.   Peristaltic pump.
(*Courtesy Randolph Co.*)

liquid in the tube, producing an even flow of liquid. The tubing must be
sufficiently flexible to allow the impeller rollers to squeeze it until it is
completely closed.

Peristaltic pumps require no check valves or packing seals. The process
liquid is completely isolated from the prime moving parts.

FACTORS WHICH AFFECT PUMP PERFORMANCE

Physical Properties of the Liquid

Viscosity. This property causes the liquid to resist flow, however small.
For a Newtonian liquid, the coefficient of viscosity μ is the factor of
proportionality between the shear stress R_s and the shear rate $\dot{\gamma}$, i.e.,

$$R_s = \mu\dot{\gamma}$$

Viscosity coefficient data are most frequently given in centipoises where
1 cp $= 0.000672$ lb$_m$/ft sec.

The coefficient of kinematic viscosity μ/ρ takes into account the liquid
density. If the coefficient of viscosity μ is in cp and the liquid density ρ
is in g/cc, then the coefficient of kinematic viscosity μ/ρ is in centistokes.
For a liquid density $\rho = 1$ g/cc, centipoises and centistokes have the same
numerical value.

The viscosity of liquids is also expressed as the time required for a given
liquid volume to flow through a particular orifice under a specified pressure

head. This method is particularly popular with pump suppliers and manufacturers. Seconds Saybolt Universal units commonly written as SSU are the most frequently used units of this type. The relationship between SSU units and centistokes is given in Table 5–1

TABLE 5-1. Viscosity Conversions

Seconds Saybolt Universal Units (SSU)	Centistokes[a]	Seconds Saybolt Universal Units (SSU)	Centistokes[a]
35	2.60	1,000	220
50	7.40	1,500	330
75	14.1	2,000	440
100	20.2	2,500	550
150	31.8	3,000	660
200	43.1	4,000	880
250	54.3	5,000	1100
300	65.1	6,000	1320
400	87.6	7,000	1540
500	110	8,000	1760
600	132	9,000	1980
700	154	10,000	2200
800	176	100,000	22,000
900	198		

[a] For liquids having a *sp gr* of 1.0, 1 centistoke = 1 centipoise.

The higher the viscosity, the greater are the head losses due to friction in the pipelines and the pump. Equations (5–4) and (5–7) show that the suction head and the available $NPSH$ both decrease with an increase in liquid viscosity for the same pumping rate. Equations (5–5) and (5–6) show that the discharge and total heads both increase with an increase in liquid viscosity for the same pumping rate. Thus the power required for pumping increases with liquid viscosity. Sometimes the viscosity of a liquid must be reduced to permit efficient pumping. This may be accomplished by using heated process lines and pumps. A jacketed pump is shown in Figure 5–6.

Shear Characteristics. For many liquids, the factor of proportionality between the shear stress R_s and the shear rate $\dot{\gamma}$ does not remain constant. These are the so-called non-Newtonian liquids discussed in Chapter 3.

In the case of some liquids, shear can lead to a permanent change in viscosity. Other liquids can be damaged by shear in a number of ways. For example, certain liquid detergents can be permanently broken down into two phases if subjected to too much shear.

Volatility. The vapor pressure is a measure of the volatility of a liquid at a given temperature. Equation (5–7) shows that an increase in vapor pressure P_{vp} leads to a decrease in available $NPSH$. As the temperature of the process liquid is increased, the vapor pressure may eventually reach a point where the $NPSH$ becomes zero, i.e., there is no head available to get the liquid through the suction piping.

The presence of vapor in the process liquid reduces the volume available for liquid in the pump. This in turn results in a fall-off in pumping rate.

Corrosiveness. Corrosion produced by a liquid may be either localized or general. Localized corrosion can be either intergranular, electrolytic, stress or pitting. In austenitic stainless steels such as 304 or 316, intergranular corrosion takes place at the grain boundaries as a result of carbide precipitation. Concentration differences occurring in pits or recesses can cause electrolytic corrosion. Stress corrosion is the acceleration of the corrosion rate by stress. It has been observed in almost all metals and their alloys. Pitting corrosion is caused by local concentrations of the corrosive liquid, by carbide precipitation or by stresses.

The corrosion rate of alloys increases as the flow rate of the corrosive liquid increases. The smoother the surface of the metal, the greater is the resistance to corrosion.

The corrosiveness of the liquid to be pumped determines the materials which can be used in the pump construction. Corrosion is more serious for intermittent than for continuous pump operation.

Lubricating Qualities. Zisman[10] has shown that a relationship does not necessarily exist between the wettability or spreadability of a liquid on a solid surface and its ability to act as a boundary lubricant. The contact angle θ between a drop of liquid and a plane solid surface is a measure of the wettability of the liquid on that surface. When $\theta = 0$, the liquid completely wets the surface; when $\theta \neq 0$, the liquid is nonspreading.

Zisman[10] has shown that the ability of a liquid to wet a solid surface is a function only of the liquid surface tension and the nature of the surface atoms of the solid.

Paraffin hydrocarbons and methyl silicones are liquids which spread freely over all metals. Paraffin hydrocarbons are among the best, and methyl silicones are among the poorest of the boundary lubricants for common metals. Liquid fatty alcohols and acids are nonspreading, yet they are excellent boundary lubricants for many metals.

The free surface energies of the common liquids are less than 100 ergs/sq cm at ordinary temperatures. Ordinary metals have free surface energies in the range 1000 to 5000 ergs/sq cm. Most organic solids have a free surface energy of less than 100 ergs/sq cm. Zisman points out that one would expect a liquid to spread freely over a high energy metal surface, since this would decrease the free energy of the whole system. He explains the fact that this does not always occur by assuming that in this case, the liquid coats the metal in such a way that it behaves like a low energy surface. With liquids having poor lubricating qualities, the wear on the moving parts of a pump is likely to be more rapid. Piston pumps are usually provided with replaceable liners in order to correct for this.

Abrasiveness. An abrasive liquid also produces wear in the pump, particularly on the moving parts. Mechanical seals should not be used with abrasive liquids. Packed seals are recommended for these. Pump speeds should be kept low with abrasive liquids in order to prolong pump life.

Suspended Solids. In addition to making the liquid abrasive, suspended solids can lead to clogging in check valves and moving parts.

Mechanical Factors

Slip. This is the leakage which occurs between the discharge and suction sides of a pump through the pump clearances. The extent of this leakage depends on the width, length and shape of these clearances, the viscosity of the pumped liquid, and the pressure differences between the discharge and suction sides of the pump. Pump speed does not influence slip.

Generally the bulk of the slip occurs at the shortest sealing surfaces, e.g., at the gears in a gear pump. Slip decreases with increasing liquid viscosity. The heating of the liquid in the pump clearance leads to some decrease in viscosity and hence an increase in slip. No slip occurs with zero pressure difference between the discharge and suction sides of the pump. Provided the internal parts of the pump do not deflect with increasing pressure, the slip increases linearly with the pressure difference across the pump if the pumped liquid is in laminar flow. For turbulent flow, slip increases with the square root of the pressure difference across the pump.

Since slip is independent of pump speed, it is an advantage to pump low viscosity liquids at high speeds. In the case of very viscous liquids, slip becomes negligible.

Condition of Pump. Wear in a pump will increase clearances and thus lead to a greater amount of slip. In rotary pumps, incorrect alignment of the rotating parts with the fixed casing can produce excessive wear. Incorrect alignment in gear pumps can cause the gears to seize. The suction and discharge pipes should be supported independently of the pump to avoid putting a strain on the pump casing.

Seals. Air leaks through the packed seals reduce the liquid pumping rate. If the packed seals are too tight, the pump will consume an excessive

amount of power. In addition, the shaft may become scored and the packing burnt. The packing gland should be adjusted to allow a very small amount of the pumped liquid to leak. This provides lubrication and cooling.

Temperature of Operation. This determines the material of construction of the pump and also the clearances on the moving parts. Frequently the packing determines the upper temperature limit of operation. Plastic component parts can only be used in pumps operating at relatively low temperatures.

Speed of Pump Cycle. The higher the speed of the moving parts in a pump, the greater is the wear. This is particularly true when pumping abrasive liquids. An increase in pump speed produces a decrease in apparent viscosity for pseudoplastic liquids and an increase in apparent viscosity for thixotropic liquids. This leads to a decrease and an increase in power consumption for pseudoplastic and thixotropic liquids, respectively. Liquids which are prone to permanent deformation or damage by shear require low pump speeds.

Rotary pumps are normally divided into two classes: large liquid cavity low speed pumps and small liquid cavity high speed pumps. The latter require more power when pumping highly viscous liquids.

Cavitation and Priming

For smooth operation, pumps should be completely filled with liquid. When liquid does not completely fill the pump chamber, a loss of capacity results. This may occur through the vaporization of some of the process liquid in the suction line or the pump chamber. The vapor bubbles are carried into higher pressure regions of the pump where they collapse, resulting in noise and vibration. This phenomenon is called cavitation.

Cavitation can also occur from air leaks through the pump seal. The repeated blows of the collapsing bubbles cause rapid wear in the pump and may also accelerate the corrosion rate. Pitting of pump parts is a common result of cavitation. The greater the slip in a pump, the smaller is the effect of cavitation. Cavitation is usually more serious with viscous liquids than with thin liquids. High speed pumps are more prone to cavitation than low speed pumps.

In a leak-free pump, cavitation can be avoided by ensuring that the available *NPSH* in the suction line is always greater than that required by the pump. Short and wide suction lines will reduce the frictional head loss term h_{fs} in Equation (5–10) and increase the available *NPSH*. Cavitation can occur in all types of pumps.

When not in operation, pumps and suction lines may be full of air. This air must be removed before the pump can start to pump liquid.

The process of removing the air and starting the pump is called priming. Normally positive displacement pumps are self-priming. For suction lifts greater than 28 ft, i.e., a suction head in Equation (5–4) of -28 ft, positive displacement pumps may require priming. This may be accomplished either by admitting liquid to the suction line to displace the air or by exhausting the air from the suction line and pump by a vacuum system.

Bearings. Heat is the main destructive factor in bearing wear. This can be reduced by a continual flow of cooling liquid through the bearing.

In positive displacement pumps, the pressure differential across the pump is balanced by the reactive force of the bearings. This so-called hydraulic imbalance increases the wear on the bearings. Pumps can be equipped with channels to carry high pressure liquid. This is fed to various bearing points to reduce the hydraulic imbalance.

Pumping Efficiencies

Volumetric Efficiency. This expresses the delivered capacity per cycle as a percentage of the true displacement per cycle. The lower the internal slip losses, the higher is the volumetric efficiency. For zero slip, the volumetric efficiency is 100 per cent. The true displacement is the delivered capacity for zero pressure difference across the pump. A knowledge of the volumetric efficiency for the required range of application is very important when the positive displacement pump is to be used for metering. Entrained air or gas in the pumped liquid reduces the volumetric efficiency of a pump.

Mechanical Efficiency. This is the liquid horsepower expressed as a percentage of the brake horsepower. The liquid horsepower is the rate of useful work done on the liquid. This is the product of the volumetric liquid flow rate into the suction side of the pump and the pressure difference across the pump divided by the appropriate conversion factor. This can be written as

$$\text{liquid horsepower} = \frac{\text{(gpm)(psi)}}{1714} \qquad (5\text{–}8)$$

Alternatively, liquid horsepower can be expressed in terms of the rate of liquid pumped in lb/min W and the head difference across the pump Δh as follows:

$$\text{liquid horsepower} = \frac{W \Delta h}{33,000} \qquad (5\text{–}9)$$

Brake horsepower is the actual power delivered to the pump by the prime mover. It is the sum of liquid horsepower and friction horsepower.

In terms of the mechanical efficiency E, the brake horsepower can be expressed in terms of Equation (5–9).

$$\text{brake horsepower} = \frac{W\Delta h}{33,000}\left(\frac{100}{E}\right) \tag{5–10}$$

Since the power required to overcome friction rises with increasing liquid viscosity, mechanical efficiency decreases as liquid viscosity increases. Some improvement in mechanical efficiency can be obtained with viscous liquids by using larger clearances in the pump. However, with thin liquids this leads to an increase in slip and hence a decrease in mechanical efficiency.

Slip is independent of pump speed. Thus the power used in pumping liquid through slip from the discharge to the suction side of the pump does not depend on pump speed. Since the ratio of liquid horsepower to slip horsepower increases with pump speed, thin liquids are pumped more efficiently at high pump speeds.

Power losses in timing gears, bearings and seals reduce mechanical efficiencies. A tightly packed seal can be a large power consumer. Contact between the rotor and the fixed casing also increases the power losses in a rotary pump. These losses are not proportional to pump size. Small pumps tend to have low efficiencies. The best efficiencies are usually found in relatively large pumps. Pumps handling tacky liquids require more power to start than those pumping noncohesive liquids.

OPERATING RANGES AND APPLICATIONS

External Gear Pumps

Advantages. These pumps are self-priming. They give constant delivery for a set rotor speed and uniform discharge with negligible pulsations, and they do not require check valves. External gear pumps can, if necessary, pump in either direction; they have small space requirements, are light in weight, and can handle liquids containing vapors and gases. Changes in capacity are small with variations in viscosity and discharge pressure, while volumetric efficiencies are high.

Disadvantages. The liquid pumped must be comparatively clean. The pump cannot be operated against a closed discharge without damage— hence, relief valves are required. Close clearances are essential between the moving parts, so alignment is critical. Shaft seals are required. Liquids containing vapors and gases tend to cause erosion; the pumps are also prone to damage by foreign bodies. They depend on the liquid pumped to lubricate the internal moving parts and can be damaged if run dry. Variable speed drives are required to provide changes in pumping rate.

Ranges. External gear pumps containing spur gears are normally low capacity pumps. The upper limit is about 200 gpm. For higher capacities, the noise level and thrust on the bearings become too great. Helical and herringbone gears are used in higher capacity pumps. Herringbone gear pumps are available with capacities up to 5000 gpm. Furthermore, helical and herringbone gear pumps can in general, handle higher viscosity liquids. Herringbone gear pumps have been known to handle liquids with viscosities up to 5,000,000 SSU.

Spur gears are invariably used in very small pumps because of the difficulty of cutting small helical and herringbone gears.

Rotor speeds up to 1800 rpm are used although the most common speed is 1150 rpm. Mechanical efficiencies depend on the liquid pumped but can be as high as 90 per cent. Line sizes range from $\frac{3}{8}$ inch NPS for small spur gear pumps to 16 inches NPS for large herringbone pumps. External gear pumps have been made to operate at temperatures up to 800°F. Normally the upper limit of pressure for external gear pumps is 500 psig although pumps have been made to operate against pressures up to 5000 psig. The costs of the pumps without motor range from $50 to $6000 for steel pumps depending on the size and construction.

Internal Gear Pumps

Advantages and Disadvantages. These are the same as listed for external gear pumps. However, in contrast to external gear pumps, the gears in an internal gear pump rotate in the same direction. The slow relative rotation and the rolling contact between the gears reduce friction, wear and turbulence. In addition, they enable more shear sensitive liquids to be pumped.

Ranges. Line sizes range from $\frac{1}{4}$ to 8 inches NPS. Internal gear pumps are available with capacities up to 1100 gpm. In general, discharge pressures are limited to 100 psig.

Lobe Pumps

Advantages and Disadvantages. These are the same as for external gear pumps with the following exceptions. The output from lobe pumps is more pulsating than from external gear pumps. Since the lobes function as gears, the greater the number of lobes, the less is the pulsation.

Lobe pumps do not tend to wear as much as external gear pumps. In some pumps, the lobe ends are fitted with packing strips. These protect the lobes from wear and can easily be replaced. The alignment is not quite as critical as for external and internal gear pumps.

Ranges. Lobe pumps are readily available in line sizes from ¾ to 6 inches NPS and in capacities up to 600 gpm. However, lobe pumps up to 2000 gpm capacity have been made. The commonly available pumps operate at temperatures up to 600°F and against discharge pressures up to 400 psig. Costs for common cast iron pumps without motor range from $300 to $2000. Commonly available stainless steel pumps without motor range in cost from $600 to $5000 depending on capacity.

Vane Pumps

Advantages. Vane pumps are self-priming and robust; they give constant delivery for a set rotor speed. These pumps produce uniform discharge with negligible pulsations. Their vanes are self-compensating for wear, and the original capacity is not affected until the vanes are critically worn. Vanes and liners are easily replaced. These pumps do not require check valves, pump in either direction, and their space requirements are small. They are light in weight, and can handle liquids containing vapors and gases. Only small changes in capacity occur with variations in viscosity and discharge pressure, while volumetric efficiencies are relatively high. In some vane pumps, the eccentricity of the rotor can be adjusted to provide changes in pumping rate for a fixed rotor speed.

Disadvantages. Vane pumps cannot be operated against a closed discharge without damage to the pump—hence, relief valves are required. They cannot handle abrasive liquids, seals are required, and foreign bodies can damage the pump.

Ranges. Vane pumps are available in line sizes from 1 to 10 inches NPS and in capacities up to 2000 gpm. These operate at temperatures up to 450°F and against discharge pressures up to 150 psig. Vane pumps can also be made which operate up to 2000 psig pressure. The commonly available pumps handle liquids with viscosities up to about 500,000 SSU. Rotor speeds up to 960 rpm are used. Costs for the commonly available basic cast iron pumps without motor range from $100 to $4000 depending on capacity.

Screw Pumps

Advantages. Screw pumps are self-priming and give uniform discharge with negligible pulsations. They do not require check valves, they produce relatively low wear on moving parts, and they can handle liquids containing vapors and gases. Liquids containing a substantial amount of solids can be pumped. Exceptionally long life and low shear are other features.

Disadvantages. These pumps are bulky and heavy, and they are subject to relatively large changes in capacity with variations in viscosity and discharge pressure. Seals are required. Pumps cannot be operated against a closed discharge without damage to the pump—hence, relief valves are essential. Variable speed drives are required to provide changes in the pumping rate.

Ranges. Screw pumps are available in line sizes from ¾ to 12 inches NPS and in capacities up to 3000 gpm.

The commonly available pumps operate at temperatures up to 500°F and against discharge pressures up to 1000 psig. Rotor speeds as high as 3600 rpm are used with single double screw pumps. With twin double screw pumps rotor speeds are normally limited to 1150 rpm. Screw pumps can pump liquids with viscosities as high as 5,000,000 SSU. Costs for single double screw pumps range from about $600 to $4000 depending on size for the basic cast iron pump without motor. Twin double screw pumps without motor range in cost from $1000 to $12,000 for cast iron pumps having internal timing gears. The corresponding price range for twin double screw pumps with external timing gears is $1300 to $14,000.

Flexible Impeller Pumps

Advantages. These pumps are self-priming and produce uniform discharge with negligible pulsation. They do not require check valves, can pump in either direction, and are of simple construction, easily disassembled and light in weight. They have small space requirements, can handle liquids containing vapors and gases, produce low shear, and can pump liquids containing solids. They can be operated against a closed discharge for short periods without damage to the pump. The flexible impellers are easily replaced at low cost.

Disadvantages. These pumps have a limited range of application, cannot pump against high pressures, and cannot be used to pump abrasive liquids. They are not suitable for heavy duty applications. Variable speed drives are required to provide changes in the pumping rate. Shaft seals are necessary.

Ranges. Flexible impeller rotary pumps are available in line sizes from ¼ to 3 inches NPS and in capacities up to 100 gpm. These pumps normally operate at temperatures up to 180°F and against discharge pressures up to 30 psig. Pumps are also available which pump up to 60 psig discharge pressure. Rotor speeds are in the range 75 to 1750 rpm. Only liquids with viscosities less than 5000 SSU can be handled satisfactorily with these pumps. Costs for the basic steel pump without motor range from $20 to $400 depending on the size.

Piston and Plunger Pumps

Advantages. These are self-priming. If the stroke is variable, they do not require variable speed drives to alter pumping rates. They can handle liquids containing vapors and gases, and they have an exceptionally long life.

Disadvantages. These pumps tend to be heavy and bulky, and have a pulsating discharge. In the case of steam pumps, a steam source must be available. Power pumps cannot be operated against a closed discharge— hence, relief valves are required. They must have inlet and outlet valves.

Ranges. Steam pumps range in capacity from 20 to 2000 gpm. Steam pumps are available which operate against discharge pressures up to 20,000 psig. Typical prices range from $450 for a cast iron duplex pump of 20 gpm capacity operating against a discharge pressure of 300 psig to $75,000 for a specially designed carbon steel duplex pump delivering 800 gpm against an 800 psig discharge head.

The expense of these pumps is offset by their complete reliability and long life. At the Seager Evans and Co. factory in England which makes "Coates' Plymouth Gin," a steam pump has been running without repair or replacement since 1855.

Power pumps range in capacity from 10 to 1000 gpm. They can operate against discharge pressures up to 1000 psi. Typical prices for power pumps range from $700 for a duplex 10 gpm plunger pump with a 5 hp electric motor operating against a discharge pressure of 500 psig to $125,000 for a 1000 gpm nonoplex pump with a 1500 hp electric motor operating against a discharge pressure of 1000 psig. Efficiencies up to 95 per cent are possible with power pumps.

Small capacity simplex plunger pumps as single or multiple units are widely used as metering or proportioning pumps. These operate at capacities as low as 0.15 gph. Typical prices for metering pumps are $170 for a 6 to 10 gph cast iron simplex pump with a ¼ hp electric motor to $9000 for a 1200 gph duplex pump with a 5 hp electric motor. In general, the smaller the plunger diameter, the greater is the discharge pressure possible. A 2 gph pump is available with a 5/16 inch diameter plunger which can operate against a discharge pressure of 50,000 psig.

Slip leakage in reciprocating piston and plunger pumps is normally less than 5 per cent and is sometimes less than 1 per cent. Piston and plunger pumps operate at temperatures up to 550°F. Power and steam pumps operate with speeds up to 500 and 150 strokes per minute, respectively.[5] The upper speed limit for metering pumps is about 350 strokes per minute.[5]

Diaphragm Pumps

Advantages. These pumps are usually self-priming. If provided with a variable stroke mechanism, they do not require variable speed drives to alter pump speeds. They can handle liquids containing vapors and gases or liquids containing a substantial amount of solids. Process liquid does not come into contact with the prime moving parts, and the pump can be run dry for an extended period of time. No packings or seals are required. Most types are adjustable while in operation. Air and hydraulically driven diaphragm pumps can be operated against a closed discharge without damage to the pump.

Disadvantages. Diaphragm pumps are bulky, and the air driven types suffer large variations in capacity with changes in discharge pressure. They have a pulsating discharge and, with mechanically driven diaphragms, cannot be operated against a closed discharge without damage to the pump. Like piston pumps, they require check valves.

Ranges. Diaphragm pumps normally range in capacity from 4 to 100 gpm. However diaphragm metering pumps are available which operate with capacities as low as 1 gph. Some diaphragm metering pumps can operate against discharge pressures up to 3500 psig. Normally diaphragm pumps are not used to handle liquids with viscosities greater than 3500 SSU.

Typical costs for air driven diaphragm pumps range from $300 for an unlined cast iron pump of 5 gpm capacity to $2000 for a cast iron pump lined with "Hypolon" of 90 gpm capacity. Typical costs for mechanically driven proportioning pumps without motor are $150 for a 1 gph polyvinyl chloride-diaphragm pump and $3000 for a 10 gpm "Teflon"-diaphragm pump.

Miscellaneous Pumps

All the pumps discussed under this heading have the following advantages: they are self-priming, do not require check valves, can pump in either direction, have small space requirements, are light in weight, can handle liquids containing vapors and gases, and produce low shear.

In addition, flexible liner and peristaltic pumps have the extra advantage that the process liquid does not come into contact with the prime moving parts of the pump. Thus no seals are required. These two pumps can also be run dry for an extended period of time.

All the miscellaneous pumps discussed are of relatively low capacity (40 gpm or below). In addition, they can operate only against a relatively low discharge pressure (100 psig or below).

In general, these pumps can only handle liquids with viscosities below 5000 SSU.

Typical costs are $100 to $250 for peristaltic pumps without motor and $150 to $600 for flexible liner pumps without motor.

AUXILIARY EQUIPMENT AND ACCESSORIES

Prime Movers

The total power consumed by a pumping system is the sum of the powers required to raise the liquid level; overcome friction in the suction line, discharge line, pump internals, bearings, shaft seals and packing glands; compensate for power losses in the drive train between the motor and pump. Normally prime movers are overpowered by about 10 per cent.

Although internal combustion engines, air and steam are used to provide power, by far the most common prime mover is the electric motor. Alternating current (AC) electric motors are widely used. Direct current (DC) motors are much less common. Synchronous and induction motors are the most readily available types of AC motors.

Synchronous Motors. These operate at a constant speed under widely varying load conditions. The designed motor speed is a function only of the frequency of the power supply. Synchronous motors are equipped with a DC generator which supplies the rotor current. The DC generator is driven either by the synchronous motor itself or by a small auxiliary AC motor. The stator uses AC power to produce the required magnetic field. This is synchronized with the DC magnetic field in the rotor—hence, the term synchronous motor.

The efficiencies of synchronous motors are high, falling between 92 and 97 per cent. Synchronous motors require complex rotor windings and control devices for the rotor's DC field. The expense of the auxiliary equipment precludes the use of synchronous motors below 250 hp. Operating speeds range between 300 and 3600 rpm. However, the most common speeds are 900 and 1200 rpm. Standard synchronous motors are available in sizes up to 10,000 hp.

Induction Motors. In these motors, AC power in the stator is used to induce a current in the rotor. Induction motors are available in two types: wound rotor and squirrel cage rotor. In the former, the rotor is wound with wires. These cut the magnetic field of the stator when the armature rotates. This action induces a current and magnetic field in the rotor.

The squirrel cage rotor is not wound with wires, but consists of numerous parallel bars. Squirrel cage motors provide a relatively constant speed. However, the variation in speed is substantially greater than with synchronous motors. Squirrel cage induction motors operate best in the range of 600 to 3600 rpm. They are the simplest and usually the least expensive of the three types discussed. Their efficiency is about 3 per cent less than for comparable synchronous motors. Squirrel cage induction motors are available in the size range fractional to 10,000 hp. However, above 500 hp, synchronous motors with their higher efficiency become more economical to operate.

Motor Enclosures. If the atmosphere in the immediate vicinity of the pump contains potentially explosive vapors, then a totally enclosed explosion-proof motor should be used. This type of enclosure prevents sparks produced at the rotor from coming into contact with the hazardous vapors. Since pumps may leak, especially at the seals, totally enclosed explosion-proof motors should be used when pumping hazardous liquids. Explosion-proof motors are expensive and bulky.

For general use in nonhazardous areas, drip-proof or splash-proof types of motor enclosures are adequate. In the drip-proof design, the working parts are shielded from falling liquids and particles. However, protection is not afforded against fumes, dust, etc., which may be carried into the motor by the air. Dust screens may be used to prevent solid particles from entering the motor.

In most open and semi-open electric motors, the natural circulation of the atmospheric air is sufficient to dissipate the heat produced during operation. For totally enclosed motors and some large open and semi-open motors, additional means of heat removal must be provided. Totally enclosed motors may be fan cooled (TEFC). Air is circulated over an internal heat transfer area. Open motors may also be equipped with fans to provide forced air circulation cooling.

Power Transmission Units

Most electric motors are constant speed units. Although the speed of a synchronous motor depends on the current frequency, the latter is normally constant. The speed of a DC motor can be changed by incorporating a rheostat into the electrical system.

If the required pump speed is the same as the speed of the electric motor, a direct coupling is used as shown in Figure 5–22. Most electric motors operate most efficiently at or near their maximum speed. Frequently this is greater than the required pump speed. In this case, it is normal practice to use a constant speed gear reduction unit.

Constant Speed Gear Reduction Units. These are available in a wide range of speed reduction ratios. For example, a 5:1 unit will enable a 1750 rpm motor to drive a 350 rpm pump. Three types of constant speed gear reduction units are available: integral motor coupled, shaft mounted and integral pump mounted. These three types are shown, respectively, in Figures 5–23, 5–24 and 5–25. All of them operate in the same manner

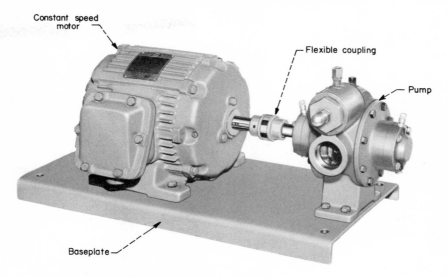

Figure 5-22.   Direct pump drive. (*Courtesy Blackmer Pump Co.*)

but differ in their position in the drive train. Each type has its own individual advantages. The integral motor coupled and pump mounted units are compact and require only one flexible coupling. Although the shaft mounted unit requires two flexible couplings, it can be removed from the drive train without disturbing the pump or motor. However, these units usually require belt drives which may not always be desirable. Furthermore, shaft mounted units may occupy more space than the integral units.

Variable Speed Units. Pumping rates should not be changed by throttling on either the discharge or the suction lines. The latter may cause cavitation and the former may produce a sufficient pressure to fracture the pump casing. Both methods can appreciably shorten the life of a positive displacement pump.

Variable speed units are readily available which enable the pumping rate of a positive displacement pump to be adjusted with no change in drive motor rpm. These units utilize gears, cones, belts and clutches to effect speed changes. Two types of variable speed unit are available: those giving an infinitely variable speed output between 0 rpm and the speed of the drive motor, and those giving a series of specific speed ratios, e.g., 10:1. Speed changes can be made while the unit is in operation.

Variable speed drives are bulky, heavy and have a high initial cost. Nevertheless, they are a good investment because of their flexibility.

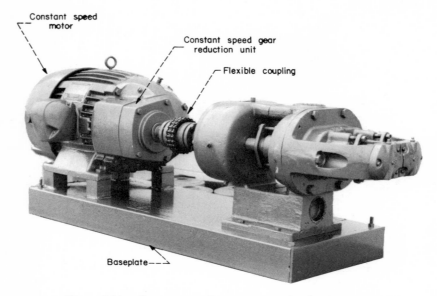

Figure 5-23.   Constant speed motor mounted reduction drive.
(Courtesy Ulrich Pump Co.)

Figure 5-24.   Constant speed shaft mounted reduction drive.
(Courtesy Ulrich Pump Co.)

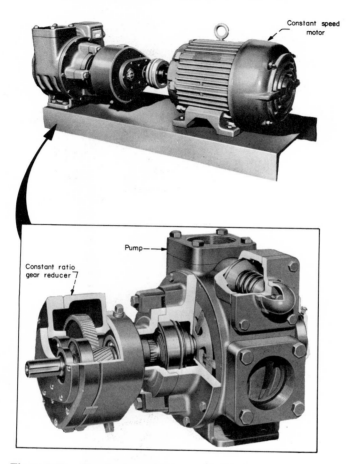

Figure 5-25. Constant speed pump mounted reduction drive.
(*Courtesy Blackmer Pump Co.*)

They may also be used to increase the life of a pump. Manufacturers have
tried to make variable speed drive units as compact as possible. Figure 5–26
shows some basic vertical variable speed drives. Horizontal units are
used when space is limited but floor area is available. Both horizontal
and vertical units are available as either "Z" or "C" units. The "C"
units are more compact than the "Z" units. The latter are usually employed when the unit is used to drive a belt. In this case it is an advantage
to have the motor on the opposite side of the speed reduction unit to avoid
interference with the belt.

Vertical Z unit

Vertical C unit

Figure 5-26.   Variable speed drives.
(*Courtesy U.S. Electrical Motors*)

Flexible Couplings

The alignment between a pump and its drive train is extremely critical; this also applies to the alignment between the component parts of the drive train. Misalignment results in excessive vibration, wasted power and ultimate damage to the pump and drive. It also leads to excessive wear at shaft seals and packing glands. Damage to gearing and bearings in reduction units, pumps and drives is a common result of misalignment. The latter does not need to be large to cause serious damage to precision parts. Two types of misalignment are possible: angular and parallel. These are illustrated in Figure 5–27. Both types may be present in the same system.

Angular misalignment occurs when the centerline of one shaft is at an angle ϕ to the connecting shaft. Parallel misalignment occurs when the centerlines of two shafts are parallel but in different planes displaced by a distance x. The allowable limits for maximum alignment depend on such factors as shaft speed, shaft length and construction of the component parts. However, angular misalignment should not generally be more than 1°. In practice, the angular misalignment should be less than 1°, although most flexible couplings can generally correct for this amount of misalignment. In general, the severity of angular misalignment increases with shaft length.

For a shaft length s and a misalignment angle ϕ, the displacement at the end of the shaft is (s) $(\sin \phi)$. If the driving shaft is rigid and the pump shaft absorbs all the angular misalignment, the circle swept out by the end of the pump shaft has a radius of (s) $(\sin \phi)$. This is true only if the pump shaft is free to adjust. Hence small angular misalignments in long shafts can exert serious strains on pumping equipment.

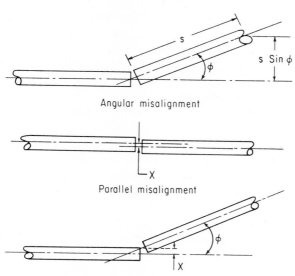

Angular misalignment

Parallel misalignment

Combined parallel and angular misalignment

Figure 5-27.   Types of shaft misalignment.

To reduce the effects of misalignment, flexible couplings may be used between shafts. Two general types of flexible couplings are available: single engagement and double engagement couplings.

Single engagement couplings are capable of transmitting power between angularly misaligned shafts. They have only one degree of freedom since they will not handle parallel misalignment. A typical example of a flexible coupling in this group is the common universal joint.

Double engagement couplings are capable of transmitting power between shafts which suffer from both angular and parallel misalignments. A number of double engagement couplings are shown in Figure 5–28. Jaw couplings consist of two meshing jaw flanges separated by a floating shock absorbent spacer block. They are used primarily for medium to high rpm's and low to moderate power consumptions. Since they consist of only three parts, they are easily installed and maintained.

Chain couplings consist of two sprocketed flanges held together by a standard-type link chain. Frequently a cover or bonnet surrounds the coupling. Another type of chain coupling, not shown in Figure 5–28, has a nylon chain. This forms its own safety cover, since the outer surface is smooth. Silent chain couplings are multi-link chains instead of the standard link type. These provide increased strength and less play.

Biscuit couplings are extremely flexible. They are available in two designs: single and double biscuit. The former type is shown in Figure 5–28. It consists of two flanges. One flange is coupled to a divider plate by flexible biscuits. The other flange is directly coupled by a floating tie link. This coupling provides excellent angular and parallel adjustment for low to moderate rpm's and moderate power loads. The double biscuit design has two sets of biscuit assemblies, one on each side of the divider plate. This arrangement gives extra flexibility.

Another type of coupling incorporates an internal gear unit. The shafts are fitted with geared hubs which fit into an internally cut gear sleeve. For low to moderate service, nonlubricated nylon sleeves are used. For heavy duty service, metallic sleeves are used. The heavy duty couplings are provided with self-contained lubrication.

Other types of flexible couplings incorporate bellows, flexible central disks, cushioned pins or radial slip clutches of various designs.

Costs of flexible couplings range from \$15 for a ½ inch shaft open roller chain unit with no safety cover to \$5000 for an 8 inch shaft radial coupling.

Shaft Packing and Seals

Any liquid when poured into a container will flow to conform to the shape of the container. Most pumps are not completely closed containers.

Roller chain coupling

Silent chain coupling

Biscuit coupling

Figure 5-28. Flexible couplings. (*Courtesy Eco Engineering Co., Morse Chain Co., Sier-Bath Bear Co., Inc.*)

Internal gear coupling

Jaw coupling

Figure 5-28. *Cont'd*

Power is transmitted to the pump mechanism by a reciprocating or rotating shaft which passes through the pump casing. In many pumps, the process liquid is in direct contact with the prime moving parts. In these pumps, the point at which the shaft passes through the casing is a potential source of leakage for the high pressure process liquid. Although the clearance between the shaft and the pump casing can be made extremely small, it can never be completely eliminated. Packings and seals are used to reduce to a minimum the leakage of process liquid from the pump.

Shaft Packings. Although these do not stop leakage entirely, they can control it to a very low level. Packing consists of pliable or semipliable material. A typical packing device is shown in Figure 5–29. The shaft passes through a stuffing box which contains the packing material. The packing material is in contact with a gland which is usually secured to the stuffing box with bolts. The latter are tightened to compress the packing around the shaft.

Some leakage of the process liquid is necessary for the packing to operate successfully. If the packing is too tight to allow a small amount of lubrication, the packing will overheat and burn or scorch. The packing surface becomes hard and smooth, no longer providing a good shaft seal. When hazardous liquids are pumped, the use of packings poses a safety problem.

The choice of packing material depends on the liquid to be pumped, temperature, pressure, shaft speed and the materials of construction of the pump. Shaft packing is available in two forms: preformed rings and flexible

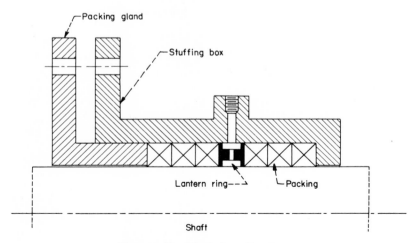

Figure 5-29.   Packed stuffing box.

spirals which can be cut to size. For heavy duty applications, laminated packings may be used. Examples of these are asbestos wrapped copper wire, aluminum foil over an asbestos core, and asbestos over a "Teflon" core. Table 5–2 gives the approximate operating temperature ranges for some common packings.

TABLE 5–2. Operating Temperature Ranges for Shaft Packings

250–525°F Range	Maximum Temperature (°F)
(1) Duck and rubber base packings	250
(2) Plant fiber base packing	250
(3) White asbestos, braided, light oil and graphite lubricant	350
(4) White asbestos, braided, solvent resistant and graphite lubricant	350
(5) Lead base packing	400
(6) "Teflon"	500

525–700°F Range	
(1) White asbestos, lattice braid	550
(2) White asbestos over "Teflon" core	550
(3) Blue African asbestos braid, asbestos over "Teflon" core, 35% "Teflon" impregnated throughout	550
(4) Blue African asbestos, square plaited braid	550
(5) 100% "Teflon" fiber yarn, lattice braid	
(6) 25% glass filled "Teflon" U-rings	550
(7) Commercial grade packings made of asbestos fiber	600
(8) White asbestos, braid over braid, mineral oil and graphite lubricant	650

700–1000°F Range	
(1) Aluminum foil over asbestos core, castor oil and graphite lubricant	750
(2) White asbestos braid over brass wire core	750
(3) "Junk rings" of braided copper wire and aluminum packings	900
(4) Aluminum foil laminations, castor oil and graphite lubricant	1000

Specially preformed seal rings are available for pressures up to approximately 8000 psi. In general, high pressure packing is weakened by a rotating shaft. High pressure packings such as braided asbestos and "Monel" over a mica-neoprene core are usually used with nonrotating or infrequently rotated shafts, e.g., on valves.

Some of the advantages and disadvantages of packings are as follows:

Advantages. Packings are relatively inexpensive, easily replaced in the field, and available in a wide variety of materials. There is also an extensive range of applications for most types.

Disadvantages. Packings require some leakage to provide lubrication. A packing gland needs frequent adjustment, and the break-in period is critical. Packing failure may result in shaft damage. If used on abrasive materials, a packing offers a short life together with increased power consumption resulting from frictional drag. Packings may corrode the gland and shaft, e.g., graphite packings corrode stainless steel shafts.

The basic source of difficulty with packed seals is that the shaft moves within a stationary packing. Mechanical seals have been designed to overcome this problem.

Mechanical Seals. In these, the sealing surface rotates with the shaft. Mechanical seals consist of two basic parts: a seal ring which fits tightly on the shaft and a stationary insert. The rotating seal ring contacts the stationary insert at a face which is precisely lapped to provide a leakproof sealing surface. A thin film of liquid must separate the two surfaces. The film may flow to the area either under the pressure of the process liquid, by capillary action or through an auxiliary feeding device. In most mechanical seals, compression springs or bellows are used to sustain good contact between the two surfaces.

Two types of mechanical seals are available: hydraulically unbalanced and balanced. The former provides no way of counteracting the hydraulic forces tending to push the seal ring against the stationary mating insert. In high pressure pumps, the force between the two faces can result in an excessive generation of heat and damage to the liquid film. To avoid this effect of hydraulic imbalance, means are available to balance the forces at the mating contact faces. The most common method is to provide a step in the shaft which decreases the direct load on the contact surfaces. More elaborate devices are also available. Some mechanical seals are totally balanced, i.e., the internal pressure does not contribute to the forces mating the contact forces.

Some common types of mechanical shaft seals are shown in Figure 5–30. In one of the seals shown, the process liquid is recirculated through the seal and a temperature control unit. This system provides lubricating liquid at the optimum temperature. It is useful when the process liquid tends either to vaporize or to crystallize. The former may lead to dry running of the sealing surfaces.

Double mechanical seals are used with valuable or hazardous liquids or under extremely high pressures.

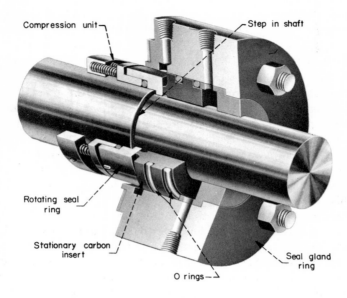

Balanced seal

Figure 5-30.   Mechanical seals. (*Courtesy Durametallic Corp.*)

For general service, mechanical seals are commonly equipped with a ceramic seal ring and a carbon insert. With highly corrosive liquids, the seal ring may be made of tungsten carbide and the insert of highly inert carbon.

Advantages. The power consumption resulting from frictional drag is only about 1/6 of that in a packing. There is relatively little wear on shafts and shaft sleeves; thus these units are run for relatively long periods without repair if seals are properly installed. Seals are good for vacuum service and for corrosive service with suitable materials of construction. Mechanical seals do not usually contaminate the process liquid, although balanced seals operating with an additional feed lubrication liquid are the exception.

Disadvantages. Mechanical seals are relatively expensive. Failure of the sealing surfaces can lead to heavy leakage. They are difficult to repair and are sensitive to mechanical abuse or maladjustment. They have relatively complicated construction and are subject to damage by liquids containing solids. Some mechanical seals require expensive auxiliary equipment.

Typical costs for mechanical seals are $25 for a 30 psi unbalanced single ⅜ inch diameter shaft seal with a ceramic seal ring and $1200 for a 600 psi

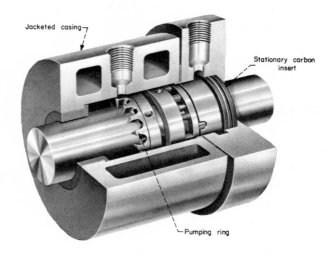

Circulating seal

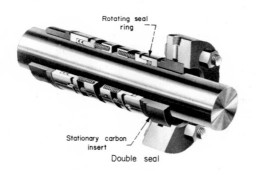

Double seal

Figure 5-30. *Cont'd*

balanced single 5 inch diameter shaft seal with a tungsten carbide seal ring. The corresponding double seal for a 5 inch diameter shaft cost $2000. The pressure balancing equipment for this seal could cost an additional $2000.

Pump Protection Equipment

Most positive displacement pumps require protection against over-pressure. If these pumps are operated against a closed or clogged discharge, a dangerous pressure buildup will take place. As the discharge pressure increases, it eventually exceeds the design limits of either the pump casing, the discharge pipeline or the shaft seal. Fracture of the weakest component can result. The danger is particularly great with mechanically driven pumps. Pressure relief and safety valves are commonly used to protect pumps from damage by overpressure. Automatic overload cutoffs on the drive motor are also used.

Pressure Relief Valves. These consist of four basic components:

(1) The main body of the valve which encases the internal parts,
(2) A movable spindle which seats into the entrance port of the valve,
(3) A spring to force the spindle against the valve seat,
(4) An adjusting screw to regulate the compression of the spring.

Relief valves are located in the discharge line of the system as close to the pump discharge port as possible. The compression in the spring is adjusted to correspond to the maximum allowable pressure in the pump. When the predetermined pressure is reached, the spindle is raised from the valve seat. This releases liquid which prevents the pump discharge pressure from rising further. The liquid discharged from the relief valve is recycled back to the suction side of the pump. The extent to which the relief valve opens is a function of the discharge pressure. Only sufficient liquid is released to allow the spindle to return to the valve seat.

In some pumps, the relief valve is not located in the discharge pipe but in its own closed loop recycle line. This facilitates maintenance and repair work since the process piping need not be disturbed.

The choice of the materials of construction for relief valves depend on the corrosiveness of the pumped liquid.

Safety Valves. These differ from relief valves in that a diaphragm or gland separates the liquid passages from the valve internals. In relief valves, the discharged liquid floods the area enclosing the compression spring. Two common types of safety valves are the balanced pressure or bellows valve and the unbalanced pressure valve. A balanced safety valve is shown in Figure 5–31. Safety valves are installed in the same way as relief valves.

Strainers and Screens. Damage can result when foreign materials enter the pump internals. Close tolerance pumps such as gear pumps are particularly prone to damage. Pipeline strainers and screens are frequently used to protect pumps from damage by foreign bodies. These are placed in the suction line prior to the pump intake port. Strainers are designed to permit rapid cleaning and replacement.

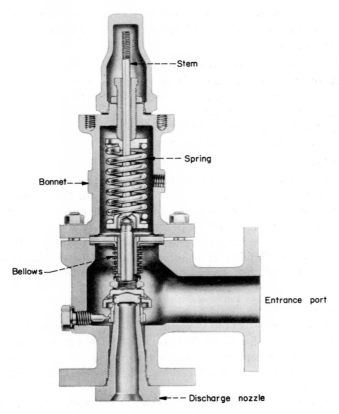

Figure 5-31. Balanced pressure safety valve.
(*Courtesy Kunkle Valve Co., Inc.*)

It is particularly important to use screens during the start-up of new pumping systems. A substantial amount of dirt, scale and welding slag is frequently present in new pipelines.

The area of a strainer should be about three to four times greater than the cross-sectional area of the pipeline. Coarse strainers are used with slurries. Oversized strainers are used with liquids of high viscosity.

PUMP INSTALLATION AND START-UP

A pump must be properly installed for it to operate efficiently and to have a long life. Improper installation frequently results in rapid and excessive wear. This also increases the down time required for repairs and replacements. The installation and start-up of a pumping system involve the following steps:

(1) Selection of the pump location,
(2) Layout of the suction and discharge pipelines,
(3) The provision of a suitable foundation for the pump and drive train,
(4) Installation of equipment,
(5) Alignment of the pump, drive train and piping,
(6) Testing of the system and start-up.

Pump Location

The pump location should be such that repair and maintenance work can be carried out easily. For example, it should not be necessary to dismantle pipelines and other equipment to get at the pump.

If possible, the pump should be positioned below the level of the liquid supply. The suction piping should be kept as short and free from bends as possible. The availability of utilities should not determine pump location. If necessary, utilities should be brought to the best available pump site.

Pipeline Layout

Suction side pipelines should be sloped to avoid air pockets. For the same reason, obstructions should be bypassed in the horizontal plane rather than the vertical. In pumping systems with suction lifts, the suction line should contain a check valve.[6] This keeps the prime on the pump when it is not in operation.

The suction and discharge pipelines should be supported independently of the pump to avoid any strain on the pump casing. For the same reason, the suction and discharge pipelines should be perfectly aligned with the pump flanges.

Since the pump is rigidly secured to a foundation, taking up misalignment in the pipe connections puts a strain on the pump casing. Some strain is unavoidable because of flexures in the pipelines. This tends to increase with pipe length. Strain on the pump casing can also result from thermal expansion of the pipes. If the pipeline expansion is likely to be greater than one- or two-hundredths of an inch, expansion joints should be used. These provide a compressive area in which to absorb the strain.[6] Strain due to piping misalignment can be avoided by incorporating damper sections in the pipelines. Dampeners are lengths of rubber pipe reinforced with multiple plies of high strength fabrics and helical steel wire reinforcement. These have the additional advantage of reducing vibration and line noises.

Excessive strain can distort the pump casing. This can lead to rapid wear and damage to the pump internals. This is especially true in close clearance pumps such as rotary gear pumps. Mechanical seals and shaft packings are very sensitive to slight distortions in pump shape. They wear excessively when strain is present.

The pipelines to the pump should not have a diameter less than the suction and discharge ports.

Pump Foundations and Alignment

The most common type of pump foundation is constructed of concrete. It is usual to bolt the pump and drive train to a cast iron or steel base plate. This is then secured to the concrete foundation.

Foundations for small pumps need only be large enough to accommodate the base plate assembly. Large pumps require foundations which are three to four times the weight of the pump and drive train assembly. Large foundations should preferably consist of concrete reinforced with steel rods.

Anchor bolts are used to secure the base plate to the foundation as shown in Figure 5–32. Each bolt is fitted with a washer and passed through a pipe sleeve which has a diameter three to four times greater than the bolt. The bolt sleeve unit is set into the concrete foundation at the predetermined base plate hole positions. A template of the base plate is used

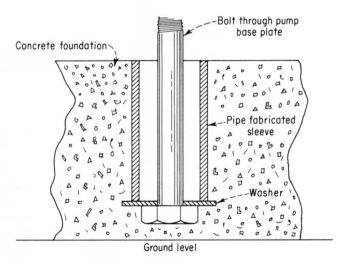

Figure 5-32.   Installation of foundation bolts.
(Courtesy Viking Pump Co.)

to position the bolts. Careful positioning of the anchor bolts is essential. The most sturdy base plate will flex to some degree if strained when the bolts are tightened. The flexibility in the sleeve washer unit allows minor adjustments to be made in the bolt position prior to final tightening. This is the case even after the concrete foundation has set.

Metal shims are used to position the pump on the foundation. Adjustments are made until the pump shafts and port flanges are completely level. Adjustments in the alignment between the pump and drive train are then made prior to connecting the pump to the suction and discharge lines. The latter should already have been aligned during the initial positioning of the base plate.

After the pipelines have been securely bolted, the entire pump assembly should be rechecked for flexure due to pipe strain. If the drive train alignment has not been changed by bolting the pipelines, the space between the base plate and the concrete foundation is filled with grouting. The latter should be sufficiently fluid to fill all the available space under the base plate.

It is essential that the alignment between the piping, pump and drive train should not change. It is preferable to make the alignments at the operating temperature of the pumping system. Although this is not easily accomplished, it eliminates any alignment changes due to thermal expansion.

In-line positive displacement pumps are now available which do not require foundations. Figure 5–33 shows an in-line double helical rotary gear pump which delivers 104 gpm of liquid at viscosities up to 100,000 SSU and pressures up to 350 psig.[4] In-line pumps save valuable floor space. A further advantage is that the straight runs of pipe into and out of the pump reduce frictional head losses.

Drives for in-line pumps are usually part of an integral frame which provides ready alignment. The alignment between the pump and the piping must be precise to avoid pipe strain on the pump casing.

Testing and Start-up

Positive displacement pumps are particularly prone to damage at start-up. Thurlow[6] suggests the use of a temporary stainless steel conical screen in the suction line. This provides protection against damage from bolts, welding slag, scale, etc., left in the pipeline during construction. A vacuum gauge in the suction line and a pressure gauge in the discharge line are useful aids in diagnosing malfunctions in a pumping system.

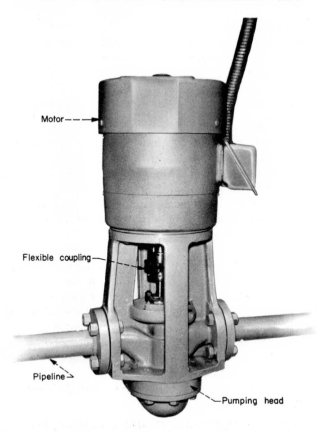

Figure 5-33. In-line rotary gear pump. (*Courtesy Warren Pumps, Inc.*)

The following procedure should be followed at start-up:

(1) Recheck alignment of pipeline connections, pump and drive train.

(2) Rotate the pump by hand. If the pump does not move freely, check for internal obstructions.

(3) Momentarily "kick in" the motor to ensure that the pump is rotating in the correct direction.

(4) Check the operation of the relief valve.

(5) Prime the pump if it is not self-priming.

(6) Open all valves in the suction and discharge lines.

(7) Ensure the tightness of all joints.

(8) Check the lubrication of packings, seals, etc.

(9) Start the pump.

(10) If the pump fails to deliver liquid within one minute, turn off the pump. A positive displacement pump should never run dry for any longer than is necessary.

The pump should also be stopped for any of the following reasons:

(1) Excessive vibration indicating misalignment,

(2) Noisy operation due to cavitation (this may be caused by an air leak in the suction line),

(3) Noisy operation caused by a foreign object inside the pump,

(4) Excessive leakage at shaft seals and packings,

(5) Overheating of the pump or drive motor (this may arise from either the binding of close tolerance moving parts, too great a discharge pressure, or inadequate cooling facilities).

Packing glands should not be taken up completely during start-up. A break-in period should be allowed to enable the packing to seat itself. If this is not done, scorching and damage to the packing and shaft can result. After the break-in period, the packing gland should be tightened to allow only sufficient leakage to provide proper lubrication.

When the pump is in operation, its performance should be checked against the manufacturer's specifications. Periodic checks on performance will provide an estimate of pump wear.

Table 5–3 lists some of the possible troubles and their causes in pump operation.

DESIGN CONSIDERATIONS AND CALCULATIONS

The important factors to consider in the design of a pumping system are the physical and chemical properties of the liquid to be transferred, the required liquid transfer rate, and the pipe dimensions and system heads. The latter are also functions of the liquid physical properties. This information enables the horsepower requirements of the system to be determined and the appropriate pump to be selected.

Liquid Properties

The cyclic speed of the moving parts of a positive displacement pump should be reduced as the viscosity of the pumped liquid increases. This minimizes noise, vibration and the loss of pumping capacity. Recommended operating speeds as a function of rated speed are given in Figure 5–34 as a function of liquid viscosity in SSU for a typical internal gear pump.[8] Similar plots are available for other pump types. Thus larger pumps are required to pump viscous liquids for the same capacity.

TABLE 5–3. Problems of Pump Operations

No Liquid Delivered	Pump Delivers Less Than Rated Capacity	Loss of Prime While Pump Is Operating	The Pump Is Noisy	Rapid Pump Wear	Pump Takes Too Much Power
(1) Pump not primed	(1) Air leaks in suction line or pump seal	(1) Liquid level falls below the suction line intake	(1) Cavitation	(1) Pipe strain on pump casing	(1) Speed too high
(2) Insufficient available NPSH	(2) Insufficient available NPSH	(2) Air leak develops in pump or seal	(2) Misalignment	(2) Grit or abrasive material in liquid	(2) Shaft packing too tight
(3) Suction line strainer clogged	(3) Suction line strainer clogged or of insufficient area	(3) Air leak develops in suction line	(3) Foreign material inside pump	(3) Pump running dry	(3) Liquid more viscous than specified
(4) End of suction line not in liquid	(4) Wear on pump leads to increased clearances and slip	(4) Liquid vaporizes in suction line	(4) Bent rotor shaft (for rotary pumps)	(4) Corrosion	(4) Misalignment
(5) Relief valve set lower than minimum required discharge pressure	(5) Relief valve wrongly set		(5) Relief valve chattering		(5) Obstruction in discharge line raises operating pressure
(6) Relief valve jammed open	(6) Relief valve jammed open				(6) Discharge line too small
(7) Pump rotates in wrong direction	(7) Speed too low				(7) Discharge valve partially closed
(8) Suction or discharge valves closed	(8) Suction of discharge valves partially closed				
(9) Bypass valve open	(9) Bypass valve partially open				
	(10) Liquid viscosity differs from that specified				

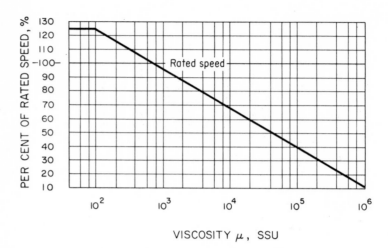

Figure 5-34.   Effect of viscosity on allowable pump speed.
(*Courtesy Viking Pump Co.*)

Since pressure heads in ft are calculated from the expression $144P/\rho$, where P is pressure in psi and ρ is density in lb/cu ft, the density of the pumped liquid effects the suction, discharge and total heads for the system. These are given by Equations (5–4), (5–5) and (5–6), respectively. The volatility of the pumped liquid at the operating temperature of the system determines the available $NPSH$. This is calculated from Equation (5–7).

The temperature of the pumped liquid and its corrosiveness also determine the materials of construction which may be used for the pump and the pipelines. The maximum allowable contamination of the pumped liquid is also a factor in materials of construction selection. In general, materials with very low corrosion rates are expensive. Cheaper materials involve higher maintenance costs. The choice will depend on the application. Table 5-4 lists the common pump materials used for a number of liquids.[8]

Pumping Rates

Positive displacement pumps provide a constant flow rate for a given cycle speed. If other liquid flow rates are required during the process, then in general, the pump must be equipped with means to vary the cycle speed. The viscosity of the liquid pumped may also vary during the process.

The system heads and horsepower requirements need to be calculated for each flow rate and liquid viscosity encountered during the process.

TABLE 5-4. Materials of Construction for Pumps[8]

Liquid Pumped	Materials of Construction					
	All Iron	Bronze Fitted	All Bronze	"Ni-Resist"	Stainless Steel	"Monel"
Acetaldehyde	X					
Acetate solvents	X	X	X			
Acetone	X	X				
Acetic anhydride					X	
Acids:						
Acetic acid (conc.)			X	X	X	X
Acetic acid (dil., cold)			X		X	X
Benzoic acid					X	
Boric acid			X		X	
Butyric acid (conc.)					X	
Carbolic acid (conc.)	X				X	
Carbolic acid (dil.)		X			X	
Chromic acid (dil.)					X	
Cyanic acids	X				X	
Fatty acids (oleic, palmitic, etc.)	X				X	X
Formic acid					X	
Hydrochloric acid (dil., cold)						X
Hydrocyanic acid	X				X	
Hydrofluoric acid (anhydrous with hydrocarbons)						X
Hydrofluoric acid (dil.)			X			X
Hydrofluosilic acid			X			X
Iron pyrite acid			X			
Lactic acid			X		X	

TABLE 5-4.—(continued)

Liquid Pumped	All Iron	Bronze Fitted	All Bronze	"Ni-Resist"	Stainless Steel	"Monel"
Naphthenic acid	X				X	
Nitric acid (conc., boiling, dil.)					X	
Oxalic acid (cold)					X	
Orthophosphoric acid					X	
Picric acid					X	
Pyrogallic acid					X	
Sebacic acid			X			
Sulfuric acid: less than 10%			X			X
Fuming	X					
Concentrated	X					
Sulfurous acid			X	X		
Tannic acid			X		X	X
Tartaric acid			X		X	X

System Heads

The system heads are a function of the liquid properties, pumping rate, pipe diameter, pipe roughness, pipe lengths and heights and the fittings in the suction and discharge pipelines.

The problem may be one of the following:
(1) The design of new pipelines and the selection of a pump,
(2) The selection of a pump to be used in an existing pipeline,
(3) The design of new pipelines to be used with an existing pump.

All these problems require the calculation of head losses in the pipelines and fittings. The frictional head loss h_f in a pipe of equivalent length ℓ_e ft and internal diameter d_i ft is given by the equation

$$h_f = 8\left(\frac{R}{\rho u^2}\right)\left(\frac{\ell_e}{d_i}\right)\left(\frac{u^2}{2g}\right) \qquad (2\text{--}38)$$

where u is the average linear velocity in the pipeline in ft/sec, g is the gravitational acceleration 32.2 ft/sec², and $j_f = R/\rho u^2$ plotted as a function of Reynolds number in Figure 2–4. The friction factor j_f is also a function of the roughness factor ϵ. Values of ϵ for various common pipeline materials are given in Table 2–1. Figure 2–4 gives separate lines for various values of the dimensionless roughness factor ϵ/d_i.

The equivalent lengths of various pipeline fittings are given in Table 4–1, and the entrance and exit losses for pipelines are given in Figure 2–6.

EXAMPLE

Calculate the system heads in the pumping system shown in Figure 5–35 on the basis of the following data.

(1) Liquid of viscosity 1000 cp, specific gravity 1.2 and vapor pressure 1.0 psia at the pumping temperature.

(2) 6 ft suction and 100 ft discharge lines of 2 inch schedule 40 steel pipe.

(3) One 90° standard radius elbow and one gate valve in the suction line (steel screwed fittings).

(4) Three 90° standard radius elbows and one globe valve in the discharge line (steel screwed fittings).

(5) Liquid transfer rate, 40 U.S. gpm.

(6) The tanks connected to the suction and discharge lines are cylindrical tanks, both 12 ft in diameter.

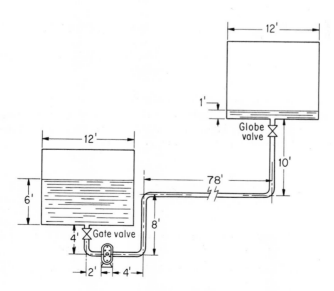

Figure 5-35.   Pumping system.

(7) Initially the liquid levels in the suction and discharge tanks are 6 ft and 1 ft, respectively, above the bottoms of the tanks.

(8) The pump is stopped when the liquid level in the suction side tank has fallen to within 1 ft of the bottom of the tank.

(9) Atmospheric pressure of 14.7 psia above the suction and discharge tanks.

The calculation procedure is as follows:

(1) Calculate the linear velocity of liquid in the pipelines: From Table A–1, a mean linear velocity of liquid of 1 ft/sec in a 2 inch schedule 40 steel pipe is given by a volumetric flow rate of 10.45 U.S. gpm. Thus a volumetric flow rate of 40 U.S. gpm gives a mean linear velocity of 3.83 ft/sec in a 2 inch schedule 40 steel pipe.

(2) Calculate the velocity head to be

$$\frac{u^2}{2g} = \frac{(3.83 \text{ ft/sec})^2}{(2)(32.2 \text{ ft/sec}^2)} = 0.228 \text{ ft}$$

(3) Calculate the liquid density to be

$$\rho = 62.4 \times 1.2 = 74.9 \text{ lb/cu ft}$$

(4) Read the inside diameter of a 2 inch schedule 40 steel pipe to be 2.067 inches from Table A–1. Therefore $d_i = 2.067/12 = 0.1723$ ft.

(5) Estimate the liquid viscosity in pound-foot-second units. Since 1 cp = 0.000672 lb/ft sec,

$$1000 \text{ cp} = 0.672 \text{ lb/ft sec}$$

(6) Calculate the Reynolds number N_{Re} in the pipelines to be

$$N_{Re} = \frac{\rho u d_i}{\mu} = \frac{(74.9 \text{ lb/cu ft})(3.83 \text{ ft/sec})(0.1723 \text{ ft})}{0.672 \text{ lb/ft sec}} = 73.6$$

Thus the liquid in the pipelines is in laminar flow.

(7) Read the value of the basic friction factor $j_f = R/\rho u^2$ corresponding to this Reynolds number from Figure 2–4. Alternatively, calculate the basic friction factor from the following formula for laminar flow in pipelines:

$$j_f = \frac{R}{\rho u^2} = \frac{8}{N_{Re}} \tag{2–36}$$

$$= 8/73.6 = 0.1086$$

(8) Estimate the equivalent length to pipe diameter ratio ℓ_e/d_i for the suction pipeline. This is made up of the following components parts:

(a) The actual length of the pipe which contributes $6/0.1723 = 34.8$ to the ℓ_e/d_i ratio.

(b) The 90° standard radius elbow which from Table 4–1 has an equivalent length to pipe diameter ratio of $8.5/0.1723 = 49.3$.

(c) The gate valve which from Table 4–1 has an equivalent length to pipe diameter ratio of $1.5/0.1723 = 8.7$.

Thus for the suction pipeline, the total equivalent length to pipe diameter ratio

$$\frac{\ell_e}{d_i} = 34.8 + 49.3 + 8.7 = 92.8$$

(9) Estimate the equivalent length to pipe diameter ratio ℓ_e/d_i for the discharge pipeline. This is made up of the following component parts:

(a) The actual length of the pipe which contributes $100/0.1723 = 580.3$.

(b) Three 90° standard radius elbows each of which from Table 4–1 has an equivalent length to pipe diameter ratio of $8.5/0.1723 = 49.3$.

(c) The globe valve which from Table 4–1 has an equivalent length to pipe diameter ratio of $54/0.1723 = 313$.

Thus for the discharge pipeline, the total equivalent length to pipe diameter ratio

$$\frac{\ell_e}{d_i} = 580.3 + 147.9 + 313 = 1041.2$$

(10) Calculate the head loss h_{fs} due to friction in the suction line. From step (7),

$$R/\rho u^2 = 0.1086$$

from step (8),

$$\ell_e/d_i = 92.8$$

and from step (2),

$$u^2/2g = 0.228 \text{ ft}$$

Therefore,

$$h_{fs} = 8(R/\rho u^2)(\ell_e/d_i)(u^2/2g) = 8 \ (0.1086)(92.8)(0.228)$$
$$= 18.4$$

the head loss due to pipe friction in the suction line. Add the contraction head loss due to liquid entering the suction line. From Figure 2–6, $K = 0.5$; therefore, $h_c = 0.1$ and $h_{fs} = 18.4 + 0.1 = 18.5$ ft.

(11) Calculate the head loss h_{fd} due to friction in the discharge line. From step (7),

$$R/\rho u^2 = 0.1086$$

from step (9),

$$\ell_e/d_i = 1041.2$$

and from step (2),

$$u^2/2g = 0.228 \text{ ft}$$

Therefore,

$$h_{\text{fd}} = 8(R/\rho u^2)(\ell_e/d_i)(u^2/2g) = 8 \ (0.1086)(1041.2)(0.228)$$
$$= 206.2$$

the head loss due to pipe friction in the discharge line. Add the expansion head loss due to liquid leaving the discharge line. From Figure 2–6, $h_e = 0.223$ ft; therefore, $h_{\text{fd}} = 206.2 + 0.223 = 206.4$.

(12) Calculate the initial suction head

$$h_s = z_s + \frac{144P_s}{\rho} - h_{\text{fs}} \tag{5–4}$$

From Figure 5–35, $z_s = 10$ ft; also

$$144P_s/\rho = 144(14.7/74.9) = 28.3 \text{ ft}$$

and from step (10), $h_{\text{fs}} = 18.5$ ft. Therefore, $h_s = 10 + 28.3 - 18.5 = 19.8$ ft—the suction head at the start of the operation.

(13) Calculate the initial discharge head

$$h_d = z_d + \frac{144P_d}{\rho} + h_{\text{fd}} \tag{5–5}$$

From Figure 5–35, $z_d = 17$ ft; also

$$144P_d/\rho = 144(14.7/74.9) = 28.3 \text{ ft}$$

and from step (11), $h_{\text{fd}} = 206.4$. Therefore, $h_d = 17 + 28.3 + 206.4 = 251.7$ ft—the discharge head at the start of the operation.

(14) Calculate the initial total head $\Delta h = h_d - h_s$. From step (13), $h_d = 251.7$ ft, and from step (12), $h_s = 19.8$ ft. Therefore, $\Delta h = h_d - h_s = 251.7 - 19.8 = 231.9$ ft—the total head at the start of the operation.

(15) Calculate the initial available net positive suction head

$$NPSH = z_s + [144(P_s - P_{\text{vp}})/\rho] - h_{\text{fs}}$$

From Figure 5–35, $z_s = 10$ ft. Since $P_{\text{vp}} = 1.0$ psia,

$$144(P_s - P_{\text{vp}})/\rho = 144\left(\frac{13.7}{74.9}\right) = 26.3 \text{ ft}$$

also from step (10), $h_{\text{fs}} = 18.5$ ft. Therefore, $NPSH = 10 + 26.3 - 18.5 = 17.8$ ft. Thus there is plenty of available head to get the liquid into the pump at the start of the operation.

(16) Proceed as in step (12) and calculate the final suction head to be h_s = 14.8 ft.

(17) Proceed as in step (13) and calculate the final discharge head to be h_d = 256.7 ft.

(18) Proceed as in step (14) and calculate the final total head to be $\Delta h = h_d - h_s$ = 256.7 − 14.8 = 241.9 ft.

(19) Proceed as in step (15) and calculate the final available net positive suction head to be NPSH = 12.8 ft. Thus there is still plenty of available head to get the liquid into the pump at the end of the operation.

Horsepower Calculations

Equation (5–9) gives the liquid horsepower in terms of the mass flow of the liquid. In terms of the volumetric flow rate of the liquid, Equation (5–9) can be rewritten as

$$\text{liquid horsepower} = \frac{(\text{gpm})(\Delta h)(sp\ gr)}{3960} \tag{5-11}$$

where $sp\ gr$ = specific gravity of the liquid referred to water at 68°F, weighing 62.3 lb/cu ft.

EXAMPLE

Calculate the liquid horsepowers at the start and finish of the pumping operation described in the previous example where the volumetric liquid flow rate is 40 U.S gpm and the specific gravity of the liquid is 1.2. Assume that a rotary gear pump is available with mechanical efficiency of 48 per cent under these conditions. Estimate the size of the drive unit.

(1) Calculate the initial liquid horsepower. Since the initial total head Δh = 231.9 ft, the initial liquid horsepower is

$$\frac{(40\ \text{gpm})\ (231.9\ \text{ft})\ (1.2)}{3960} = 2.81\ \text{hp}$$

(2) Calculate the final liquid horsepower. Since the final total head Δh = 241.9 ft, the final liquid horsepower is

$$\frac{(40\ \text{gpm})\ (241.9\ \text{ft})\ (1.2)}{3960} = 2.93\ \text{hp}$$

(3) Calculate the brake horsepower on the basis of the final liquid horsepower of 2.93 hp:

$$\text{mechanical efficiency} = \frac{\text{liquid horsepower}}{\text{brake horsepower}} \times 100$$

Therefore,

$$\text{brake horsepower} = \frac{2.93}{48} \times 100$$

$$= 6.12 \text{ hp}$$

A 7.5 hp electric motor may be used to drive the rotary gear pump. If the liquid is tacky, the additional power available in the motor will be required to start the rotary gear pump.

Usually brake horsepower (bhp) is given in manufacturers' bulletins in the form of a plot of bhp vs pump discharge pressure in psig for a particular liquid viscosity. Frequently plots for two different viscosities μ_1 and μ_2 are given.

Zalis[9] has given a method for calculating the brake horsepower of rotary pumps at viscosities other than those specified for a particular pump discharge pressure. The basis of the method is as follows:

$$\text{brake horsepower} = \text{liquid horsepower} + \text{friction horsepower}$$

The liquid horsepower is calculated as already described. However, in this case the volumetric flow rate into the pump is used in the calculation, i.e., the pumping capacity with zero slip. The friction horsepower (fhp) is the bhp value at zero discharge pressure. This can be read from the bhp vs pump discharge pressure plot for each of the two known viscosities μ_1 and μ_2. A plot is made of fhp vs liquid viscosity on logarithmic coordinates by joining the two points to form a straight line. The fhp values at other viscosities can be read from this plot.

Alternatively the equation

$$\frac{\text{fhp}}{\text{fhp}_1} = \left(\frac{\mu}{\mu_1} \right)^{m_1} \tag{5–12}$$

can be used to obtain the friction horsepower at a particular liquid viscosity μ where

$$m_1 = \frac{\log_{10} \text{fhp}_2 - \log_{10} \text{fhp}_1}{\log_{10} \mu_2 - \log_{10} \mu_1} \tag{5–13}$$

In Equation (5–13), fhp_1 and fhp_2 are the known friction horsepowers, respectively, at the given liquid viscosities μ_1 and μ_2.

The brake horsepower is then obtained by adding the calculated liquid horsepower to the friction horsepower which is calculated from Equation (5–12), where fhp_1 and μ_1 are known. The exponent m_1 is calculated from the known values of μ_1, fhp_1, μ_2 and fhp_2 using Equations (5–13).

EXAMPLE

Consider the previous example. Head h in ft is related to pressure P in psi by the equation

$$h = 144\left(\frac{P}{\rho}\right)$$

where ρ is the liquid density in lb/cu ft. The final discharge head was calculated in step (17) of the first example to be 256.7 ft. Since the liquid density $\rho = 74.9$ lb/cu ft, the discharge head is calculated to be 133.5 psia which is 118.8 psig. The liquid has a viscosity of $\mu_1 = 1000$ cp and a specific gravity of 1.2. Thus the kinematic viscosity is 833 centistokes which is equivalent to a viscosity of $\mu = 3790$ SSU.

Calculate the brake horsepower under the above conditions if the friction horsepowers at viscosities $\mu_2 = 10,000$ SSU and $\mu_1 = 1000$ SSU are $fhp_2 = 4$ hp and $fhp_1 = 2$ hp, respectively, at a pump discharge pressure of 118.8 psig.

(1) Find the value of m_1 in Equation (5–12):

$$m_1 = \frac{\log_{10} 4 - \log_{10} 2}{\log_{10} 10,000 - \log_{10} 1000} = 0.301$$

(2) Calculate fhp at $\mu = 3790$ SSU from Equation (5–12):

$$fhp_1 = 2 \text{ and } \mu_1 = 1000 \text{ SSU}$$

Therefore fhp $= 2(3.79)^{0.301} = 2.99$.

(3) Obtain the brake horsepower by adding fhp $= 2.99$ to the liquid horsepower value of 2.93 calculated in step (2) of the last example. Therefore, bhp $= 5.92$.

This method of obtaining brake horsepower is less accurate than the method of direct calculation already described.

Slip Calculations

Zalis[9] has also given a method for calculating the liquid flow from the discharge to the suction side of a rotary pump for a particular pressure at viscosities other than those specified.

Usually the capacity of a rotary pump is given in manufacturers' bulletins in the form of a plot of gpm vs pump discharge pressure in psig for a particular liquid viscosity. Frequently plots for two different viscosities μ_1 and μ_2 are given. The basis of the Zalis method is as follows:

The pump capacity with no slip is the capacity at 0 psig discharge pressure. This can be read from the appropriate gpm vs discharge pressure plot together with the capacity at the particular discharge pressure in question. The difference between the two values is the slip capacity. This can be calculated for each viscosity μ_1 and μ_2 at the discharge pressure required. A plot is then made of slip gpm vs liquid viscosity on logarithmic coordinates by joining the two points to form a straight line. The slip gpm values at other viscosities μ can be read from this plot.

Alternatively the equation

$$\frac{\text{slip gpm}}{\text{slip gpm}_1} = \left(\frac{\mu}{\mu_1}\right)^{m_2} \tag{5-14}$$

can be used to obtain the slip gpm at a particular viscosity where

$$m_2 = \frac{\log_{10} \text{slip gpm}_2 - \log_{10} \text{slip gpm}_1}{\log_{10} \mu_2 - \log_{10} \mu_1} \tag{5-15}$$

m_2 has a negative value since slip capacity decreases with increasing viscosity. In Equation (5-14), slip gpm$_1$ and slip gpm$_2$ are the known slip capacities, respectively, at the given liquid viscosities μ_1 and μ_2.

The pump capacity at the discharge pressure and liquid viscosity μ in question is then obtained by subtracting the slip capacity calculated from Equation (5-14) from the capacity at 0 psig discharge pressure.

EXAMPLE

Consider the previous example. The liquid viscosity is $\mu = 3790$ SSU and the final discharge is calculated to be 118.8 psig.

Calculate the slip and discharge capacity under the above conditions if the slip capacities at viscosities of $\mu_2 = 10,000$ SSU and $\mu_1 = 1000$ SSU are 0.3 and 0.7 gpm, respectively, at a pump discharge pressure of 118.8 psig.

(1) Find the value of m_2 in Equation (5-15):

$$m_2 = \frac{\log_{10} 0.3 - \log_{10} 0.7}{\log_{10} 10,000 - \log_{10} 1000} = -0.368$$

(2) Calculate the slip gpm at $\mu = 3790$ SSU from Equation (5-14):
$$\text{slip gpm} = 0.7 \text{ at } \mu_1 = 1000 \text{ SSU}$$

Therefore,

$$\text{slip gpm} = 0.7(3.79)^{-0.368}$$
$$= 0.43 \text{ gpm}$$

(3) Calculate the pump capacity at a discharge pressure of 118.8 psig and a liquid viscosity of $\mu = 3790$ SSU. If the pump capacity at 0 psig discharge pressure is 40.00 gpm, the pump capacity under the above conditions is 40.00 − 0.43 = 39.57 gpm.

Piston and Plunger Pump Calculations

At the peak of the suction stroke in a piston or plunger pump the available net positive suction head can be calculated from the equation

$$NPSH = z_s + [144(P_s - P_{vp})/\rho] - h_{fs} \qquad (5\text{-}7)$$

which was discussed earlier.

The following equation[1] gives the minimum net positive suction head required by the pump system at this point to avoid cavitation,

$$NPSH_{min} = 25D_i\left(\frac{h_{fs}}{\ell_e}\right) \qquad (5\text{-}16)$$

where D_i is the inside diameter of the suction pipe in inches, h_{fs} is the frictional head loss in the suction line in ft and ℓ_e is the equivalent length of pipe in the suction line in ft.

At the start of the suction stroke, the liquid has no velocity. The available net positive suction head at this point is thus given by the equation

$$NPSH = z_s + [144(P_s - P_{vp})/\rho] \qquad (5\text{-}17)$$

The following equation[1] gives the minimum net positive suction head required by the pump system to avoid cavitation at the start of the suction stroke,

$$NPSH_{min} = \frac{\ell L D^2 N^2}{(5.2 \times 10^4)D_i^2} \qquad (5\text{-}18)$$

where

ℓ = actual length of the suction pipeline including fittings in ft,
L = pump stroke length in inches,
D = plunger diameter in inches,
N = pump speed in strokes per minute,
D_i = inside diameter of the suction pipe in inches.

EXAMPLE

Calculate the maximum allowable pump speed N in strokes per minute for a plunger pump on the basis of the following data: pipeline system data, $z_s = 10$ ft, $P_s = 14.7$ psia, $P_{vp} = 1.0$ psia, $\rho = 72.0$ lb/cu ft, $\ell = 20$ ft, $\ell_e = 50$ ft, $h_{fs} = 1.0$ ft and $D_i = 1.049$ inches (1 inch schedule 40 steel pipe). Pump data, $L = 4$ inches and $D = 1.5$ inches.

(1) Calculate the available $NPSH$ from Equation (5–17):

$$NPSH = 10 + \left[\frac{144}{72}(14.7 - 1.0) \right] = 37.4 \text{ ft}$$

(2) For the $NPSH$ value calculated in step (1), calculate the stroke speed N from the Equation (5–18):

$$N = \left(\frac{5.2 D_i{}^2 NPSH}{\ell L D^2} \right)^{\frac{1}{2}} 10^2 = \left[\frac{(5.2)(1.049)^2(37.4)}{(20)(4)(1.5)^2} \right]^{\frac{1}{2}} 10^2$$

$$= 109 \text{ strokes per minute}$$

This is the maximum allowable pump speed. At greater pump speeds, cavitation will occur.

(3) Calculate the available NPSH from Equation (5–7):

$$NPSH = 10 + \left[\frac{144}{72}(14.7 - 1.0) \right] - 1.0 = 36.4 \text{ ft}$$

(4) Calculate the minimum required $NPSH$ from Equation (5–16):

$$NPSH_{min} = 25(1.049)\left(\frac{1.0}{50} \right) \cong 0.5 \text{ ft}$$

Thus there is adequate $NPSH$ available at the peak of the suction stroke.

EXAMPLE

Recalculate the maximum allowable pump speed N for a vapor pressure of 10.0 psia with all the other data remaining the same. In practice, the frictional head loss changes with liquid flow rate. The same value is taken here only for illustration purposes.

(1) Calculate the available $NPSH$ from Equation (5–17):

$$NPSH = 10 + \left[\frac{144}{72}(14.7 - 10.0) \right] = 19.4 \text{ ft}$$

(2) For the $NPSH$ value calculated in step (1), calculate the stroke speed N from Equation (5–18):

$$N = \left(\frac{5.2 D_i{}^2 NPSH}{\ell L D^2} \right)^{\frac{1}{2}} 10^2 = \left[\frac{(5.2)(1.049)^2(19.4)}{(20)\,(4)(1.5)^2} \right]^{\frac{1}{2}} 10^2$$

$$= 78 \text{ strokes per minute}$$

This is the maximum allowable pump speed.

Equations (5–16) and (5–18) give required $NPSH_{min}$ values which are too low for pumps with heavy suction valves and very restricted inlet passages.

NOMENCLATURE

bhp	brake horsepower
d_i	inside pipe diameter, ft
D_i	inside pipe diameter, inches
D_T	inside tank diameter, ft
D	plunger diameter, inches
E	mechanical efficiency, per cent
f	Fanning friction factor (dimensionless)
g	gravitational acceleration, 32.2 ft/sec²
g_c	conversion factor, 32.174 ft lb$_m$/lb$_f$ sec²
gpm	gallons per minute
hp	horsepower
fhp	friction horsepower
h	head, ft
h_f	head loss due to friction, ft
h_s	suction head, ft
h_d	discharge head, ft
h_c	head loss due to contraction, ft
h_e	head loss due to expansion, ft
j_f	basic friction factor (dimensionless) $= R/\rho u^2$
ℓ	actual pipe length, ft
ℓ_e	equivalent pipe length, ft
L	stroke length of pump, inches
m_1	factor in Equation (5–13), hp/SSU
m_2	factor in Equation (5–15), gpm/SSU
N_{Re}	Reynolds number (dimensionless) $= \rho u d_i/\mu$
$NPSH$	net positive suction head
N	pump speed, rpm or strokes/min
P	pressure, psi
P_{vp}	vapor pressure of liquid, psi
psi	pounds per square inch
R_s	shear stress, poundals/sq ft
s	shaft length, ft
u	mean linear velocity of liquid inside a pipe, ft/sec
W	mass flow rate of liquid, lb/min
z	liquid height, ft
α	factor in Equation (5–1), (dimensionless)
μ	viscosity of liquid, lb/ft sec, cp or SSU
ρ	density of liquid lb/cu ft

$\dot{\gamma}$ shear rate, sec^{-1}

Δh total head, ft

θ liquid contact angle, degrees

ϕ angular misalignment, degrees

REFERENCES

1. "Controlled Volume Pumps, Bulletin 553–1," Milton Roy Co., Philadelphia, Pa.
2. Coulson, J. M., and Richardson, J. F., "Chemical Engineering," Vol. 1, p. 33, New York, The Macmillan Co., 1964.
3. "Hydraulic Institute Standards," Eleventh ed., p. E(I)—7, New York, The Hydraulic Institute, May 1965.
4. "Roline Gear-Type Rotary In-Line Pumps," Warren Pumps, Inc., Warren, Mass.
5. Thurlow, C., *Chem. Eng.*, **72**, No. 11 (1965).
6. Thurlow, C., *Chem. Eng.*, **72**, No. 12 (1965).
7. "Vari-Flo Controlled Volume Pumps, Bulletin 600," Blackmer Pump Co., Grand Rapids, Michigan.
8. "Viking Rotary Pumps," Viking Pump Co., Cedar Falls, Iowa.
9. Zalis, A. A., *Hydrocarbon Process. Petrol. Refiner*, **40**, No. 9 (1961).
10. Zisman, W. A., Naval Research Lab. Report 4932, Washington D.C., 1957.

CHAPTER 6

Liquid Transport With Centrifugal Pumps

Pumps are devices for supplying energy or head to a flowing liquid. In centrifugal pumps, the energy or head is imparted by centrifugal action. In a conventional volute-type centrifugal pump, liquid enters the pump near the axis of a high speed impeller and is thrown radially outward into the pump casing. The velocity head imparted to the liquid by the vanes of the impeller is converted into pressure head. The efficiency of this conversion depends on the design of the impeller and the casing and on the physical properties of the liquid. The action of a typical volute-type centrifugal pump is illustrated in Figure 6-1.

System and Pump Heads

The important heads to consider in a pumping system are the suction, discharge, total and available net positive suction heads. These have been defined in Chapter 5. Frictional head losses increase with liquid flow rate. Thus the suction and available net positive suction heads for a system decrease with liquid throughput. The corresponding discharge and total heads for a system increase with throughput. A plot of system total head vs liquid flow rate is shown in Figure 6-2.

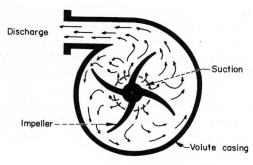

Figure 6-1. Action of a volute centrifugal pump.

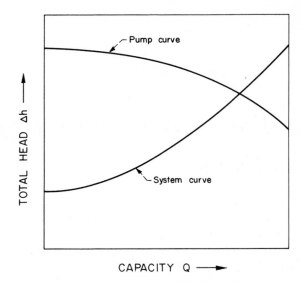

Figure 6-2.   System and pump total head vs capacity curves.

At a given rotational speed, a centrifugal pump can operate at any capacity ranging from zero to a maximum value depending on the size and the design of the pump. A typical total head vs capacity characteristic curve for a centrifugal pump is also shown in Figure 6–2. Pump manufacturers normally give these curves only for operation with water. However, methods are available for obtaining the total head vs capacity characteristic curves for other liquid viscosities from the plot for water.

The total head in ft developed by a centrifugal pump at a given impeller rotational speed and capacity is independent of the liquid density. A column of water approximately 2.31 ft high will produce a pressure of 1 psia at its base. A centrifugal pump with a total head Δh of 231 ft therefore pumps against a net pressure of 100 psi for water, but the corresponding pressure is $100 \times 1.2 = 120$ psi for a liquid with a specific gravity of 1.2 and $100 \times 0.8 = 80$ psi for a liquid with a specific gravity of 0.8. The pressure developed when the pump runs on air is clearly very small and, in fact, a conventional centrifugal pump can never prime itself when operating on a suction lift. To do this, a specially designed self-priming pump must be used.

A centrifugal pump can only operate at one particular capacity along its total head vs capacity characteristic curve and that is the point at which the pump total head curve meets the system total head curve as shown in Figure 6–2. It is assumed here that the available $NPSH$ in the system is adequate to support the flow rate of liquid into the suction side of the pump. If the available $NPSH$ is lower than that required by the pump, cavitation occurs and the normal curves are not applicable.

Centrifugal Pump Relations

As with agitators operating in liquids, the power P required in a centrifugal pump can be expected to be a function of the liquid density ρ, the impeller diameter D and the rotational speed of the impeller N.

Thus the power P for an ideal frictionless pump can be expressed by the following equation:

$$P = \mathcal{f}\,(\rho, N, D) \tag{6-1}$$

Assume the appropriate equation can be written as

$$P = C\rho^a N^b D^c \tag{6-2}$$

where C is a constant which depends on the geometry of the system. The dimensions of each term may be expressed in terms of mass M, length L and time T units.

Since power can be expressed as force times distance per unit time, Equation (6–2) can be written dimensionally as:

$$\left(\frac{ML}{T^2}\right)\left(\frac{L}{T}\right) = \left(\frac{M}{L^3}\right)^a \left(\frac{1}{T}\right)^b (L)^c \tag{6-3}$$

Equate the exponents for mass, length and time, respectively, to give

$$M: 1 = a$$

$$L: 2 = -3a + c$$

$$T: -3 = -b$$

Therefore,

$$a = 1$$

$$b = 3$$

$$c = 5$$

Thus Equation (6–2) can be rewritten as

$$P = C\rho N^3 D^5 \qquad (6\text{--}4)$$

The power P is also proportional to the product of the volume flow rate Q and the total head Δh developed by the pump.

The volume flow rate

$$Q \propto ND^3 \qquad (6\text{--}5)$$

and the total head

$$\Delta h \propto N^2 D^2 \qquad (6\text{--}6)$$

Eliminate the diameter D from Equations (6–5) and (6–6) to give

$$D^3 \propto \frac{Q}{N} \propto \frac{\Delta h^{3/2}}{N^3}$$

Therefore,

$$\frac{N^2 Q}{\Delta h^{3/2}} = \text{a constant}$$

or

$$\frac{N\sqrt{Q}}{\Delta h^{3/4}} = \text{a constant} \qquad (6\text{--}7)$$

The constant in Equation (6–7) is known as the specific speed N_s when the rotational speed N of the impeller is in rpm, the volume flow rate Q is in gpm and the total head Δh is in ft. The specific speed is always evaluated using the head and capacity at the best efficiency point of the pump (bep). Specific speed is often used as an index of pump types.

Therefore, specific speed can be written as

$$N_s = \frac{\text{rpm } \sqrt{\text{gpm}}}{\Delta h^{3/4}} \qquad (6\text{--}8)$$

Two pumps are said to be geometrically similar when the ratios of corresponding dimensions in one pump are equal to those of the other pump. Hence geometrical similarity exists between two different size pumps when the wetted surfaces in each have the same shape. Geometrically similar pumps are also said to be homologous.

The specific speed of a centrifugal pump is defined as the rpm at which a theoretical homologous pump of smaller size would operate to deliver 1 gpm against a total head of 1 ft.

Another common expression used to characterize the performance of centrifugal pumps is the suction specific speed S.

$$S = \frac{\text{rpm} \sqrt{\text{gpm}}}{(NPSH)^{3/4}} \tag{6-9}$$

In Equations (6–8) and (6–9), gpm, Δh and required $NPSH$ are all taken at the best efficiency point (bep).

The suction specific speed of a centrifugal pump is defined as the rpm at which a theoretical homologous pump of smaller size would operate to give 1 gpm at 1 ft required $NPSH$.

The definitions for specific speed and suction specific speed have a doubtful practical significance. However, they provide a convenient means of characterizing pumps.

Equation (6–9) shows that

$$(NPSH)^{3/4} \propto \text{rpm} \sqrt{\text{gpm}} \tag{6-10}$$

where the $NPSH$ in Equation (6–10) is the $NPSH$ required by the centrifugal pump.

Equation (6–5) can be rewritten as

$$\text{gpm} \propto \text{rpm} \, D^3 \tag{6-11}$$

Combine Equations (6–10) and (6–11) to give

$$NPSH \propto \text{rpm}^2 \, D^2 \tag{6-12}$$

Equations (6–4), (6–5), (6–6), (6–11) and (6–12) are the basis of a set of formulas known as the affinity laws. These govern centrifugal pump performance for homologous pumps at various impeller speeds. The formulas for capacity, total head, required $NPSH$ and horsepower are listed, respectively, as follows:[5]

$$\text{gpm}_2 = \left(\frac{\text{rpm}_2}{\text{rpm}_1}\right) K^3 \, \text{gpm}_1 \tag{6-13}$$

$$\Delta h_2 = \left(\frac{\text{rpm}_2}{\text{rpm}_1}\right)^2 K^2 \, \Delta h_1 \tag{6-14}$$

$$NPSH_2 = \left(\frac{\text{rpm}_2}{\text{rpm}_1}\right)^2 K^2 \, NPSH_1 \qquad (6\text{-}15)$$

$$\text{hp}_2 = \left(\frac{\text{rpm}_2}{\text{rpm}_1}\right)^3 K^5 \, \text{hp}_1 \qquad (6\text{-}16)$$

where K is the ratio of linear dimensions between the two systems.

The following equations[1]

$$\text{gpm}_2 = \left(\frac{\text{rpm}_2}{\text{rpm}_1}\right)\left(\frac{D_2}{D_1}\right) \text{gpm}_1 \qquad (6\text{-}17)$$

$$\Delta h_2 = \left(\frac{\text{rpm}_2}{\text{rpm}_1}\right)^2\left(\frac{D_2}{D_1}\right)^2 \Delta h_1 \qquad (6\text{-}18)$$

$$\text{hp}_2 = \left(\frac{\text{rpm}_2}{\text{rpm}_1}\right)^3\left(\frac{D_2}{D_1}\right)^3 \text{hp}_1 \qquad (6\text{-}19)$$

can be used to calculate the effect of changes in impeller speed and diameter on the performance of a given centrifugal pump. These equations only hold for small changes in impeller diameter.

If the performance curves are available for a centrifugal pump operating at a given rpm, Equations (6–17), (6–18) and (6–19) enable the performance curves to be plotted for other operating speeds and impeller diameters.

COMPARISON OF CENTRIFUGAL PUMPS

Centrifugal pumps can be broadly classified into the following types: volute, diffuser, turbine or regenerative and propeller.

Each of these general pump types can be further classified by impeller shape and operating characteristics. Impellers may be enclosed, semi-enclosed or open. In addition, they may be single or double suction. On the basis of the main direction of the liquid discharge, impellers are classified as: radial, axial and mixed flow.

Other means of classification are: casing design (vertical or horizontal split case); axis of shaft rotation (vertical, horizontal or inclined); direction of pump suction or discharge (side, top or bottom); number of impellers or stages (single or multistage); type of motor-to-pump coupling (close coupled or frame mounted); position of the pump in relation to the liquid supply (wet or dry pit mounted or in-line) and pump service (water, corrosive chemicals, abrasive slurries, etc.).

Volute Pumps

The volute pump is by far the most common type of centrifugal pump. Liquid enters at the eye of the impeller and is thrown radially outward to the periphery. This creates a partial vacuum which causes more liquid to flow in through the suction line. Thus the flow from the pump is continuous.

In volute pumps, the impeller discharges liquid into a progressively widening spiral casing as shown in Figure 6–3. This design facilitates the conversion of velocity head into pressure head by gradually reducing the velocity of the liquid as it flows from the impeller into the discharge line.

Some of the more common kinds of impellers are shown in Figure 6–4. The impeller vanes are curved to ensure a smooth flow of liquid. Both turbulence and circulation are reduced as the number of vanes is increased. The effect of circulation is to decrease the developed head. To a large extent, the characteristics of a centrifugal pump depend on the angle of the tip of the blades.

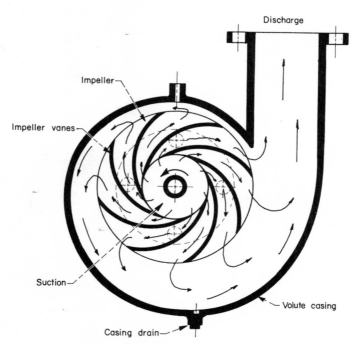

Figure 6-3.　Volute centrifugal pump casing design.

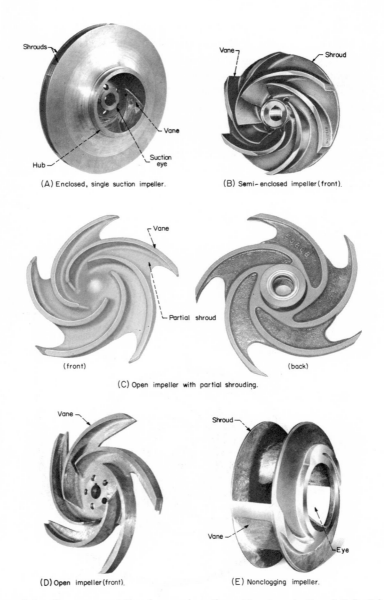

(A) Enclosed, single suction impeller.

(B) Semi-enclosed impeller (front).

(front)

(back)

(C) Open impeller with partial shrouding.

(D) Open impeller (front).

(E) Nonclogging impeller.

Figure 6-4.   Common centrifugal pump impellers. (*Courtesy A, D and E-Buffalo Forge Co.; B-Stnd. Pump Div., Worthington Corp.; C-Goulds Pumps, Inc.*)

Closed impellers generate head between the two walls of the rotating impeller. However, semi-open impellers generate head between the one wall of the rotating impeller and one stationary wall of the casing. Open impellers generate head between the two stationary walls of the casing.

Closed impellers have the following advantages: their maintenance is low, their wearing surfaces are relatively uncritical, and their original efficiencies are maintained over most of their lives.

Open and semi-open impellers require close clearances between the rotating vanes and the corresponding wall of the casing. Wear results in increased clearances, greater leakage losses and lower efficiencies. Open impellers are used for pumping liquids containing suspended solids.

Figure 6–5 shows a typical end suction, single stage, single suction volute pump with a closed impeller. The bearings should be designed to withstand the axial hydraulic thrust resulting from the unbalanced hydraulic pressures on the impeller (see Figure 6–6).

Figure 6–7 shows a double suction volute pump. In this pump, liquid is fed from identical suction chambers located at each side of the impeller. This design substantially eliminates hydraulic imbalance, as shown in

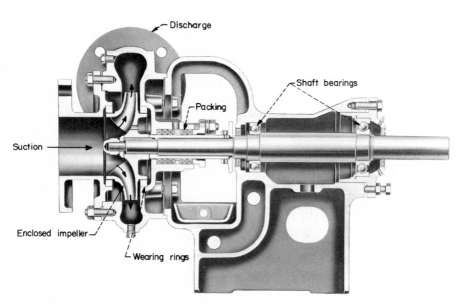

Figure 6-5.   End suction, single-stage, single suction volute pump.
(*Courtesy Goulds Pumps, Inc.*)

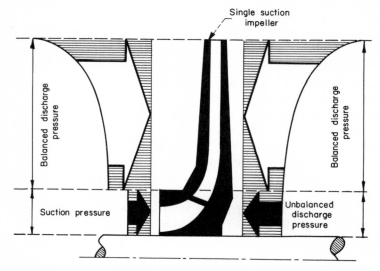

Figure 6-6.   Hydraulically unbalanced centrifugal pump impeller.

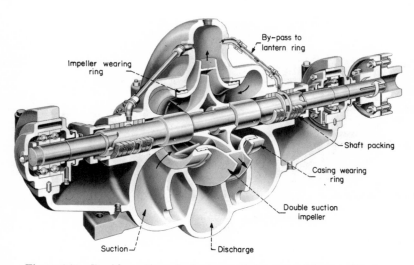

Figure 6-7.   Double suction, single-stage volute pump. (*Courtesy Peerless Pump Hydrodynamics Div., FMC Corp.*)

Figure 6–8. Thus double suction pumps can be used for higher operating pressures than single suction pumps.

Double suction pumps also allow lower liquid velocities at the eye of the impeller. This results in relatively low *NPSH* requirements.

Usually single suction pumps have vertically split casings. In contrast, double suction pumps normally have horizontally split casings. Pumps with horizontally split casings may be disassembled without removing the lower half of the casing from the pipeline. Most vertically split pumps (except the newer AVS pumps discussed later) must be removed from the pipeline before they are disassembled. However, double suction horizontally split pumps require more highly skilled labor than single suction vertically split pumps.[17]

In order to reduce internal recirculation from the high to low pressure sides of the impeller, and hence increase efficiency, impeller and casing seal rings or wearing rings are used. These are shown installed on the pumps illustrated in Figures 6–5, 6–7, 6–9 and 6–15. A set of impeller and casing seal rings is called a leakage joint. Wearing rings may be either renewable or nonrenewable. When renewable rings become worn they may be easily replaced and the pump clearances restored to their original specifications. When permanent wearing rings become worn, they cannot be replaced. In this case, pump clearances may be restored by any of the following methods. (1) the worn surfaces may be machined and replaceable rings

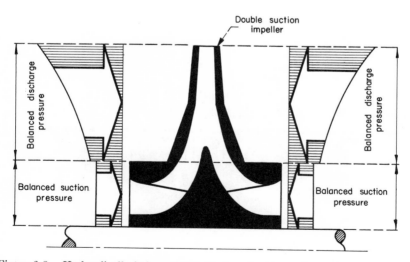

Figure 6-8. Hydraulically balanced impeller in a double suction volute centrifugal pump.

installed, (2) the worn surfaces may be renewed by building them up with welding and then remachining, or (3) the impeller, the casing or both may be replaced.[1] For small, inexpensive pumps, the latter alternative is usually the least costly. Seal rings are not used with open impellers. With these, the close clearances between the exposed vanes and the casing wall provide the necessary seal. Open impellers are replaced when they become worn.

Single-stage volute centrifugal pumps are normally used to generate heads up to 500 ft when operating at 3500 rpm. For higher heads, multistage pumps are available. Figure 6–9 shows a four-stage horizontally split case, opposed closed impeller volute centrifugal pump. This pump is used for high pressure service such as boiler feed. It is capable of delivering 900 gpm against a total head of 1375 ft at the bep.

In multistage pumps, the delivery from each stage becomes the feed of the next stage. The head generated by the various impellers is cumulative.

Multistage centrifugal pumps may have either single or double suction impellers. Single suction impellers are hydraulically unbalanced (see Figure 6–6). For this reason, they are usually arranged in multistage pumps to have equal numbers discharging in opposite directions (as in the four-stage boiler feed pump shown in Figure 6–9).

Hydraulic imbalance is not a problem in multistage pumps with double suction impellers. Each impeller is hydraulically balanced (see Figure 6–8).

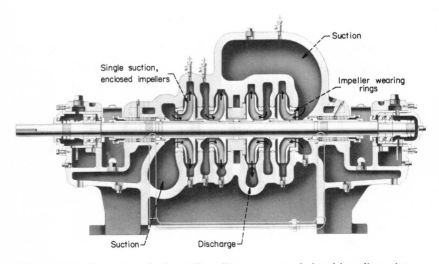

Figure 6-9.   Four-stage, horizontally split case, opposed closed impeller volute pump. (*Courtesy Goulds Pumps, Inc.*)

In this case, it is not necessary to have equal numbers of impellers discharging in opposite directions.

Volute centrifugal pumps may be either cradle mounted (frame mounted) or close coupled. In cradle mounted units, the drive motor is connected to the pump through a coupling. In close coupled units (see Figure 6–10), the impeller is mounted directly on the motor shaft. Close coupled units can operate in any position. In contrast, cradle mounted units with oil lubricated bearings must be used horizontally. Although close coupled units have no alignment problems, in cradle mounted units the motor can be changed and repaired without breaking into the pipeline.[17] Normally, close coupled units are not used for temperatures greater than 200°F.

Horizontal Packingless Centrifugal Pumps. These do not require packing or mechanical seals to prevent leakage at the point of shaft entry into the volute or casing. One type is the canned pump used for handling hazardous chemicals, especially at high pressures. A canned pump is illustrated in Figure 6–11. In this unit, a combined rotor and impeller assembly is driven by the rotating magnetic field of an induction motor. Some of the pumped liquid is recirculated via a bypass tube from the discharge to the rear of the rotor cavity. As this liquid flows through the rotor chamber, it cools the motor and lubricates the bearings. Leakage of the cooling liquid into the stator winding portion of the pump is prevented by completely sealing

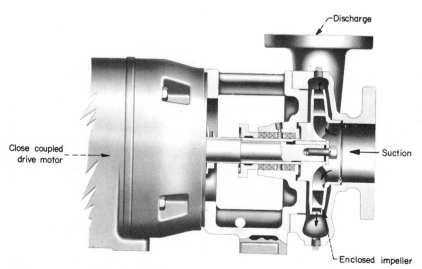

Figure 6-10.   Close coupled process pump. (*Courtesy Dean Bros. Pumps, Inc.*)

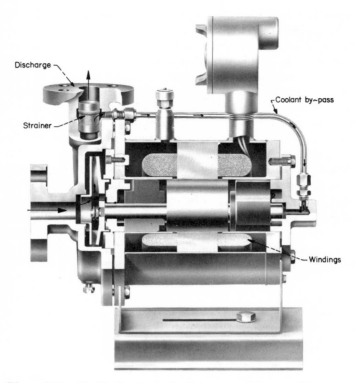

Figure 6-11.   Packingless canned volute pump. (*Courtesy Chempump
Div., Crane Co.*)

the stator from the rotor chamber by a metal shell or sleeve. If the pumped
liquid contains solids, the recirculation tube should be equipped with a
filter to prevent any particles from entering the rotor chamber. Self-cleaning
filters are normally used.

Canned pumps are available in sizes up to 1400 gpm. The special design
features of this type of pump make it usable (with various modifications)
at temperatures ranging from −400 to +1000°F. Discharge pressures up
to 5000 psi are possible in high pressure designs. Although most canned
pumps are base plate mounted, in-line units are available.

Specially designed sealless pumps are available to handle gritty pulps,
slurries, sludges and other highly abrasive materials. An effective seal is
provided by the action of a reversed turbine or slinger located in the suction
port. During pump operation, the entire shaft and impeller assembly
slides forward due to axial thrust. Thus no rubbing contact is made at

the point where the shaft enters the casing. The turbine or slinger prevents material from entering the open area. When the pump stops, a spring pushes the shaft and impeller back to make contact between a flexible shaft diaphragm and the rear of the casing. This prevents leakage when the pump is not running. Since no rubbing contact is made during pump operation, there is no wear on the shaft. Similar pumps are also available from the same manufacturer for use with highly corrosive liquids and acid sludges. These pumps are supplied in a variety of abrasion resistant alloys, plastics or ceramic wear parts. Steam jacketed models are also available.

The packingless pump shown in Figure 6–12 also has a radially vaned auxiliary turbine in addition to the pump impeller. However, in this unit, packing is required to prevent leakage when the pump is not operating. During operation, a low pressure area is produced in front of the stuffing box. This prevents the process liquid from entering the area. The manufacturer claims that the packing may be removed during pump operation with no resulting leakage, since there is zero pressure on the stuffing box. Although rubbing contact is not completely eliminated during operation, packing and shaft wear are substantially reduced, and there is no leak through the seal.

Volute centrifugal pumps are also available which have an integral magnetic drive. In these units, magnets are attached to the impeller and a

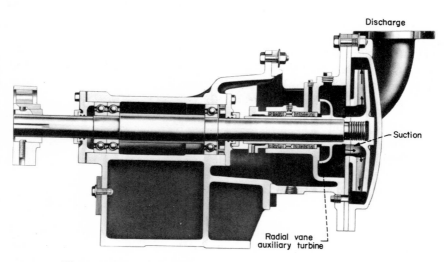

Figure 6-12. Centrifugal process pump with auxiliary turbine.
(*Courtesy Allis-Chalmers*)

drive plate. The drive plate is separated from the impeller and pumping chamber by a diaphragm seal. No shaft seals or packing are required.

In-line Centrifugal Pumps. In recent years, in-line centrifugal pumps have become popular in the chemical process industries. Figure 6–13 shows a typical in-line centrifugal pump. The initial and installation costs for these units are about 20 per cent less than for conventional centrifugal pumps. The reasons for these savings are:

(1) Less space requirement: The pump consists of a flanged head mounted directly in the process line. Drives are usually close coupled and positioned above the pump casing.

(2) No permanent foundation required: Small in-line units are mounted directly in horizontal pipelines. Large units should have a rest plate to relieve any strain on the pipe. Small and large in-line units are mounted directly in vertical pipelines. In addition to the reduced costs, valuable floor area is saved.

(3) Ease of maintenance: The connection between the drive and the pump is usually made using four to eight studs. To disassemble the pump for repairs, these are loosened and the entire motor-impeller unit is lifted clear of the pump casing. Since the latter remains in the pipeline, realignment is not necessary on reassembly. This considerably reduces the downtime required for repairs.

In-line pumps are available in capacities up to 1000 gpm against a total head of 450 ft. Materials of construction vary widely, depending on the liquids handled.

Standard Pumps. This term usually means AVS pumps (American Voluntary Standard pumps). In recent years, pump manufacturers and users have agreed on the need for centrifugal pumps of standard design suitable for the Chemical Process Industries. The most widely used pumps have the following characteristics:

> Single suction
> Single stage
> Horizontal centerline discharge
> End suction
> Capacity range of 5 to 500 gpm
> Total heads up to 250 ft at temperatures not exceeding 500°F

At the present time, the various organizations involved have not yet reached a firm agreement. However, many of the suggested standards have been voluntarily adopted by a number of pump manufacturers. Hence the term "American Voluntary Standard pump" is often used.

One of the outstanding features of the standard pump concept is the large capacity range available from a relatively few interchangeable impellers, casings, backplates and motor end frames. An additional advantage is the substantially smaller inventory needed to keep a plant on-stream. At the present time, manufacturers have standardized the overall linear dimensions of the pump and base plate; the distance from the face of the suction flange to the end of the drive shaft is either 17½ or 23½ inches. Base plate mounting holes and other assembly points have also been standardized. Impellers, internal designs and capacities for similar pumps have not yet been standardized. Thus pumps with the same mounting dimensions made by different manufacturers are not interchangeable. However, pumps made by a single manufacturer have interchangeable parts.

AVS pumps are designed to rigid standards of shaft deflection, clearances and bearing life. They can also be used with a wide selection of packings or mechanical seals. AVS pumps are available with a back pullout feature. This enables the rotating parts to be removed without disturbing the piping, casing or motor. AVS pumps are more expensive than centrifugal pumps which do not have all the advantages of AVS units.

Solids Handling and Sewerage Pumps. These are designed to pump liquid-solid mixtures without clogging. Thus sewerage and industrial waste pumps have large suction and discharge ports which are free of obstructions. Nonclogging pumps usually have specially designed impellers which are self-cleaning and therefore pass materials that would build up and clog other types of pumps. Figures 6–14 illustrates one type of nonclogging impeller. This has rounded edges and large vane clearances. The narrow repelling vanes on the outer shroud dislodge solids caught between the shroud and the casing wall. This impeller is recommended for pumping sewage disposal, slaughterhouse refuse, cannery by-products and paper stock. The shaft on nonclog pumps is usually kept clear of the suction port and chamber. This avoids clogging prior to reaching the impeller eye. Figure 6–15 illustrates the shaft position in a high capacity, low head water pump used for sewage or slurry service. This particular pump has a single suction, fully enclosed impeller with an oversized eye and large clearances between the vanes. This impeller pumps sewage without clogging and also operates efficiently on clear liquids. The pump shown in Figure 6–15 is available in line sizes ranging from 16 to 54 inches and capacities up to 100,000 gpm against a total head of 75 ft. End clearance impeller and casing wearing rings are provided to maintain the optimum clearance for efficient operation.

Some volute pumps used to transfer paper stock have semi-enclosed

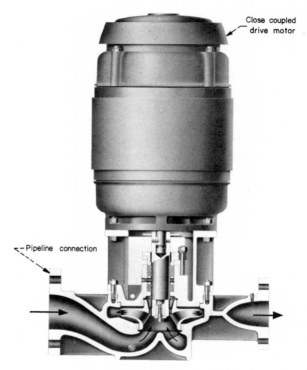

Figure 6-13.   In-line volute centrifugal pump. (*Courtesy Ingersoll-Rand Co.*)

impellers with combined screw and radial streamlined vanes.[7] The screw end of the impeller conveys material from the suction port to the center of the pump.

Lined Pumps. In centrifugal pumps used for abrasive slurries, it is common practice to cover the internal surface which is exposed to the liquid with a resilient lining. Natural and synthetic rubbers are used for this service, since they have excellent wearing characteristics in the presence of abrasives. The lining may be either permanently bonded to these surfaces or of a replaceable type.

Pumps used with acids and acid sludges are often lined with materials such as "Hypalon," a polyethylene elastomer, or plastic compounds such as "Kynar." Pumps lined with these materials resist corrosion and are substantially less expensive than pumps fabricated from corrosion resistant alloys such as molybdenum and titanium. Removable liner pumps are more expensive than the bonded liner units, but the additional expense is frequently worthwhile.

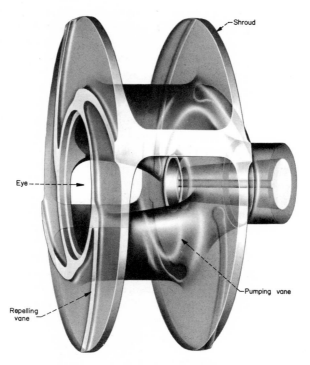

Figure 6-14.   Nonclogging impeller. (*Courtesy Peerless Pump Hydrodynamics Div., FMC Corp.*)

Centrifugal pumps lined with glass or stoneware are also used to transport corrosive liquids. A stoneware lined pump is shown in Figure 6–16. The enclosed impeller and pump chamber are lined with "Alite," which is a high alumina, nonporous ceramic of extreme hardness. This pump may be used up to temperatures of 400° F. with nearly all corrosives except hydrofluoric acid and hot concentrated caustics. These materials attack the silica components in the "Alite" lining. Semi-enclosed impellers are also available for pumping solid suspensions of liquids of high viscosity. The pump in Figure 6–16 can be obtained in capacities up to 600 gpm against a total head of 180 ft.

Vertical Volute Pumps. In these units, the impellers discharge radially against the bowl. The pressure developed forces liquid up through the vertical column. Single or multistage units are available. Vertical volute pumps are of two general types: wet pit mounted and dry pit mounted. In the former, the pumping chamber is located below the liquid supply level, with a discharge line usually to ground level. Wet pit mounted pumps are commonly bottom suction units, although side suction types are also available. In dry pit mounted units, the pumping chamber is located above the liquid supply level. Some vertical pumps have cantilevered impeller shafts. This avoids problems which may arise with bearings, bushings and sleeves. The shaft is supported at two points at the top of the shaft. The remainder of the shaft runs completely free. As with vertically mounted agitators in mixing vessels, the shaft must be shorter than a critical length to prevent excessive vibration. For this reason, cantilevered shafts rarely extend more than 6 or 7 ft below the bottom outboard steady bearing. For greater lengths, the required shaft diameters become too large. A typical vertical cantilevered pump is shown in Figure 6–17.

Vertical Packingless Centrifugal Pumps. As with horizontal units, vertical centrifugal pumps tend to wear rapidly at the seals with abrasive or corrosive liquids. Packingless vertical centrifugal pumps are used in severe service.

Bottom suction, wet pit mounted, sealless vertical centrifugal pumps are used in sulfuric acid plants. These circulate 93 per cent acid over the drying towers, 98 per cent acid over the absorbing towers, and pump product acid to storage and oleum at concentrations up to 40 per cent. The pump

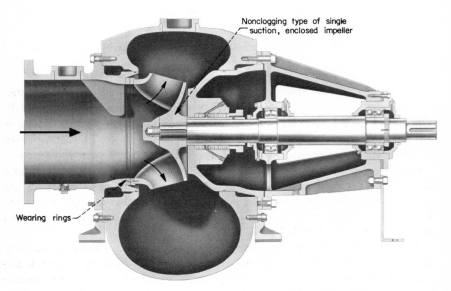

Figure 6-15.   High capacity, low head, water, sewage and slurry pump.
(*Courtesy Allis-Chalmers*)

does have one shaft seal, but this serves only to prevent dirt and moist air from entering the pump or vapors from escaping. At no time is this seal subjected to more than atmospheric pressure, and it does not come in contact with the pumped liquid. The seal is isolated by a vented pump boot surrounding the shaft. Vents maintain the liquid in the boot at

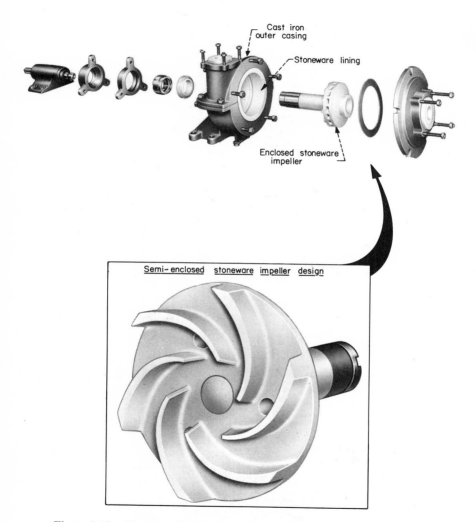

Figure 6-16.   Stoneware lined volute process pump. (*Courtesy The United States Stoneware Co.*)

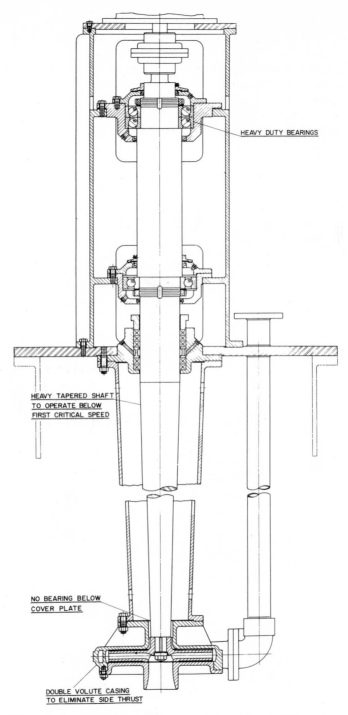

HEAVY DUTY BEARINGS

HEAVY TAPERED SHAFT
TO OPERATE BELOW
FIRST CRITICAL SPEED

NO BEARING BELOW
COVER PLATE

DOUBLE VOLUTE CASING
TO ELIMINATE SIDE THRUST

Figure 6-17. Vertical, cantilevered, bottom suction volute pump.
(*Courtesy Lawrence Pumps, Inc.*)

substantially the same level as the bulk liquid. Any leakage between the impeller and casing wearing rings into the boot area is returned to the bulk acid via the vent holes. Thus the seal and boot are never subject to any part of the discharge pressure. These pumps can be obtained in the capacity range of 50 to 2500 gpm.

Pumps of a similar design are used with liquid sulfur trioxide, molten sulfur and phosphoric acid.

Figure 6–18 shows a vertical packingless pump with a kinetic or hydraulic seal. The latter operates on the principal of a rotating U-tube filled with liquid. The effective weight of the liquid is increased by centrifugal force. The pump has an area with a U cross section. Liquid entering is whirled around by auxiliary turbine vanes. The weight of the liquid is increased and an effective seal formed. Since the drive shaft enters the pump on the suction side, the seal need only work against atmospheric pressure. Kinetic seals only function when the pump is in operation. If there is a positive pressure on the suction line when the pump is not in operation, this pump cannot be used, since leakage would occur through the clearances between the shaft and the sealing chamber. Normally,

Figure 6-18. Packingless pump with kinetic seal. (*Courtesy* *LaBour Pump Co.*)

the power consumed in the kinetic seal is less than in a stuffing box and packing. The pump shown in Figure 6–18 has a cantilevered shaft. This requires less maintenance than packed or mechanically sealed shafts.

Characteristic Curves. The most common shape of the total head vs capacity characteristic curve for a conventional volute centrifugal pump is that shown in Figure 6–19(A). The maximum head for a pump with this curve is developed at zero capacity. As the throughput is increased, the head developed decreases. Some pumps have very steep total head vs capacity curves as in Figure 6–19(B) or very flat ones as in Figure 6–19(C). A less common curve is that shown in Figure 6–19(D). The latter is known as a drooping curve. In this case, the same head can be developed for two different capacities. A small amount of droop is normally acceptable, but there is a danger of the throughput hunting back and forth between the two capacities and setting up dangerous vibrations.[4]

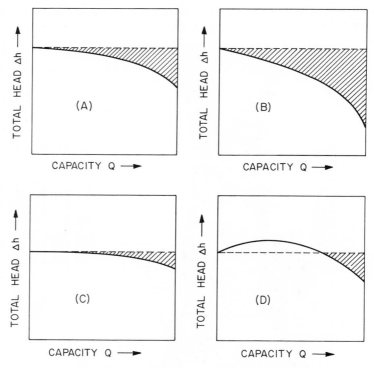

Figure 6-19.   Total head vs capacity characteristic curves for volute centrifugal pumps.

Power vs capacity characteristic curves also display a variety of shapes. Some of these are shown in Figure 6–20. For curve A, the power has a maximum value at a certain capacity. This is the curve of a nonoverloading pump. These pumps are only obtainable in certain specific speed ranges. Curve B illustrates a normal overloading curve where the power continues to increase with capacity. Curve C shows an overloading curve where the power increases continuously with a decrease in capacity.

The geometry of the impeller and pump casing determines the shapes of the various characteristic curves. Pumps may be designed with characteristic curves which are a combination of those shown in Figures 6–19 and 6–20. For example, the total head vs capacity characteristic curve may be flat over a range of capacities as in Figure 6–19(C) and then may become very steep as in Figure 6–19(B) beyond a certain capacity. This type of curve is produced by what is known as a nonoverloading impeller. It has fewer vanes than normally used and a greater wrap to the individual vanes.[4]

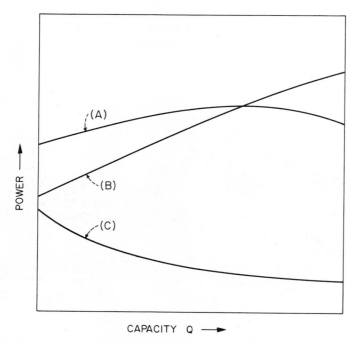

Figure 6-20. Power vs capacity characteristic curves for volute centrifugal pumps.

The capacity obtained from a centrifugal pump at a given total head, pump speed and liquid viscosity is determined by the characteristic curve. The capacity of a constant speed centrifugal pump may be decreased with a throttling valve. Throttling, however, consumes additional power and increases the wear on a centrifugal pump, since the energy ordinarily used to transport liquid is absorbed by the internal pump parts. The variable capacity pump shown in Figure 6–21 avoids the adverse effects of throttling. This pump is equipped with an adjustable internal bypass to control the capacity at a constant head or the head at a constant capacity. The bypass is a movable sleeve on the suction side of the pump. The amount of liquid pumped internally from the discharge to the suction side is determined by the sleeve position. Figure 6–21 shows the sleeve in close proximity to the vanes of the semi-enclosed impeller. In this position, internal leakage is at a minimum and the pump capacity is at a maximum. As the sleeve is moved away from the impeller vanes, the clearance and hence the amount of internal pumping increases and the pump capacity decreases. The sleeve can be adjusted either manually or automatically. The pump shown in Figure 6–21 is available in sizes from 1¼ to 36 inches NPS and in capacities up to 45,000 gpm at 270 ft of total head.

Nonclogging pumps are relatively low head pumps. They have steep total head vs capacity characteristic curves similar to the one shown in Figure 6–19(B).

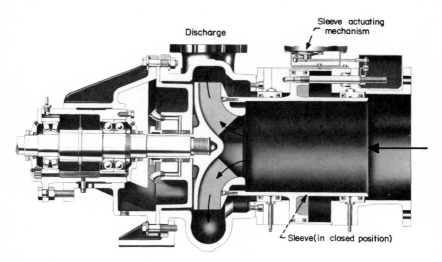

Figure 6-21. Variable capacity volute process pump. (*Courtesy Allis-Chalmers*)

Diffuser Pumps

Figure 6–22 shows a section through a diffuser-type centrifugal pump. In a centrifugal pump, all the additional head is obtained by adding velocity to the liquid. The velocity is then reduced, which results in an increase in pressure head according to the Bernoulli equation. In diffuser pumps, after the liquid has left the impeller, it is passed through a ring of fixed diffuser vanes. This provides a more controlled flow and allows a more efficient conversion of velocity head into pressure head. The change from high velocity to pressure takes place gradually. This eliminates shock losses. Thus diffuser pumps have high efficiencies. Some of the larger pumps have efficiencies over 90 per cent.[8]

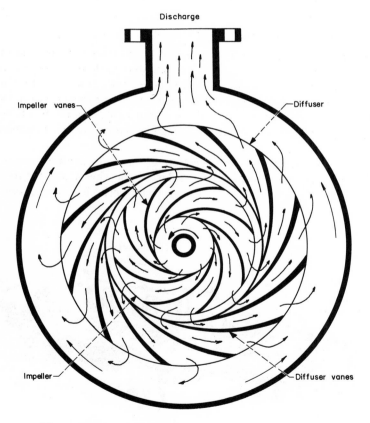

Figure 6-22. Action of a diffuser-type centrifugal pump.

Diffuser-type centrifugal pumps are commonly used for high head applications. As with volute pumps, they are available in more than one stage. An eight-stage horizontally split diffuser pump is shown in Figure 6–23. The single suction enclosed impellers are arranged so that equal numbers discharge in opposite directions. This reduces the axial thrust caused by hydraulic imbalance. Radial thrust is reduced by the diffusers. This type of pump is used in mine and refinery service. The pump shown in Figure 6–23 has a capacity of 700 gpm at pressures between 300 and 1000 psi. Both higher capacity and higher head units are also available.

Diffuser pumps have the further advantage of a balanced radial loading on the impeller. In volute pumps, an unequal pressure distribution along the volute may result in a heavy radial thrust on the impeller which tends to deflect the shaft. Since these loads are pulsating, the shaft may fail through fatigue.[8]

Turbine or Regenerative Pumps

In a turbine or regenerative pump, the liquid does not discharge freely from the tip of the impeller but is recirculated back to a lower point on the impeller diameter. The liquid recirculates many times before it finally leaves the impeller. As a result of this recirculation or regeneration, turbine pumps develop high heads. A turbine pump can generate heads several times greater than a volute pump having the same impeller diameter and speed.

Figure 6–24 illustrates the operation of typical turbine pumps. The impeller has vanes located on both sides of the rim which rotate in an annular channel in the pump's casing. Relatively close clearances exist

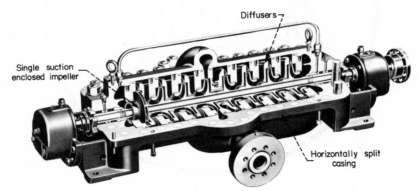

Figure 6-23.   Eight-stage diffuser pump. (*Courtesy Ingersoll-Rand Co.*)

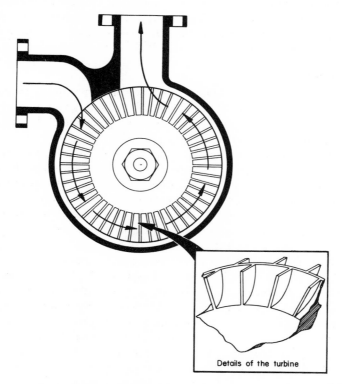

Details of the turbine

Figure 6-24. Action of a regenerative turbine pump.

between the vanes of the impeller and the walls of the channel. The casing also contains a sealing wall through which the impeller passes with very close clearances. Twin suction passages pass around the sealing wall and feed into the impeller chamber. As the liquid enters the pump casing, it flows to both sides of the impeller. It then passes into the cavities between the vanes of the rotating impeller. Velocity is imparted to the liquid which, after a number of recirculations, is thrown out into the annular channel. The velocity is gradually reduced and the energy is converted to pressure head which increases linearly around the circumference of the pumping chamber. Because of the close clearances between the turbine and the casing, only clear liquids may be pumped.

The total head vs capacity characteristic curves for turbine pumps are steep, as shown in Figure 6–19(B). The corresponding power vs capacity characteristic curves have a maximum power value at shut-off as in

Figure 6–20(C). Turbine pumps are available in multistage units. Capacities range from 1 to 200 gpm. Single-stage units generate heads up to 500 ft. Heads up to 2500 ft are generated with five-stage units. Liquid viscosities should not exceed 500 SSU.

Propeller Pumps

Propeller pumps are sometimes called axial flow pumps since the liquid flows parallel to the axis. The additional head is generated by vortex action and the propelling or lifting action of the vanes.[3] A typical horizontal propeller pump is shown in Figure 6–25.

The discharge volute required in conventional centrifugal pumps is not necessary in propeller pumps. However, diffusion vanes are used in the discharge port of the pump to eliminate the rotational velocity of the liquid imparted by the propeller. Vertical propeller pumps are widely used. They are very compact and can be located in the suction well to maintain prime. The mounting is commonly wet pit, illustrated by the vertical propeller pump in Figure 6–26.

Total head vs capacity and power vs capacity characteristic curves for a typical propeller pump are shown in Figure 6–27. Propeller pumps have the disadvantage that a higher power is required to operate against a closed discharge. This difficulty can be avoided by using an adjustable blade propeller.[9] The blades can be adjusted to improve the characteristics of the pump under any particular set of operating conditions. The adjustment may be made either manually or automatically. Capacities range from 300 to 100,000 gpm. Port sizes up to 5 ft are used. Heads up to 40 ft are generated.

Mixed Flow Pumps

Volute pumps discharge liquid radially from the impeller and propeller pumps discharge liquid axially. In mixed flow pumps, liquid is discharged both radially and axially into a volute-type casing. The head is generated by a combination of the processes occurring in volute and propeller pumps. Mixed flow impellers are often used in deep well and other vertical turbine pumps.

Vertical Turbine Pumps

This is a broad classification for bottom suction centrifugal pumps with vertical shafts to which one or more impellers are attached. The impeller(s) are of either the volute or the mixed flow type. Discharge occurs along the shaft axis and in some units is stabilized by the use of diffuser vanes located at the bowl wall. Vertical turbine pumps are further classified as water lubricated or oil lubricated.

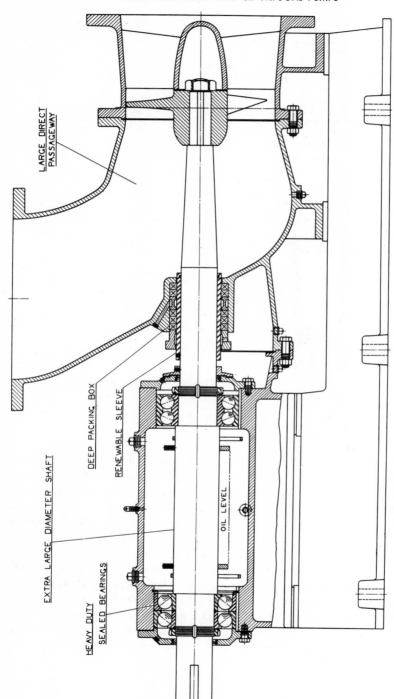

LARGE DIRECT PASSAGEWAY

DEEP PACKING BOX

RENEWABLE SLEEVE

EXTRA LARGE DIAMETER SHAFT

HEAVY DUTY SEALED BEARINGS

OIL LEVEL

Figure 6-25.   Horizontal propeller pump.   (*Courtesy Lawrence Pumps, Inc.*)

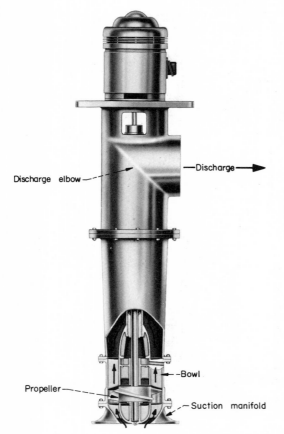

Discharge elbow

Discharge

Bowl

Propeller

Suction manifold

Figure 6-26. Single-stage vertical propeller pump. (*Courtesy Peerless Pump Hydrodynamics Div., FMC Corp.*)

In water lubricated units, the drive shaft is located directly in the path of the discharge process liquid which lubricates the shaft bushings, packing and stabilizers. Figure 6–28 shows a three-stage water lubricated unit with semi-enclosed impellers and bowl diffuser vanes. Since each stage has a separate bowl and impeller, additional stages can be added without difficulty. Thus extremely high suction lifts are possible by merely increasing the number of stages. This pump is used for raising liquids to the surface from extremely deep subterranean sources and is often called a deep well pump. Deep well pumps are used in mine dewatering and well water supply service. In the latter, the drilled well diameters range from 4 to 48 inches. They have capacities up to 30,000 gpm against total heads up to 1000 ft or more.

Water lubricated pumps are prone to rapid wear at the shaft packing and bushings when used with abrasive or corrosive liquids. Oil lubricated pumps are used for this service. A tube enclosing the drive shaft is filled with oil to lubricate the bushings and sleeves. In these units, the latter do not come in contact with the process liquid. Both water and oil lubricated vertical deep well pumps usually have a screen or strainer in the suction line to prevent clogging. The screen area should be about four times the eye area of the impeller. A disadvantage of oil lubricated pumps is the tendency of the lubricant to contaminate the process liquid.

In deep installations, long shafts can be avoided by using a close coupled totally submersible motor, located beneath the pump chamber. The motors are of either the water filled or the oil filled type. Water filled units have hermetically sealed stator windings and a pressure equalizing diaphragm to compensate for expansion and contraction under varying temperatures. A mechanical seal and slinger prevent solid particles from entering the motor area.

Oil filled motors are completely isolated from the process liquid. A mechanical seal and slinger prevent oil from leaking out or process liquid and foreign material from entering the motor.

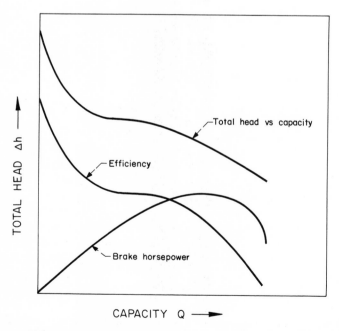

Figure 6-27.   Characteristic curves for a propeller pump.

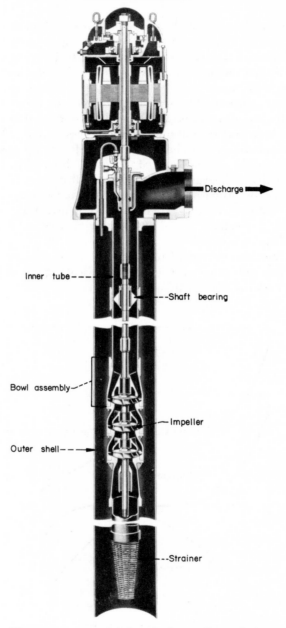

Figure 6-28.   Three-stage, water lubricated, deep well, vertical turbine pump.
(*Courtesy Deming Pump Div., Crane Co.*)

Figure 6–29 shows a pump with a submersible, close coupled motor. Like the pump in Figure 6–28, it has semi-enclosed impellers and bowl stabilizing vanes. Submersible motor turbine pumps require less space at ground level and use less power than the long shaft units.

Close coupled vertical turbine pumps are used in air conditioning systems, settling tank recirculation loops, fire protection systems, plant cooling lines, industrial waste handling, storage vessel transfer lines, pipeline booster service, and pumping water from lakes and sumps, etc. Capacities range from 15 to 40,000 gpm at total heads exceeding 1000 ft. The unit bowl construction allows additional stages to be added. Since the suction lies below the liquid surface, these pumps when primed require no further repriming. Figure 6–30 shows a vertical turbine pot (low NPSH) pump which incorporates a self-contained sump. These pumps are extensively used in the petroleum industry as booster pumps on long transfer lines.

Rotative Speed and Efficiency

Figure 6–31 shows typical efficiency vs capacity characteristic curves for volute-type centrifugal pumps. Maximum efficiency is reached at a particular total head and capacity. This point is determined by the design of the pump.

There is a general tendency to design pumps with higher rotative speeds. Centrifugal pumps operating at 3500 rpm are in common use. High speed pumps tend to be more efficient than low speed pumps. Furthermore, for a given service, pumps with high rotative speeds have correspondingly smaller diameters. This is an important advantage when the material of construction is an expensive alloy. Smaller pumps are more easily installed and require smaller foundations. However, when pumping abrasive liquids, the higher speed impellers tend to erode more quickly.

Since lower speed pumps transmit more torque for a given horsepower, they require larger shaft diameters.[18] This in turn increases the possibility of leakage. Lower speed pumps have the advantages of lower NPSH requirements and generally lower noise levels.

For a given service, Equation (6–8) shows that pumps with high rotative speeds have correspondingly high specific speeds. Low specific speed impellers are narrow with relatively large diameters. High specific speed impellers are wide with relatively small diameters. Generally, low specific speed pumps are high head pumps.

A typical propeller pump operating at 1750 rpm and delivering 10,000

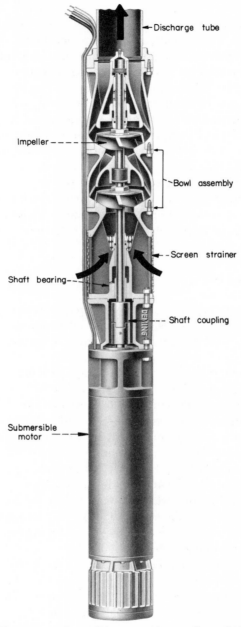

Figure 6-29.   Two-stage, submersible motor, deep well, vertical turbine pump.
(Courtesy Deming Pump Div., Crane Co.)

gpm against a total head of 40 ft at its best efficiency point has a specific speed

$$N_s = \frac{1750 \sqrt{10,000}}{(40)^{0.75}} = 11,000$$

A typical turbine pump operating at 1750 rpm and delivering 100 gpm against a total head of 500 ft at its best efficiency point has a specific speed

$$N_s = \frac{1750 \sqrt{100}}{(500)^{0.75}} = 164$$

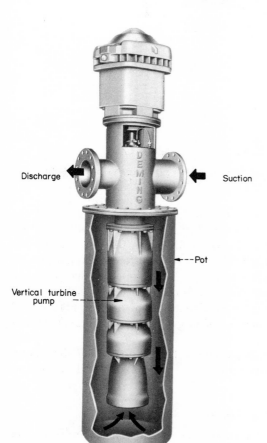

Discharge

Suction

Pot

Vertical turbine pump

Figure 6-30. Vertical turbine pot pump. (*Courtesy Deming Pump Div., Crane Co.*)

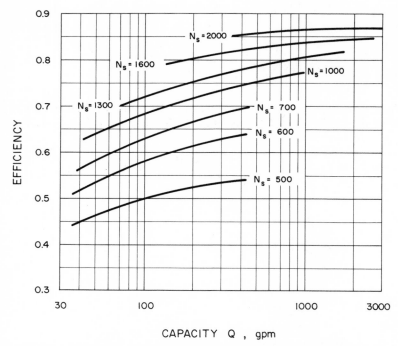

Figure 6-31.　Efficiency vs capacity characteristic curves for volute centrifugal pumps.[17]

Volute centrifugal pumps, in general use in the processing industries, normally have specific speeds under 3000.[17] Specific speed is a very approximate measure of efficiency. Figure 6–31 shows the relationship between efficiency, capacity and specific speed for volute centrifugal pumps. The plot shows that for a given capacity, higher specific speed pumps are more efficient. In general, this rule holds up to specific speeds of about 3000. However, efficiencies decrease at higher specific speeds. Figure 6–31 also illustrates the greater efficiencies of larger pumps for a given specific speed.

In general, high efficiency pumps have a high required $NPSH$. Sometimes a compromise has to be made between efficiency and $NPSH$ requirements.

Priming Characteristics of Centrifugal Pumps

Volute, diffuser and propeller pumps are normally not self-priming. Turbine pumps are self-priming provided there is sufficient liquid to seal the close clearances.[3] Conventional volute and diffuser pumps will transfer liquids containing only a small amount of vapor before losing prime. The positive displacement characteristics of regenerative turbine pumps enable them to transfer liquids containing a substantial amount of vapor.

Specially designed volute pumps are available which can handle liquid-vapor mixtures moderately well. In these pumps, the flow pattern is such that the liquid leaves the wall at certain points creating low pressure regions into which vapor is drawn. This facilitates the pumping of vapor by the impeller and reduces the possibility of vapor binding.

Although conventional volute pumps are not self-priming, they can be made so with additional equipment. Figure 6–32 shows a pump with a

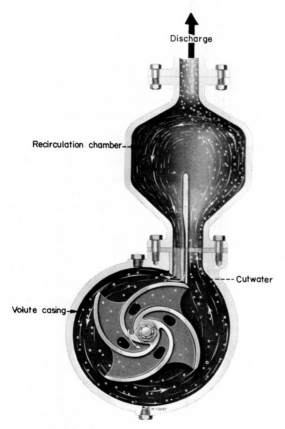

Figure 6-32.   Action of a self-priming centrifugal pump with recirculation chamber.
(*Courtesy Stnd. Pump Div., Worthington Corp.*)

recirculation chamber located at the discharge side of the volute casing. This chamber serves to separate air or gas present in the process liquid during priming. The deaerated liquid is recycled back to the impeller through a recirculation port until the pump is primed. At this point, the uniform pressure distribution around the impeller prevents further recirculation. A check valve at the entrance to the suction chamber is recommended to maintain prime when the pump is not in operation.

Another type of self-priming centrifugal pump is illustrated in Figure 6–33. A small sliding vane positive displacement pump located directly behind an opening in the centrifugal pump impeller creates a suction which increases with the degree of eccentricity of the rotor. The latter is controlled by the back pressure in the discharge line. During priming, the amount of entrained air in the liquid decreases and hence the back pressure increases. This moves the rotor to a less eccentric position through a slide valve linkage. When full prime has been achieved, the rotor has no eccentricity and the vane pump creates no suction. A check valve isolates the vane pump from the centrifugal pump during normal operation to avoid recirculation through the passage in the centrifugal pump impeller. This pump is used in the petroleum industry and can operate on static suction lifts of 14 ft. Capacities range up to 1600 gpm at total heads of 400 ft.

In diffuser pumps, prime is achieved through the action of a diffuser ring concentric with the impeller. Initially, the pump chamber is filled with liquid, usually through a filler plug located at the top of the discharge chamber. The impeller is then rotated in the initially primed liquid. Air is entrained in the liquid as it discharges through small holes around the diffuser ring's periphery. This air is then free to escape to the discharge chamber. The process continues until the suction line is free from air or gas. At this point, the flapper check valve located at the suction inlet swings fully open under the pressure of the incoming liquid. The flapper check valve also keeps the pump full of liquid and thus facilitates repriming after a stoppage. The pump functions as a conventional diffuser pump when primed.

Pump Performance

Conventional volute pumps have a long life and require little maintenance. Furthermore, a substantial amount of corrosion or erosion can take place before the performance is seriously affected. In contrast, turbine pumps have only about one-third the life of a volute pump for comparable service with clean noncorrosive liquids. In addition, the performance of turbine pumps is seriously affected by only a small amount of corrosion.

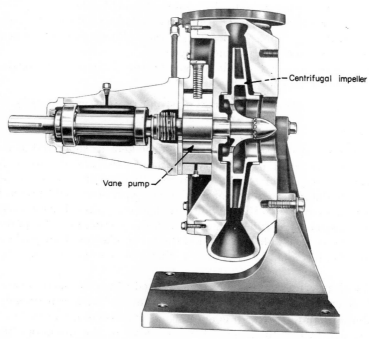

Centrifugal impeller

Vane pump

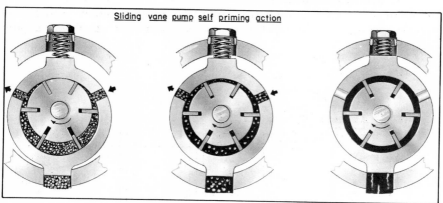

Sliding vane pump self priming action

Figure 6-33.   Centrifugal pump with vane pump self-priming device.
(*Courtesy Gilbert & Barker Mfg. Co.*)

Nevertheless, turbine pumps are ideal for relatively high head vs low capacity applications in which conventional volute pumps would be required to operate too close to their shut-off point.[3]

The major disadvantage of centrifugal pumps is that performance is very sensitive to changes in liquid viscosity. Pump capacity is seriously reduced by an increase in liquid viscosity.

The advantages and disadvantages of the various centrifugal pump types are listed in Table 6–1.

INSTALLATION AND OPERATION OF CENTRIFUGAL PUMPS

Installation

Suction and discharge pipelines should be kept as short and as straight as possible to avoid unnecessary friction losses. For the same reason, reducers in the pipelines must be tapered. Pipeline diameters are never to be smaller than the pump nozzles. Suction pipelines should preferably be wider in diameter than the suction nozzle of the pump. Figure 6–34 shows the recommended position of a reducer in the suction line of a pump. The use of an eccentric reducer prevents the accumulation of air pockets. The suction piping should be free of any high points where air pockets could form.

If at all possible, pumps should be located below the suction side liquid level. Suction problems are extremely common with centrifugal pump installations and it is worth going to some expense to avoid them.

It is worthwhile to include a check valve in the discharge line of a centrifugal pump. This affords protection against sudden surges and reverse rotation of the impeller. In the case of a discharge line of greater

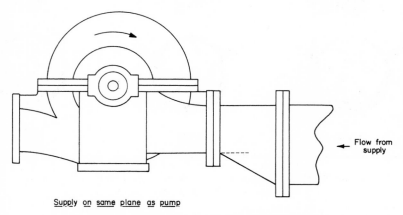

Supply on same plane as pump

Figure 6-34.   Correct installation of suction line reducers.

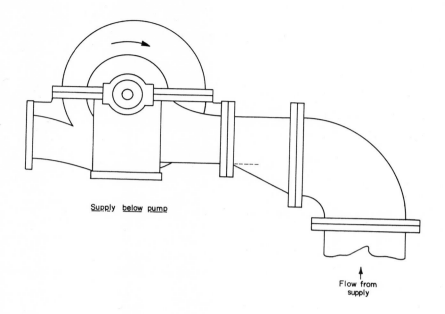

Supply below pump

Flow from
supply

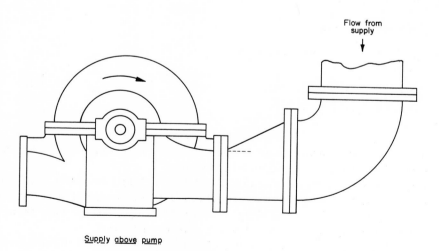

Flow from
supply

Supply above pump

Figure 6-34. *Cont'd*

TABLE 6-1.   Advantages and Disadvantages of Various Centrifugal Pumps

	PUMP TYPES			
	Volute Pumps	Diffuser Pumps	Turbine Pumps	Propeller Pumps
ADVANTAGES				
Available in a wide range of sizes	X	X		X
Simple construction	X			X
Relatively quiet operation	X	X	X	X
Robust with a long life	X	X		X
Available in a wide variety of materials	X	X		X
Can handle liquids containing solids	X	X		X
Can handle liquids with a high proportion of vapor			X	
Self-priming			X	
Variable speed drive units not required to adjust the capacity	X	X	X	X
Pressures and powers developed are limited at shutoff	X	X	X	X
DISADVANTAGES				
Unsuitable for pumping high viscosity liquids	X	X	X	X
Heads developed are limited	X	X	X	X
Close clearances required			X	

diameter than the discharge nozzle, the order of fittings should be the tapered increase, check valve and gate valve.

A strainer is commonly employed in the suction line of a centrifugal pump used to transfer liquids containing foreign matter. This prevents the impeller from becoming clogged. Strainers are unnecessary when pumps having specially designed nonclogging impellers are used.

At the time of installation, pumps must be carefully checked for correct alignment. Pipelines should place no strain on the pump so that misalignment does not occur. The latter leads to accelerated wear and premature replacements. Expansion joints in the suction and discharge pipelines obviate undue strain on the pump casing. These are commonly used in long pipelines handling hot liquids. The information given in Chapter 5 for installing positive displacement pumps also applies to centrifugal pumps.

Suction lines on a new pump installation should be carefully checked for tightness to avoid drawing air into the pump. Entrained air tends to accumulate in the center of the impeller. This in turn reduces the head developed by a centrifugal pump. If the pump is fed from an open shallow tank, entrained air may also enter the pump because of vortex formation.[13] Baffles placed at the entrance to the suction pipeline may be used to break up the vortexes.

Effect of Insufficient Available NPSH

A centrifugal pump should operate at the total head and capacity given by the intersection of the total head vs capacity characteristic curve of the pump with the corresponding system curve. This is only the case if the available NPSH in the system is greater than the NPSH required by the centrifugal pump. The latter is a measure of the head necessary to transfer liquid into the impeller vanes without cavitation affecting the performance of the pump. If the available NPSH in the system is less than the required NPSH, the pump cavitates and the pumping rate is reduced. In this case, the actual operating line of the centrifugal pump departs sharply from the normal total head vs capacity characteristic curve. The dotted and full lines in Figure 6–35 graphically illustrate the relationship between the normal curve with adequate suction conditions and the new curve with inadequate available net positive suction head.

The required NPSH of a centrifugal pump increases approximately with the square of the liquid throughput. The available NPSH in a system decreases as the liquid throughput increases because of the greater frictional head losses. The relationship between available and required NPSH in a pump system is illustrated in Figure 6–36. The intersection of the two NPSH curves corresponds to the capacity at which the dotted line departs from the full line in Figure 6–35. Thus the pump will operate normally at a point on its total head vs capacity characteristic curve until the available NPSH curve falls below the required NPSH curve. Beyond this point, the total head generated by a centrifugal pump falls drastically as the pump begins to operate in cavitation conditions.

The available NPSH depends on the viscosity and density of the liquid being pumped as these affect the value of the frictional head loss. Similarly,

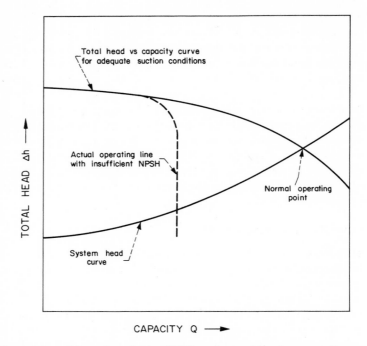

Figure 6-35.   Effect of available $NPSH$ on the total head vs capacity curve
for a centrifugal pump.

the physical properties of the liquid pumped affect the required $NPSH$.
However, it is normal practice to use the required $NPSH$ values for cold
water as these are, in most cases, on the conservative side when applied
to any other liquid.[16]

Suction specific speed defined in Equation (6–9), is a measure of a
centrifugal pump's performance with regard to cavitation. Below suction
specific speeds of 5000, single suction centrifugal pumps have very poor
cavitation characteristics. Above suction specific speeds of 11,000, single
suction centrifugal pumps have very good cavitation characteristics.
However, partial cavitation is characteristic even with suction specific
speeds as high as 12,000.[6] Normally, design values of suction specific speed
do not exceed 10,000 for single suction pumps and 9000 for double suction
units.[6] Most centrifugal pumps have suction specific speeds in the range
7000 to 10,000.

A knowledge of suction specific speed greatly assists in deciding where to
locate a centrifugal pump.

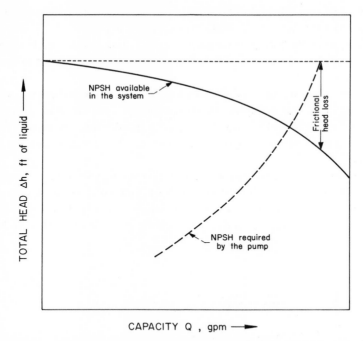

Figure 6-36.   Relationship between available and required $NPSH$ in pumping systems.

Noise and Vibration

The operation of centrifugal pumps may sometimes be accompanied by excessive noise and vibration. In cavitating pumps, vapor bubbles are formed. When these bubbles are carried into a higher pressure region in the pump, they collapse, subjecting the impeller and casing to liquid hammer. This produces a characteristic crackling sound. If cavitation is the source of the noise, then reducing the pump capacity by throttling the pump discharge valve should eliminate the trouble.

Excessive noise may not necessarily be produced in the pump itself but may arise from excessive velocities in the connecting pipelines. Improperly supported pipelines may also be the cause.

Centrifugal pumps with high impeller rotational speeds are not necessarily noisier than low speed pumps. Hydraulic noises are low in well-designed and well-built pumps irrespective of the impeller speed. However, motor and bearing noises are less in slower speed pumps. Pumps operating at their best efficiency point will be substantially quieter than when operating at lower or higher flows.[14] Thus pumps should not be oversized or undersized for a particular application.

Vibration of the pump or driver may result in a considerable amount of noise. In addition, excessive vibration may lead to equipment failure such as a broken shaft.

Excessive vibration may sometimes be caused by operating a volute centrifugal pump at reduced capacities. In this case, unbalanced hydraulic forces act radially on the impeller. Usually these forces are greatest at zero capacity and become progressively less as the design capacity is approached.[15]

In pumps required to operate at widely varying capacities, the problem of radial thrust can be eliminated by using a dual volute unit. Alternatively, the pump can be fitted with a bypass which will enable the pump to be operated at its design capacity. The desired flow rate can then be tapped from the loop.

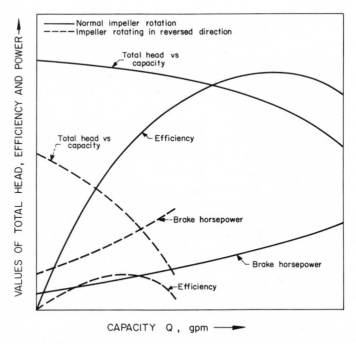

Figure 6-37.   Effect of reversed impeller rotation on the total head vs capacity curve of a centrifugal pump.

Direction of Impeller Rotation

Centrifugal pumps are available either as right-hand or left-hand units. Right-hand pumps have a clockwise rotation when observed from the motor side of the pump. Left-hand pumps have a counterclockwise rotation and normally have an arrow cast on the pump casing which marks the direction of impeller rotation.

If the impeller of a centrifugal pump is rotated in the reverse direction, the head and capacity generated by the pump are both substantially reduced. In addition, the power consumed by the pump at a given liquid throughput is increased. Figure 6–37 shows the normal total head vs capacity characteristic curve of a volute centrifugal pump together with the corresponding characteristic curve when the impeller is rotated at the same speed in the reverse direction.

The performance of a volute centrifugal pump can also be adversely affected if the impeller is reversed even though the direction of rotation is correct. A closed impeller can easily be installed by mistake in the reverse direction after a pump overhaul. Figure 6–38 shows the normal total head

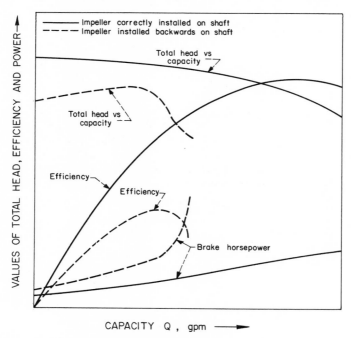

Figure 6-38. Effect of reversed impeller installation on the total head vs capacity curve of a centrifugal pump.

vs capacity characteristic curve of a volute centrifugal pump together with the probable corresponding characteristic curve when the reversed impeller is operated at the same speed. The reversed impeller also consumes more power at a given liquid throughput.

Flow Regulation

A centrifugal pump can only operate at one particular flow rate along its total head vs capacity characteristic curve and that is the point at which the pump curve meets the corresponding system curve. This is shown as point A in Figure 6–39. If the valve on the discharge side of the centrifugal pump is throttled, the system total head vs capacity curve is altered to incorporate the increased frictional head loss. The new system curve may be, for example, the dotted curve in Figure 6–39. This cuts the pump total head vs capacity characteristic curve at point A′ which represents a decreased capacity and an increased total head relative to point A.

The system total head is composed of static and dynamic or frictional heads. The control valve should have a design head differential equal to

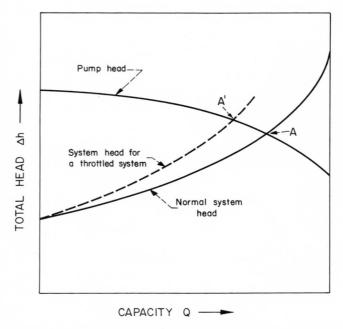

Figure 6-39.   Effect of throttling the discharge valve on the total head vs capacity curve of a centrifugal pump.

at least 30 per cent of the dynamic head of the system at design flow.[6] A decrease in the ratio of the control valve head loss to the dynamic head loss diminishes the ability of the valve to control the flow. However, an increase in this ratio adds to the initial and operating cost of the pump.

Valves used to control the output from centrifugal pumps are usually of the equal percentage type. In these valves, the change in flow rate caused by a unit change in lift is a fixed percentage of the liquid flow rate just before the change is made. Control valves are normally one or two sizes smaller than the line size.

Operating Problems

Table 6–2 lists some of the common problems encountered in centrifugal pump operation together with some of the possible reasons. In the column dealing with the failure of a centrifugal pump to deliver any liquid is listed the rotation of the impeller in the wrong direction. Although in this case the pump is capable of generating total head as seen in Figure 6–37, this may be less than the system total head. Under these circumstances the pump will fail to deliver any liquid. If the system head is not less than the pump total head, the pump will deliver liquid at a reduced capacity.

DESIGN CONSIDERATIONS AND CALCULATIONS

Application of the Affinity Laws

EXAMPLE

Consider a volute centrifugal pump with the following performance data at the best efficiency point (bep):

$$\begin{aligned}
\text{capacity} &= 80 \text{ gpm} \\
\text{total head} &= 50 \text{ ft} \\
\text{required } NPSH &= 13 \text{ ft} \\
\text{horsepower} &= 2 \text{ hp} \\
\text{impeller speed} &= 1750 \text{ rpm}
\end{aligned}$$

The pump has an impeller diameter of 8 inches. Evaluate the performance data when this pump is operated at 3500 rpm using Equations (6–13), (6–14), (6–15) and (6–16). In this case $K = 1$ since the linear dimensions of the pump do not change.

Calculate the speed ratio.

$$\frac{\text{rpm}_2}{\text{rpm}_1} = \frac{3500}{1750} = 2$$

TABLE 6–2. Problems in Centrifugal Pump Operation

No Liquid Delivered	Pump Delivers Less Than Rated Capacity	Loss of Prime While Pump Is Operating	Pump Is Noisy	Pump Takes Too Much Power
(1) Pump not primed	(1) Air leak in suction line or pump seal	(1) Liquid level falls below the suction line intake	(1) Cavitation	(1) Impeller speed too high
(2) Insufficient available $NPSH$	(2) Insufficient available $NPSH$	(2) Air leak develops in pump or seal	(2) Misalignment	(2) Shaft packing too tight
(3) Suction line strainer clogged	(3) Suction line strainer partially clogged or of insufficient area	(3) Air leak develops in suction line	(3) Foreign material inside pump	(3) Liquid more viscous than specified
(4) End of suction line not in liquid	(4) System total head higher than calculated	(4) Liquid vaporizes in suction line	(4) Bent shaft	(4) Misalignment
(5) System total head higher than pump total head at zero capacity	(5) Partially clogged impeller		(5) Impeller touching casing	(5) Impeller touching casing
				(6) System total head too low causing the pump to deliver too much liquid

(6) Liquid viscosity higher than specified

(7) Impeller rotates in the wrong direction

(8) Suction or discharge valves partially closed

(9) Impeller speed too low

(10) Impeller installed in reverse direction

(7) Liquid denser than specified

(8) Impeller rotates in the wrong direction

(9) Impeller installed in the wrong direction

From Equation (6–13), calculate the new capacity.

$$\text{gpm}_2 = 2 \times \text{gpm}_1 = 2 \times 80 = 160 \text{ gpm}$$

From Equation (6–14), calculate the new total head.

$$\Delta h_2 = 2^2 \times \Delta h_1 = 4 \times 50 = 200 \text{ ft}$$

From Equation (6–15), calculate the new required $NPSH$:

$$NPSH_2 = 2^2 \times NPSH_1 = 4 \times 13 = 52 \text{ ft}$$

From Equation (6–16), calculate the new horsepower:

$$\text{hp}_2 = 2^3 \times \text{hp}_1 = 8 \times 2 = 16 \text{ hp}$$

EXAMPLE

Consider a volute centrifugal pump geometrically similar to the pump in the previous example but with an impeller diameter of 12 inches. Evaluate the performance data when the pump is operated at 3500 rpm using Equations (6–13), (6–14), (6–15) and (6–16).

Calculate the ratio of linear dimensions between the two systems:

$$K = \frac{12}{8} = 1.5$$

Calculate the speed ratio:

$$\frac{\text{rpm}_2}{\text{rpm}_1} = \frac{3500}{1750} = 2$$

From Equation (6–13), calculate the new capacity:

$$\text{gpm}_2 = 2 \times 1.5^3 \times \text{gpm}_1 = 2 \times 1.5^3 \times 80 = 540 \text{ gpm}$$

From Equation (6–14), calculate the new total head:

$$\Delta h_2 = 2^2 \times 1.5^2 \times \Delta h_1 = 2^2 \times 1.5^2 \times 50 = 450 \text{ ft}$$

From Equation (6–15), calculate the new required $NPSH$:

$$NPSH_2 = 2^2 \times 1.5^2 \times NPSH_1 = 2^2 \times 1.5^2 \times 13 = 117 \text{ ft}$$

From Equation (6–16), calculate the new horsepower:

$$hp_2 = 2^3 \times 1.5^5 \times hp_1 = 2^3 \times 1.5^5 \times 2 = 121\frac{1}{2} \ hp$$

EXAMPLE

Consider the same volute centrifugal pump as in the first example. Assume the impeller is then cut down from a diameter of 8 inches to a diameter of 7 inches. Use Equations (6–17), (6–18) and (6–19) to calculate the performance data for the 7 inch impeller operating at 1750 rpm.

From Equation (6–17), calculate the new capacity:

$$gpm_2 = \left(\frac{7}{8}\right) gpm_1 = \frac{7}{8} \times 80 = 70 \ gpm$$

From Equation (6–18), calculate the new total head:

$$\Delta h_2 = \left(\frac{7}{8}\right)^2 \Delta h_1 = \left(\frac{7}{8}\right)^2 50 = 38.3 \ ft$$

From Equation (6–19), calculate the new power:

$$hp_2 = \left(\frac{7}{8}\right)^3 hp_1 = \left(\frac{7}{8}\right)^3 2 = 1.34 \ hp$$

The original performance of the pump may be restored by increasing the operating speed of the 7 inch impeller diameter to $8/7 \times 1750 = 2000$ rpm.

Temperature Rise in a Pump with Closed Discharge

EXAMPLE

Consider a centrifugal pump operating against a closed discharge. Assume that the pump contains 10 lb of water and that the power consumption is 2 hp.

Calculate the rate of increase of the temperature of the water in the pump casing assuming that all the energy supplied goes into heating the water. Take the heat capacity of water as 1 Btu/lb °F and 1 hp = 42.4 Btu/min. Calculate the heat input as:

$$Q = 2 \times 42.4 = 84.8 \ Btu/min$$

Calculate the temperature rise $\Delta T°F$ in 1 minute from the equation

$$\Delta T = \frac{Q}{M}$$

where M is the mass of water in lb in the pump casing. Therefore $\Delta T = 84.8/10 \cong$ $8\frac{1}{2}°F$ temperature rise per minute

It is not advisable to operate centrifugal pumps against a closed discharge for any appreciable length of time.

Multiple Centrifugal Pump Systems

Diskind[2] has described a simple graphical method for determining the operating conditions for centrifugal pumps in parallel or in series.

In parallel operation, the total head for each pump must be the same as the total head for the system. The individual pump capacities at this total head when added together must equal the system flow.

In series operation, the capacity for each pump must be the same as the system flow. The individual pump total heads at this capacity when added together must equal the system total head.

For the parallel operation of two centrifugal pumps, the procedure is as follows:

(1) Draw the total head vs capacity characteristic curves for both pumps together with the system total head vs capacity curve on the same plot as shown in Figure 6–40.

(2) Draw a horizontal constant total head line intersecting the two pump curves at capacities Q_1 and Q_2, respectively, and the system curve at capacity Q_s.

(3) Add the two pump capacities obtained in step (2) to give $Q_1 + Q_2 = Q_t$.

(4) Compare Q_t obtained in step (3) with Q_s obtained in step (2). If Q_t does not equal Q_s, repeat steps (2), (3) and (4) until $Q_t = Q_s$. This is the point of stable operation.

Alternatively the total head vs capacity characteristic curve for two centrifugal pumps in parallel can be plotted directly by adding the capacities of the individual pumps for various total heads. The system total head vs capacity curve is then plotted on the same graph, and the point of intersection of the two curves gives the operating capacity and total head for stable operation.

For the series operation of two centrifugal pumps, the procedure is as follows:

(1) Draw the total head vs capacity characteristic curves for both pumps together with the system total head vs capacity curve on the same plot as shown in Figure 6–41.

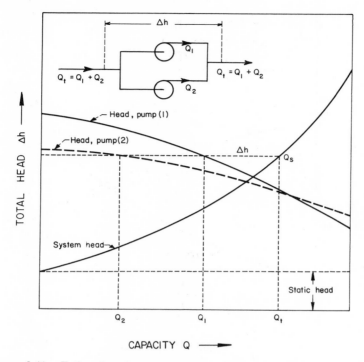

Figure 6-40.   Estimation of total head and capacity for centrifugal pumps in parallel.

(2) Draw a vertical constant capacity line intersecting the two pump curves at total heads Δh_1 and Δh_2, respectively, and the system curve at total head Δh_s.

(3) Add the two pump total heads obtained in step (2) to give $\Delta h_1 + \Delta h_2 = \Delta h_t$.

(4) Compare Δh_t obtained in step (3) with Δh_s obtained in step (2). If Δh_t does not equal Δh_s, repeat steps (2), (3) and (4) until $\Delta h_t = \Delta h_s$. This is the point of stable operation.

Alternatively the total head vs capacity characteristic curve for two centrifugal pumps in series can be plotted directly by adding the total heads of the individual pumps for various capacities. The system total head vs capacity curve is then plotted on the same graph, and the point of intersection of the two curves gives the operating capacity and total head for stable operation.

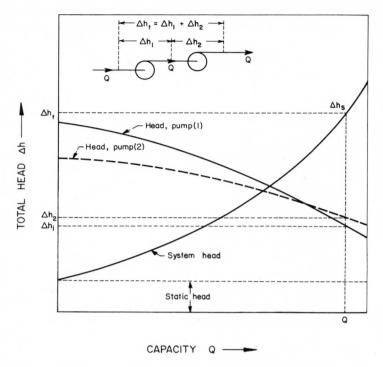

Figure 6-41.   Estimation of total head and capacity for centrifugal pumps in series.

Two centrifugal pumps are commonly used either in series or in parallel to take care of varying capacity requirements. Either series or parallel operation may be the most suitable depending on the shape of the system total head vs capacity curve. In order to determine the optimum arrangement, the total head vs capacity characteristic curves for both the parallel and the series pump systems must be plotted on the same graph as the system curve. Horsepower vs capacity characteristic curves for both the parallel and the series pump systems should also be plotted to aid in the evaluation.

Karassik[11] states that the widest range in capacity between single and two pump operation is given by two centrifugal pumps in parallel if the static component is a large proportion of the system total head and the friction losses are low. In this case, the system total head vs capacity curve is relatively flat. However, series operation provides more capacity if the system total head is composed almost entirely of friction. In this case, the total system head vs capacity curve is steep.

However, series operation has the disadvantage that the stuffing box pressure of the second pump is increased by the total head developed by the first pump.[12] This may increase the maintenance costs on the pump.

In parallel systems, a valve should be located in the discharge line of each centrifugal pump. This not only enables either pump to be isolated for one pump operation but facilitates control of the system. If only one centrifugal pump is in operation and a two pump operation is required, the second pump should be brought up to full speed and pressure before opening its discharge valve.[10]

In addition to the control and isolation valve, a check valve should be located in the discharge line of each centrifugal pump. This prevents the buildup of back pressure from one pump adversely affecting the operation of the other.

The piping and valves may be arranged to enable two centrifugal pumps to be operated either in series or in parallel in the same system. This provides a very flexible arrangement. If the two pumps are identical, the series system provides a liquid flow capacity Q against a total head $2\Delta h$. The parallel system provides a liquid flow capacity $2Q$ against a total head Δh where Q and Δh are the corresponding capacity and total head of a single pump. The efficiency of either the parallel or the series two pump system is practically the same as for a single pump.

Effect of Liquid Viscosity on Centrifugal Pump Performance

Total head vs capacity, horsepower vs capacity and efficiency vs capacity characteristic curves for centrifugal pumps are normally available only for operation with water. Corresponding characteristic curves for higher viscosity liquids can be obtained by using the performance correction chart in Figure 6–42. This chart is only applicable for conventional volute centrifugal pumps. The procedure is as follows:

(1) On the efficiency vs capacity characteristic curve for water, locate the water capacity at the point of maximum efficiency Q_{nw}. Read the value E_{nw} of this maximum efficiency.

(2) From the total head vs capacity curve for water, read the total head Δh_{nw} corresponding to the capacity Q_{nw}.

(3) Locate the value of Q_{nw} on the abscissa of the chart in Figure 6–42. Draw a vertical line from this point up to an ordinate value equal to the total head Δh_{nw} found in step (2). Draw a line horizontally from this latter point (either left or right) to the appropriate liquid viscosity in SSU. At this point draw a vertical line upward to cut the curves in the upper part of the chart at ordinate values, C_E, C_Q and $C_{\Delta h}$, respectively.

(4) Multiply the water efficiency from step (1) by the correction factor

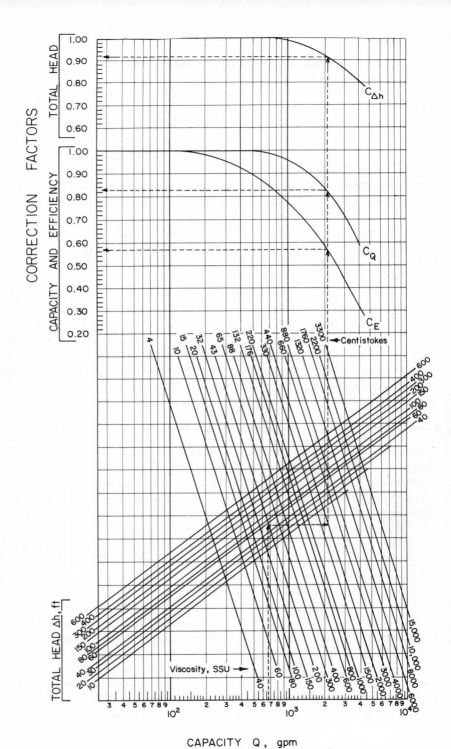

Figure 6-42.   Performance correction chart for centrifugal pumps.
(*Courtesy Stnd. Pump Div., Worthington Corp.*)

C_E from step (3). Multiply the water capacity Q_{nw} from step (1) by the correction factor C_Q from step (3). Multiply the water total head Δh_{nw} from step (2) by the correction factor $C_{\Delta h}$ from step (3). These data are the corresponding points for the liquid having a viscosity greater than water. Additional points can be obtained as described in subsequent steps. It should be noted that at zero capacity, the total head is not affected by viscosity and the pump efficiency is zero.

(5) From the value of Q_{nw} obtained in step (1), calculate the capacities $0.6Q_{nw}$, $0.8Q_{nw}$ and $1.2Q_{nw}$.

(6) For each of the capacities $0.6Q_{nw}$, $0.8Q_{nw}$ and $1.20Q_{nw}$, repeat steps (2), (3) and (4).

(7) Calculate the brake horsepower for each capacity from the formula

$$\text{bhp} = \left(\frac{W\Delta h}{33,000}\right)\left(\frac{100}{E}\right)$$

where W is the liquid flow rate in lb/min.

(8) From these data, plot the total head vs capacity, horsepower vs capacity and efficiency vs capacity characteristic curves for the liquid having a viscosity greater than water.

The performance correction chart shown in Figure 6–42 should only be used when dealing with Newtonian liquids. The chart cannot be used to correct the performance curves of axial and mixed flow pumps. It is only valid for conventional volute centrifugal pumps. Adequate available NPSH is assumed in all calculations. The chart applies either to a single-stage pump or to a single stage of a multistage pump.

The characteristic curves for a viscous liquid obtained by the above procedure are not exact for a particular pump. Accurate characteristic curves can only be obtained by conducting performance tests on the pump with the liquid in question. Nevertheless the calculation procedure described provides a rapid method for predicting the approximate performance of a volute centrifugal pump with a viscous liquid.

EXAMPLE

Characteristic curves for a volute centrifugal pump operating on water are shown as full lines in Figures 6–43(A), 6–43(B) and 6–43(C). The pump has a 9½ inch diameter impeller which rotates at 1450 rpm. Obtain the corresponding characteristic curves for pumping a liquid having a viscosity of 2000 SSU and density of 10 lb/gal. It is assumed that adequate NPSH is available in all cases.

(1) On the efficiency vs capacity characteristic curve for water, locate the water capacity at the point of maximum efficiency to be $Q_{nw} = 670$ gpm. Read the efficiency E_{nw} to be 78.7 per cent.

(2) From the total head vs capacity curve for water, read the total head Δh_{nw} to be 55 ft corresponding to the capacity $Q_{nw} = 670$ gpm.

(3) On Figure 6–42, draw a vertical line from an abscissa value of 670 gpm to a total head $\Delta h_{nw} = 55$ ft. Draw a line horizontally to the liquid viscosity line of 2000 SSU. Draw a vertical line from this latter point to cut the efficiency, capacity and total head correction curves at $C_E = 0.57$, $C_Q = 0.85$ and $C_{\Delta h} = 0.92$, respectively.

(4) Multiply the water efficiency $E_{nw} = 78.7$ per cent by the correction factor $C_E = 0.57$ to give 44.9 per cent. Multiply the water capacity $Q_{nw} = 670$ gpm by the correction factor $C_Q = 0.85$ to give 569 gpm. Multiply the water total head $\Delta h_{nw} = 55$ ft by the correction factor $C_{\Delta h} = 0.92$ to give 50.6 ft. The calculated values 44.9 per cent, 569 gpm and 50.6 ft are corresponding points on the characteristic curves for the centrifugal pump operating on a liquid of viscosity 2000 SSU.

(5) Calculate the capacities $0.6Q_{nw}$, $0.8Q_{nw}$ and $1.2Q_{nw}$: where $0.6Q_{nw} = 402$ gpm, $0.8Q_{nw} = 536$ gpm and $1.2Q_{nw} = 804$ gpm.

(6) Steps (2), (3) and (4) are repeated for these capacities to give three additional points on each of the characterictic curves for a 2000 SSU liquid. The calculations are shown in Table 6–3.

(7) Calculate the mass flow rates W in lb/min for each capacity by multiplying the flow rate in gpm by the liquid density in lb/gal.

In this case $W = 10 \times$ gpm in lb/min. Calculate the brake horsepower for each capacity from the formula bhp $= (W \Delta h/33,000) (100/E)$ where Δh and E are the

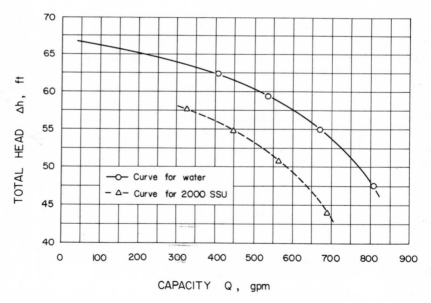

Figure 6-43(A).   Effect of viscosity on the total head vs capacity
curve of a centrifugal pump.

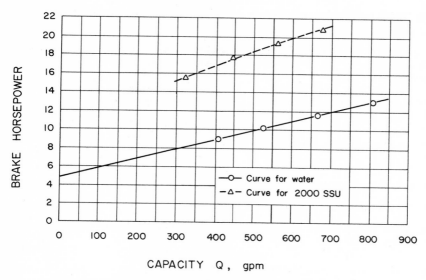

Figure 6-43(B).   Effect of viscosity on the power vs capacity
curve of a centrifugal pump.

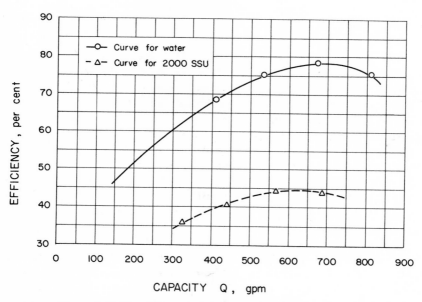

Figure 6-43(C).   Effect of viscosity on the efficiency vs capacity
curve of a centrifugal pump.

total head in ft and efficiency in per cent, respectively. The calculations are listed in Table 6–3.

(8) From the data calculated in Table 6–3, plot the pump characteristic curves for a liquid having a viscosity of 2000 SSU and a density of 10 lb/gal as dotted lines in Figure 6–43.

TABLE 6-3. Centrifugal Pump Performance Calculations

	$0.6Q_{nw}$	$0.8Q_{nw}$	Q_{nw}	$1.2Q_{nw}$
Water capacity Q_w, gpm	402	536	670	804
Water total head Δh_w, ft	62.6	59.6	55	47.7
Water efficiency E, %	68.9	75.8	78.7	76.1
C_Q from Figure 6–42	0.81	0.83	0.85	0.85
$C_{\Delta h}$ from Figure 6–42	0.92	0.92	0.92	0.92
C_E from Figure 6–42	0.53	0.55	0.57	0.58
Viscous capacity C_Q and Q_w, gpm	326	445	569	684
Viscous total head $C_{\Delta h}$ and Δh_w, ft	57.6	54.9	50.6	43.9
Viscous efficiency C_E and E_w, %	36.5	41.7	44.9	44.1
Viscous brake horsepower	15.6	17.8	19.4	20.6

The previous example demonstrates that the effect of an increase in liquid viscosity is to increase the brake horsepower and to decrease both the total head and the capacity of a volute centrifugal pump.

The chart in Figure 6–42 can also be used to select a volute centrifugal pump which will transport a liquid having a known viscosity and density at a particular flow rate Q and total head Δh. The procedure is as follows:

(1) Locate the value of Q on the abscissa of the chart in Figure 6–42. Draw a vertical line from this point up to an ordinate value of Δh. Draw a line horizontally from this latter point (either left or right) to the viscosity of the liquid to be pumped in SSU. At this point draw a vertical line upward to cut the curves in the upper part of the chart at ordinate, C_E, C_Q and $C_{\Delta h}$, respectively.

(2) Divide the capacity of the viscous liquid Q by the correction factor C_Q to give the corresponding water capacity Q_w. Divide the total head Δh for the viscous liquid by the correction factor $C_{\Delta h}$ to give the corresponding water total head Δh_w.

(3) Select a pump which has a total head vs capacity characteristic curve for water which passes through the point Δh_w, Q_w.

(4) Obtain the water efficiency E_w at this point and multiply it by the correction factor C_E to give the corresponding efficiency E for the viscous liquid.

(5) Calculate the brake horsepower for the viscous liquid from the formula

$$\text{bhp} = \left(\frac{W \, \Delta H}{33,000}\right)\left(\frac{100}{E}\right)$$

where W is the flow rate of the viscous liquid in lb/min.

The method described above for selecting a volute centrifugal pump to transfer a viscous liquid is only approximate. However, it does provide a rapid and convenient means for preliminary pump selection.

EXAMPLE

Select a volute centrifugal pump to transfer a liquid of viscosity 2000 SSU and density 10 lb/min at a rate of 1000 gpm against a total head of 80 ft.

(1) Locate 1000 gpm on the abscissa of the chart in Figure 6–42. Draw a vertical line from this point up to a total head ordinate value of 80 ft. Draw a line horizontally to the liquid viscosity line of 2000 SSU. Draw a vertical line from this latter point to cut the efficiency, capacity and total head correction curves at $C_E = 0.63$, $C_Q = 0.89$ and $C_{\Delta h} = 0.95$, respectively.

(2) Divide the capacity of the viscous liquid $Q = 1000$ by the correction factor $C_Q = 0.89$ from step (1) to give the corresponding water capacity $Q_w = 1125$ gpm. Divide the total head $\Delta h = 80$ ft for the viscous liquid by the correction factor $C_Q = 0.95$ from step (1) to give the corresponding water total head $h_w = 84.2$ ft.

(3) Select a pump which has a total head vs capacity characteristic curve for water which passes through the point $\Delta h_w = 84.2$ ft and $Q_w = 1125$ gpm in the region of maximum efficiency.

(4) For example, assume that this maximum water efficiency $E_{nw} = 80$ per cent. Multiply this water efficiency by the correction factor $C_E = 0.63$ to give the corresponding efficiency $E = 50.4$ per cent for the liquid of viscosity 2000 SSU.

(5) For the values $W = 10,000$ lb/min, $\Delta h = 80$ ft and $E = 50.4$ calculate the brake horsepower to be bhp $= 48$.

System Heads

System total heads and available net positive suction heads for various liquid flow rates can be calculated as described in Chapter 5 for pipelines containing valves and fittings.

System total heads should be estimated as accurately as possible. Safety factors should never be added to these total head values. Consider the result of adding a safety factor for a particular system.

In Figure 6–44 suppose that OA_1 is the correct system curve and that the

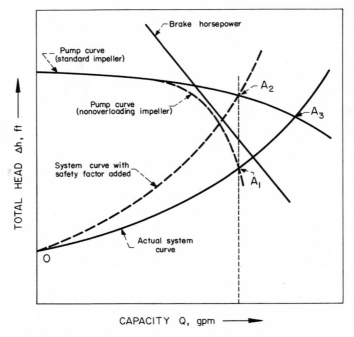

Figure 6-44.   Effect of safety factors on system total head vs capacity curves.

centrifugal pump is required to operate at point A_1. However, a safety factor is added to the total head values to give a system curve OA_2. On the basis of this latter system curve, the manufacturer will supply a pump to operate at point A_2. However, since the total head at the required capacity is A_1 and not A_2, the pump will operate at point A_3, i.e., the point at which the pump total head vs capacity characteristic curve meets the true system curve. Not only is the capacity higher than that specified, but the motor may be overloaded.[4]

One way of guarding against this type of error in specifications is to fit a nonoverloading impeller which has a total head vs capacity characteristic curve shown by the dotted line in Figure 6–44. However, pumps with nonoverloading impellers operate at lower efficiencies and thus have higher operating costs.

Cost Calculations

The cost of centrifugal pumps can be obtained using Tables 6–4, 6–5 and Figure 6–45.

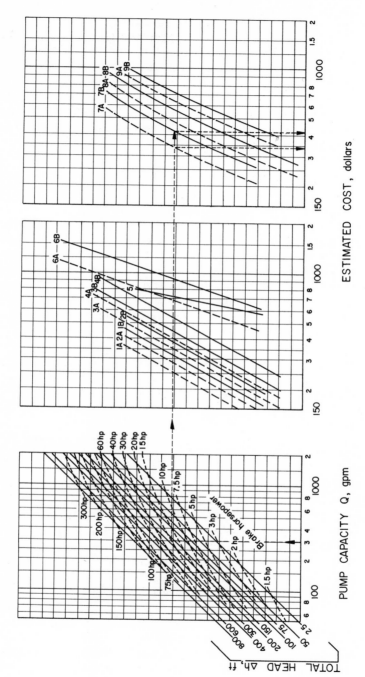

ESTIMATED COST, dollars

Figure 6-45. Centrifugal pump cost vs total head and capacity.

Costs given in Figure 6–45 (curves 1B, 2B, 3B, 4B, 5, 6B, 7B, 8B and 9B) are with low cost steel channel base plates. For solid cast iron base plates, these costs are 10 to 30 per cent higher. This addition is made only after any correction factors for pump materials of construction have been applied. For example, consider a solid cast iron base plate on a titanium AVS pump rated at 3500 rpm. If the cast iron cost obtained from Figure 6–45 (curve 7B) is $500, the adjusted cost is

$$(\$500)(9.20) + (\$500)(0.30) = \$4750$$

for a base plate cost addition of 30 per cent.

Tabulated costs are based on inexpensive jaw or chain-type flexible couplings suitable for medium to high speeds at low to moderate power transmission. Pumps with heavy loads require radial or other types of heavy duty couplings. For these, add 5 per cent to the cost for cast iron pumps as with base plate additions. If a coupling guard is required, add 3 to 8 per cent of the coupling correction. If the pump used in the above example were fitted with a heavy duty coupling and cover, the corrected cost would be

$$(\$500)(9.2) + (\$500)(0.30) + (\$500)(0.05) + (\$500)(0.05)(0.08) = \$4777$$

for the maximum coupling guard addition of 8 per cent.

Flexible coupling costs vary widely and may account for a considerable increase in total pump cost, especially for heavy duty types used in the larger pumps, e.g., the cost of an open roller chain coupling for a ½ inch shaft is $15, while a radial clutch-type coupling for an 8 inch shaft costs $5000.

Cost additions for mechanical seals are less accurate than for base plates and couplings. This is due to the wide variety of seals available and the considerable variations between costs, especially when high pressure, corrosive or high temperature service is required. Sniffen and Serven[19] of the Worthington Corp. have given broad cost factors for mechanical seals. For simple bellows-type mechanical seals used with water and oils at normal temperatures and suction pressures below 100 psi, they suggest an addition of 5 per cent to curves 1A, 2A, 3A, 4A, 7A and 8A, and 13 per cent to curves 5, 6A and 9A. These seals are recommended only on iron and steel pumps where corrosion is not a problem. A factor of 30 per cent for 316 stainless steel and 40 per cent for "Worthite" seals should be used with curves 1A, 2A, 3A, 4A, 7A and 8A. Curves 5, 6A and 9A require a factor of 17 or 21 per cent for 316 stainless steel and "Worthite,"

TABLE 6-4. Operating Ranges for Common Centrifugal Pumps

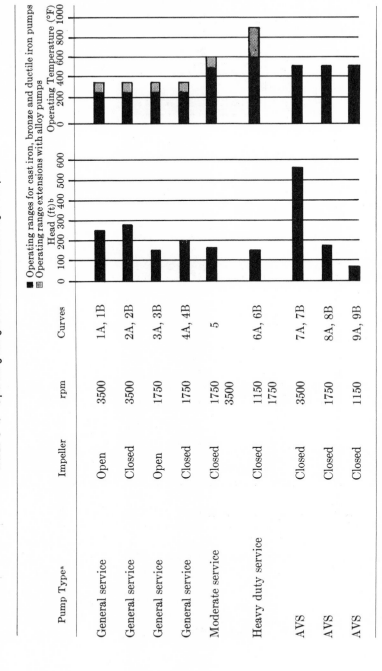

Pump Type[a]	Impeller	rpm	Curves
General service	Open	3500	1A, 1B
General service	Closed	3500	2A, 2B
General service	Open	1750	3A, 3B
General service	Closed	1750	4A, 4B
Moderate service	Closed	1750 3500	5
Heavy duty service	Closed	1150 1750	6A, 6B
AVS	Closed	3500	7A, 7B
AVS	Closed	1750	8A, 8B
AVS	Closed	1150	9A, 9B

[a] All pumps are single-stage, single suction designs.
[b] Heads taken at the best efficiency point (bep).

TABLE 6-5.   Cost Correction Factors for Centrifugal Pump Materials of Construction

Curve	All Cast Iron	All Ductile Iron	All Cast Steel	304 or 316 SS Fitted	All 304 or 316 SS	Cast "Goulds-A-Loy #20"[e]	All Bronze	All "Worth-ite"[c]	All "Hastel-loy C"[c]	All "Monel"	All Nickel	All "ISO B"[d]	All "ISO C"[e]	All Titanium
1A	1.00	1.10	1.25	1.06	1.91	2.00	1.80	2.35	2.95	3.00	3.25	4.95	4.60	9.50
1B	1.00	1.07	1.15	1.03	1.85	1.90	1.65	2.20	2.55	2.80	2.90	4.75	4.45	9.20
2A	1.00	1.10	1.25	1.06	1.91	2.00	1.80	NA	2.95	3.00	3.25	4.95	4.60	9.50
2B	1.00	1.07	1.15	1.03	1.85	1.90	1.65	NA	2.55	2.80	2.90	4.75	4.45	9.20
3A	1.00	1.10	1.25	1.06	1.91	2.00	1.80	2.50	2.95	3.00	3.25	4.95	4.60	9.50
3B	1.00	1.07	1.15	1.03	1.85	1.90	1.65	2.30	2.55	2.80	2.90	4.75	4.45	9.20
4A	1.00	1.10	1.25	1.06	1.91	2.00	1.80	NA	2.95	3.00	3.25	4.95	4.60	9.50
4B	1.00	1.07	1.15	1.03	1.85	1.90	1.65	NA	2.55	2.80	2.90	4.75	4.45	9.20
5	1.00	1.15	1.35	1.15	2.00	2.00	1.90	2.60	2.95	3.30	3.50	4.95	4.60	9.70
6A	1.00	1.25	1.35	1.15	2.10	2.00	1.75	2.40	2.95	3.30	3.50	4.95	4.60	9.70
6B	1.00	1.10	1.20	1.05	1.95	1.90	1.65	2.10	2.55	3.00	3.15	4.75	4.45	9.45
7A, 8A, 9A	1.00	1.10	1.25	1.06	1.91	2.00	1.80	2.60	2.95	3.00	3.25	4.95	4.60	9.50
7B, 8B, 9B	1.00	1.07	1.15	1.03	1.85	1.90	1.65	2.40	2.55	2.80	2.90	4.75	4.45	9.20

[a] Factors based on Feb. 1966 cost data. Figure 6-45 gives base prices for cast iron.
[b] Highly alloyed austenitic steel, 20% Cr, 29% Ni, 1.75% Mo.
[c] Highly alloyed austenitic steel, 20% Cr, 24% Ni, 3% Mo.
[d] 4–6% Fe, 1.0% Cr, 26–30% Mo, balance Ni.
[e] 4.5–7.5% Fe, 15.5% Cr, 16–18% Mo, balance Ni.

Legend for Table 6-5 Cost Correction Data and Curves in Figure 6-45

Curve	Pump Type[a]	Impeller	rpm	Cost Obtained Includes [d]: Bare Pump Only[a]	Cost Obtained Includes [d]: Bare Pump, Base Plate and Flexible Coupling[c]
1A	Standard service	Open	3500	X	
1B	Standard service	Open	3500		X
2A	Standard service	Closed	3500	X	
2B	Standard service	Closed	3500		X
3A	Standard service	Open	1750	X	
3B	Standard service	Open	1750		X
4A	Standard service	Closed	1750	X	
4B	Standard service	Closed	1750		X
5	Medium duty service	Closed	3500, 1750		X
6A	Heavy duty service	Closed	1750, 1150	X	
6B	Heavy duty service	Closed	1750 1150		X
7A	AVS	Closed	3500	X	
7B	AVS	Closed	3500		X
8A	AVS	Closed	1750	X	
8B	AVS	Closed	1750		X
9A	AVS	Closed	1150	X	
9B	AVS	Closed	1150		X

[a] All pumps are single-stage, single suction units. Standard service and AVS pumps are end suction. Medium duty and heavy duty service pumps are both end suction and top suction. All pumps have a packed stuffing box.

[b] Feb. 1966 costs are for cast iron pumps. Table 6–5 gives appropriate cost multipliers for other materials of construction.

[c] These couplings are moderately priced flexible units suitable for medium loads. Low cost steel channel base plates are used. For solid cast iron base plates, heavy duty couplings and mechanical seals, the cost multipliers given in Table 6–6 must be applied to the base prices obtained from Figure 6–45.

[d] Costs are for single pump purchases only. Quantity discounts from suppliers range from 10 to 50%. Cost data are based on an average industrial user discount and not manufacturers' list prices.

respectively. The factors should be doubled for double seals used at pressures over 100 psi.

Examples of mechanical seal costs are $25 for a 30 psi unbalanced single $\frac{3}{8}$ inch diameter shaft seal with a ceramic seal ring, and $1200 for a 600 psi balanced single 5 inch diameter shaft seal with a tungsten carbide seal ring.

EXAMPLE

Estimate the cost of a single titanium AVS pump with a capacity of 300 U.S. gpm against a total head of 175 ft. The operating temperature is 400°F; a double mechanical seal, a heavy duty flexible coupling with safety cover and a solid cast iron base plate are required. The pump is to be purchased without a motor.

(1) Select the operating speed to be 3500 rpm from Table 6–4.

(2) Obtain the cost of a cast iron pump with a channel steel base plate, a medium duty flexible coupling and a packed stuffing box from Figure 6–45, curve 7B to be $415.

(3) Multiply the cost from step (2) by the titanium multiplication factor from Table 6–5 to give $415 × 9.2 = $3820.

(4) From Table 6–6, obtain the additional cost for a solid cast iron base plate to be 30 per cent of the cost in step (2), i.e., $415 × 0.30 = $125.

(5) From Table 6–6, obtain the additional cost for a heavy duty flexible coupling with safety cover to be 13 per cent of the cost in step (2), i.e., $415 × 0.13 = $54.

(6) Obtain the cost of a cast iron pump without base plate or coupling from Figure 6–45, curve 7B, to be $330.

(7) From Table 6–6, obtain the additional cost of a double mechanical seal to be 2 × 40 per cent of the cost in step 6, i.e., $330 × 0.80 = $264.

(8) Find the cost of a titanium AVS pump with a double mechanical seal, a heavy duty flexible coupling with safety cover and a solid cast iron base plate by adding the cost from steps (3), (4), (5) and (7) to be $3820 + $125 + $54 + $264 = $4263.

Approximate brake horsepower requirements to pump liquids having the density and viscosity of water can also be obtained from Figure 6–45. This information can be used to estimate the cost of both pump and driver if cost data for motors are available.

The centrifugal pump cost data given in Figure 6–45 are based on 1966 prices. These can be updated using either the "Marshall and Stevens Cost Index" (Table 6–6) or the "Chemical Engineering Plant Cost Index" (Table 6–7). The former had a value of 100 in 1926 and the latter a value of 100 for the period 1957–1959.

The "Chemical Engineering Plant Cost Index" is probably more accurate since it gives factors for specific types of equipment such as pumps and compressors, pipes, valves and fittings, etc. In contrast, the "Marshall and Stevens Cost Index" is an over-all chemical processing equipment index.

EXAMPLE

Estimate the cost in October 1970 of the titanium centrifugal pump in the previous example, assuming that the "Chemical Engineering Plant Cost Index" will then be 106.0.

$$\text{cost (1970)} = \text{cost (1966)} \left(\frac{\text{index for 1970}}{\text{index for 1966}} \right)$$

$$\text{cost (1970)} = \$4263 \left(\frac{106.0}{104.2} \right) = \$4335$$

TABLE 6-6. "Marshall and Stevens Equipment Cost Index"[a]

Process Industries	YEAR																		
	1947	1948	1949	1950	1951	1952	1953	1954	1955	1956	1957	1958	1959	1960	1961	1962	1963	1964	1965
Cement manufacturing	144.3	156.5	156.5	161.6	172.7	172.8	174.6	177.6	182.6	199.4	216.4	222.8	228.7	232.1	231.1	231.8	232.5	235.9	239.3
Chemical industries	151.5	164.5	164.5	169.6	180.7	181.1	183.1	186.2	191.5	209.1	226.5	232.3	236.5	239.2	237.7	238.0	238.7	241.1	243.8
Clay products	139.8	151.5	151.5	156.6	167.7	167.8	169.5	172.4	177.3	193.8	210.2	216.8	222.2	225.7	224.6	225.5	225.8	229.2	232.6
Glass manufacturing	142.3	154.6	154.6	159.7	170.8	171.0	173.0	176.0	180.9	197.5	213.8	219.3	223.2	225.3	224.4	224.7	225.4	227.6	230.1
Paint manufacturing	145.9	157.8	157.8	162.9	174.0	174.4	176.3	179.3	184.3	201.2	217.6	223.2	226.9	229.5	230.0	231.5	232.1	235.2	238.1
Paper manufacturing	146.9	158.1	158.1	163.2	174.3	174.7	176.6	179.6	184.6	201.5	218.2	223.8	227.8	229.9	229.0	229.3	229.9	232.3	234.8
Petroleum industries	147.1	160.9	160.9	166.0	177.1	177.6	179.1	182.8	188.0	205.4	222.2	228.0	231.8	234.3	235.0	238.2	238.8	243.0	244.9
Rubber industries	151.2	163.3	163.3	168.4	179.5	180.0	182.1	185.2	190.5	207.5	224.9	230.8	234.6	237.3	237.9	239.2	240.0	243.0	246.2

[a] Base period: 1926 = 100.

TABLE 6-7. "Chemical Engineering Equipment Cost Index"[a]

	YEAR																		
	1947	1948	1949	1950	1951	1952	1953	1954	1955	1956	1957	1958	1959	1960	1961	1962	1963	1964	1965[b]
Equipment, machinery and supports (Averages)	60.3	65.6	67.2	69.8	77.6	77.8	80.9	82.3	85.1	92.7	98.5	99.6	101.9	101.7	100.2	100.6	100.5	101.2	102.1
Fabricated equipment	63.2	68.4	69.6	71.5	78.4	79.0	81.3	81.4	84.2	92.5	99.5	99.6	100.9	101.2	100.1	101.0	101.7	102.7	103.4
Process machinery	58.4	63.1	66.2	69.4	76.5	77.5	80.6	82.8	85.3	92.2	98.1	100.1	101.8	101.8	101.1	101.9	102.0	102.5	103.6
Pipe, valves and fittings	53.2	60.1	61.9	64.7	73.1	73.8	78.0	79.5	85.2	94.8	97.9	98.8	103.3	104.1	101.1	100.6	100.7	101.6	103.0
Process instruments and controls	64.2	68.2	69.3	71.9	79.8	80.0	82.9	85.1	86.7	91.2	96.7	100.4	102.9	105.4	105.9	105.9	105.7	105.8	106.5
Pumps and compressors	53.8	58.2	62.3	65.4	73.9	73.4	77.5	79.5	81.7	90.0	97.5	100.0	102.5	101.7	100.8	101.1	100.1	101.0	103.4
Electrical equipment and materials	61.8	64.2	64.2	68.3	79.7	79.3	82.0	83.0	84.3	93.5	98.4	100.6	101.0	95.7	92.3	89.4	87.6	85.5	84.1
Structural supports, insulation and paint	66.6	73.5	75.0	77.6	82.0	83.0	86.0	88.6	90.5	92.5	98.0	100.4	101.6	101.9	99.8	99.2	97.3	98.3	98.8

[a] Courtesy of Chemical Engineering Magazine. Based period: 1957-1959 = 100.

[b] Preliminary estimate. Annual price data for 1965 were not available at time of publication.

NOMENCLATURE

a	exponent in Equation (6–3)
b	exponent in Equation (6–3)
bep	best efficiency point
bhp	brake horsepower
c	exponent in Equation (6–3)
C	constant in Equation (6–2), (dimensionless)
C_E, C_Q and $C_{\Delta h}$	correction factors in Figure 6–42
D	impeller diameter
E	mechanical efficiency, per cent
gpm	gallons per minute
hp	horsepower
h	head, ft
K	ratio of linear dimensions in Equations (6–13), (6–14), (6–15) and (6–16)
N_s	specific speed $= \text{rpm}\sqrt{\text{gpm}}/\Delta h^{3/4}$
$NPSH$	net positive suction head
N	pump speed, rpm
Q	volume flow rate of liquid
S	suction specific speed $= \text{rpm}\sqrt{\text{gpm}}/(NPSH)^{3/4}$
μ	viscosity of liquid, SSU
ρ	density of liquid, lb/cu ft
Δh	total head, ft
ΔT	temperature rise, °F

REFERENCES

1. Carter, R., and Karassik, I. J., *Water & Sewage Works*, **98**, 212 (1951).
2. Diskind, T., *Chem. Eng.*, **66**, No. 22 (1959).
3. Dolman, R. E., *Chem. Eng.*, **59**, No. 3 (1952).
4. Holland, F. A., *Chem. & Process Eng.*, **44**, 630 (1963).
5. Horwitz, R. P., *Water & Sewage Works*, **111**, 343 (1964).
6. Jacobs, J. K., *Hydrocarbon Process.*, **44**, No. 6 (1965).
7. Kristal, F. A., and Annett, F. A., "Pumps," p. 80, New York, McGraw-Hill Book Co. Inc., 1953.
8. *Ibid.*, p. 106.
9. *Ibid.*, p. 135.
10. *Ibid.*, p. 325.
11. Karassik, I. J., "Engineers' Guide to Centrifugal Pumps," p. 65, New York, McGraw-Hill Book Co. Inc., 1964.
12. *Ibid.*, p. 67.
13. *Ibid.*, p. 133.
14. *Ibid.*, p. 226.
15. *Ibid.*, p. 261.
16. Mills, H. E., *Chem. Eng.*, **71**, No. 12 (1964).
17. Pollak, H. M., *Chem. Eng.*, **70**, No. 3 (1963).
18. Serven, E. J., *Chem. Eng.*, **70**, No. 7 (1963).
19. Sniffen, T. J., and Serven, E. J., *Chem. Eng.*, **69**, No. 24 (1962).

CHAPTER 7

Liquid Flow Measurement in Pipelines

The rate of flow of liquids through pipes is most commonly measured using head flowmeters. These are designed to cause a pressure drop which can be conveniently measured. Since the pressure drop is a function of the liquid flow rate, the latter may be read directly from a calibrated instrument. Orifice and venturi meters, pitot tubes and flow nozzles all operate on this principle. Head flowmeters consist of a primary element which produces the pressure drop and a secondary element which measures it. The primary element of head flowmeters does not contain any moving parts.

Flowmeters are also in common use which operate on different principles. Some of these flowmeters have primary elements which contain moving parts. These are referred to as mechanical flowmeters. Included in this category are rotameters, positive displacement meters and velocity meters. The latter operate on the windmill principle using either a propeller or a turbine.

Flowmeters are also available which do not involve restrictions in the pipeline (as is the case with head flowmeters); these do not have moving parts (as is the case with mechanical flowmeters). Electromagnetic flowmeters fall into this category. The moving liquid in the pipe cuts the lines of force in a magnetic field and generates a voltage which is directly proportional to flow rate.

HEAD FLOWMETERS

The Orifice Meter

In its simplest form, an orifice meter is a flat plate with a centrally drilled hole located in a pipeline perpendicular to the direction of liquid flow. The liquid is accelerated at the sudden constriction in the pipeline. The increase in velocity head produced results in a decrease in pressure head. The latter is measured by a differential manometer placed across the orifice.

Consider the horizontal pipeline and orifice in Figure 7–1. Let

ρ = density of liquid in lb/cu ft,

P = pressure of liquid in psi,

u = mean velocity of flowing liquid in ft/sec,

A_1 = cross-sectional flow area of pipe in sq ft,

d_1 = inside diameter of pipe in ft,

A_o = cross-sectional flow area of orifice hole in sq ft,

d_o = diameter of orifice hole in ft,

A_2 = smallest cross-sectional area of flow reached in sq ft,

d_2 = diameter of smallest cross-sectional area of flow reached in ft.

The smallest cross-sectional area of flow is reached at a point known as the vena contracta. This occurs at one-half to two pipe diameters downstream from the orifice plate. The location of the vena contracta is a function of the liquid velocity and the ratio of the pipe to orifice hole diameters.

Consider a point 1 in the pipe shown in Figure 7–1. At this point the liquid flow is undisturbed by the orifice plate. Consider also the liquid

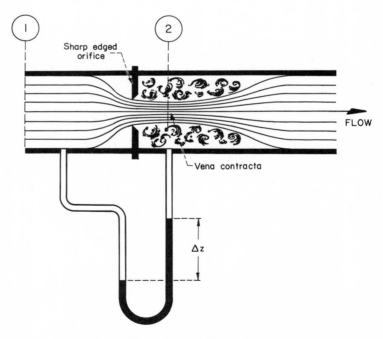

Figure 7-1.   Orifice meter.

flow at the vena contracta point 2. For the case of frictionless liquid flow, the Bernoulli equation can be written for points 1 and 2 as follows:

$$\frac{144P_1}{\rho}\left(\frac{g_c}{g}\right) + \frac{u_1{}^2}{2\alpha_1 g} = \frac{144P_2}{\rho}\left(\frac{g_c}{g}\right) + \frac{u_2{}^2}{2\alpha_2 g} \qquad (7\text{--}1)$$

where $(144P/\rho)\,(g_c/g)$ and $u^2/2g$ are the pressure and velocity heads respectively in ft. Equation (7–1) can be rearranged in the form

$$\frac{1}{2g}\left(\frac{u_2{}^2}{\alpha_2} - \frac{u_1{}^2}{\alpha_1}\right) = \frac{144}{\rho}\left(\frac{g_c}{g}\right)(P_1 - P_2) \qquad (7\text{--}2)$$

In Equations (7–1) and (7–2), the dimensionless correction factors α_1 and α_2 are unity for turbulent flow and one-half for laminar flow[2], g is the gravitational acceleration in ft/sec², and g_c is a constant having the dimensions lb_m ft/lb$_f$ sec²; g_c is numerically almost equal to the gravitational acceleration, i.e., 32.2.

For this case the principle of continuity can be expressed by the equation

$$W = \rho A_1 u_1 = \rho A_2 u_2 = \rho A_o u_o \qquad (7\text{--}3)$$

where W is the mass flow rate in lb/sec. Equation (7–3) can be rearranged to give

$$u_1 = \frac{A_o u_o}{A_1} \qquad (7\text{--}4)$$

and

$$u_2 = \frac{A_o u_o}{A_2} \qquad (7\text{--}5)$$

Combine Equations (7–2), (7–4) and (7–5) to give

$$(P_1 - P_2)(g_c/g) = u_o{}^2 \frac{\rho}{288\alpha_2 g}\left[\left(\frac{A_o}{A_2}\right)^2 - \frac{\alpha_2}{\alpha_1}\left(\frac{A_o}{A_1}\right)^2\right]$$

$$= u_o{}^2 \frac{\rho}{288\alpha_2 g}\left(\frac{A_o}{A_2}\right)^2\left[1 - \frac{\alpha_2}{\alpha_1}\left(\frac{A_2}{A_1}\right)^2\right] \qquad (7\text{--}6)$$

Since $A_o = \pi d_o{}^2/4$, $A_1 = \pi d_1{}^2/4$ and $A_2 = \pi d_2{}^2/4$, Equation (7–6) can be written as

$$(P_1 - P_2)(g_c/g) = u_o{}^2 \frac{\rho}{288\alpha_2 g}\left(\frac{d_o}{d_2}\right)^4\left[1 - \frac{\alpha_2}{\alpha_1}\left(\frac{d_2}{d_1}\right)^4\right] \qquad (7\text{--}7)$$

Rearrange Equation (7–7) to read

$$u_o = \left(\frac{d_2}{d_o}\right)^2 \sqrt{\frac{2g[144(P_1 - P_2)g_c/\rho g]\alpha_2}{\left[1 - \frac{\alpha_2}{\alpha_1}\left(\frac{d_2}{d_1}\right)^4\right]}} \tag{7–8}$$

Combine Equations (7–3) and (7–8) to give

$$W = \rho A_o \left(\frac{d_2}{d_o}\right)^2 \sqrt{\frac{2g[144(P_1 - P_2)g_c/\rho g]\alpha_2}{\left[1 - \frac{\alpha_2}{\alpha_1}\left(\frac{d_2}{d_1}\right)^4\right]}} \tag{7–9}$$

the mass flow rate through the system in lb/sec. Alternatively, Equation (7–4) can be combined with Equation (7–8) to give the mean linear liquid velocity in the pipe before the orifice

$$u_1 = \left(\frac{d_2}{d_1}\right)^2 \sqrt{\frac{2g[144(P_1 - P_2)g_c/\rho g]\alpha_2}{\left[1 - \frac{\alpha_2}{\alpha_1}\left(\frac{d_2}{d_1}\right)^4\right]}} \tag{7–10}$$

Equations (7–8), (7–9) and (7–10) have been derived on the assumption that the liquid flow through the orifice is frictionless. In practice, this is not the case. Boundary layer separation occurs on the downstream side of the orifice plate resulting in a substantial pressure loss from form friction. Because of friction, the actual liquid flow rate for a given pressure drop $(P_1 - P_2)$ is less than the theoretical.

For frictional liquid flow, an equation analogous to Equation (7–10) can be written as follows:

$$u_1 = C_d \sqrt{\frac{2g[144(P_1 - P_2)g_c/\rho g]}{[1 - (d_o/d_1)^4]}} \tag{7–11}$$

where C_d is the dimensionless discharge coefficient which accounts for geometry and friction. In Equation (7–11), d_o/d_1 is the ratio of the diameter of the orifice hole to the inside diameter of the pipe. This ratio does not vary as does the ratio d_2/d_1 in Equation (7–10).

In Equation (7–11), the term $144(P_1 - P_2)g_c/\rho g$ has the dimensions of ft. Thus since the gravitational acceleration g has the dimensions ft/sec^2, the velocity u_1 in Equation (7–11) has the dimensions ft/sec. The ratio g_c/g is numerically almost equal to unity.

The discharge coefficient C_d is obtained by calibrating the meter.

The mean linear liquid velocity in the pipe before the orifice may also be written as

$$u_1 = K \sqrt{2g[144(P_1 - P_2)g_c/\rho g]} \qquad (7\text{--}12)$$

where K is known as the flow coefficient.[6]

In the case of a horizontal orifice meter in which the orifice diameter d_o is small compared with the diameter of the pipe d_1, Equations (7–11) and (7–12) become almost identical and $K \rightarrow C_d$.

In terms of the liquid flowing through the pipe, the head loss across the orifice can be written as

$$\Delta h = 144(P_1 - P_2)g_c/\rho g \qquad (7\text{--}13)$$

In this case, Equation (7–12) becomes

$$u_1 = K \sqrt{2g\Delta h} \qquad (7\text{--}14)$$

and Equation (7–11) becomes

$$u_1 = C_d \sqrt{\frac{2g\Delta h}{[1 - (d_o/d_1)^4]}} \qquad (7\text{--}15)$$

For the case of liquid flowing upward through an orifice meter which is not horizontal, Equation (7–14) becomes

$$u_1 = K \sqrt{2g(\Delta h + \Delta z)} \qquad (7\text{-}16)$$

where Δz is the vertical distance between the pressure taps. Therefore, Equation (7–15) becomes

$$u_1 = C_d \sqrt{\frac{2g(\Delta h + \Delta z)}{[1 - (d_o/d_1)^4]}} \qquad (7\text{-}17)$$

The holes in orifice plates may be either concentric, eccentric or segmental as shown in Figure 7–2. Concentric orifice units are used for clean liquids at pipe Reynolds numbers of 500 or greater. In general, the liquid should have a viscosity less than about 300 SSU. Accurate discharge coefficients C_d are available for pipe sizes in the range 1½ to 14 inches. The upstream edge of the orifice may be sharp and square. Eccentric orifice units have the hole circumference flush with the inside of the pipe. They are used with liquids containing either a small amount of nonabrasive

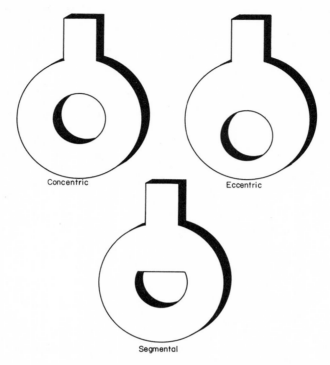

Figure 7-2.   Concentric, eccentric and segmental orifice plates.

solids or small amounts of gas. In the former case, the opening is at the bottom of the pipe, and in the latter case, it is at the top. In segmental orifice plates, the opening is a circular segment of the internal pipe diameter. These units are used with liquids containing nonabrasive solids which are substantially denser than the liquid. Predictable accuracy of eccentric and segmental orifice plate units is inferior to that of concentric orifice plates. Orifice plates have the disadvantage of being sensitive to damage by erosion.

The most common locations for the taps to transmit the differential pressure across the orifice plate are shown in Figure 7–3. Vena contracta taps are normally located one pipe diameter upstream from a standard concentric orifice plate and one-half of a pipe diameter downstream. These taps should not be used for pipe sizes under 4 inches since the flange interferes with the downstream tap. The allowable orifice to pipe diameter ratio d_o/d_1 range for vena contracta tap systems is 0.10 to 0.80. Flange taps are located 1 inch upstream from one face of the orifice plate and 1

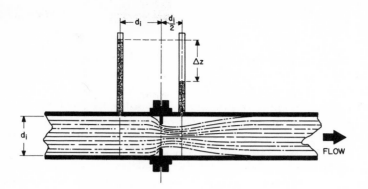

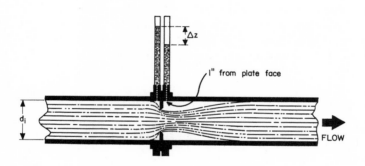

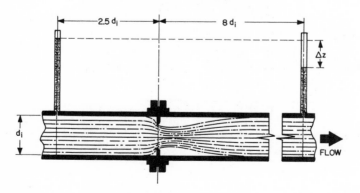

Figure 7-3.   Pressure tap locations for orifice plates.

inch downstream from the other face. The allowable orifice to pipe diameter ratio d_o/d_1 range for flange tap systems is 0.10 to 0.75 for pipe sizes of 4 inches and above, and 0.20 to 0.70 for pipe sizes of $3\frac{1}{2}$ inches and under. These ranges also apply to pipe taps. The latter are located two and one-half pipe diameters upstream from the orifice plate and eight pipe diameters downstream. Corner taps are located immediately adjacent to the faces of the orifice plate, upstream and downstream.

The coefficient of discharge C_d for a given orifice type is a function of the location of the pressure taps, the orifice to pipe diameter ratio d_o/d_1 and the Reynolds number in the pipeline N_{Re}. C_d is also a function of the plate thickness unless this is less than (1) $d_o/8$; (2) $d_1/30$ to $d_1/50$; (3) $(d_1 - d_o)/8$. Authoritative references for orifice coefficients should be consulted.[8]

When considering discharge coefficient Reynolds number data, it should be noted whether the Reynolds numbers are based on the orifice diameter or the inside pipe diameter. A typical plot of discharge coefficient data for a sharp-edged concentric orifice is shown in Figure 7–4.

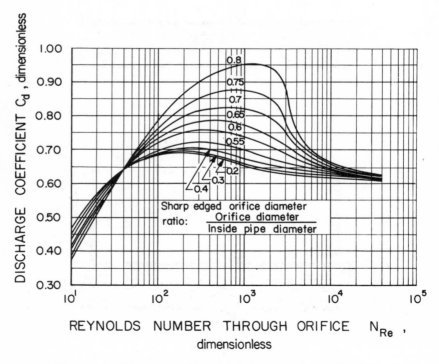

Figure 7-4.   Discharge coefficient data for concentric orifice plates.

Orifice meters suffer from high frictional head losses. Thus, most of the pressure drop is not recoverable. The high velocity liquid flowing through the orifice mixes with the relatively static liquid on the downstream side. This results in the generation of turbulence and the dissipation of the excess kinetic energy as heat. Only about 5 to 10 per cent of the excess kinetic energy is recovered as pressure energy.[2]

The high inherent energy losses with orifice meters has led to the development of other head flowmeters in which eddy formation and turbulence are reduced to a minimum.

The Venturi Meter

The theory of the Venturi meter is the same as for the orifice meter. However, the venturi meter is designed to reduce eddy formation and consequent energy loss by making the approach to, and the exit from, the orifice, gradual. Figure 7–5 shows the geometry of the venturi meter. The streamlined shape substantially eliminates boundary layer separation. Thus, form drag is reduced to a minimum.

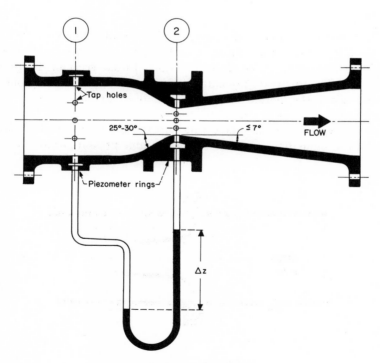

Figure 7-5.   Venturi meter.

The venturi meter consists of an inlet section of substantially the same diameter as the pipeline, an entrance cone with a fixed angular convergence of between 25 and 30°, an accurately machined throat section and a discharge cone with fixed angular divergence not exceeding 7°.

The inlet section has a series of tap connections in an annular pressure ring. This device gives an average value for the upstream pressure. A similar pressure ring at the throat gives an average value for the downstream pressure.

Venturis can meter up to 60 per cent more flow than orifice plates for the same pipe diameter and differential pressure.[4] Venturis have the same additional advantage of being able to meter liquids containing solids. In the latter application, averaging pressure rings should not be used.

The nonrecoverable pressure drop across a venturi is only about 10 per cent of the total pressure drop. Discharge coefficients C_d for venturis are about 0.98 compared with only about 0.6 for orifice plates. However, venturi meters tend to be bulky. In addition, their initial and installation costs are relatively high compared with orifice plates.

Nozzles

A flow nozzle is a modified version of the venturi. As shown in Figure 7–6, the inlet cone of the venturi is replaced by a short flared bell which provides a curved entrance to a cylindrical throat section. There is no outlet cone. The upstream pressure tap is located approximately one pipe diameter from the nozzle entrance. The downstream pressure tap is located at the point of smallest jet area.

A flow nozzle can handle flow rates up to 60 per cent higher than an orifice of the same diameter. The nonrecoverable pressure drop is less than

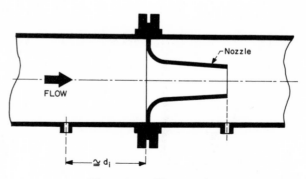

Figure 7-6.   Flow nozzle.

with an orifice. However, flow nozzles are more expensive than orifice plates, although less in cost than venturis.

Flow nozzles are more suitable than orifice plates for metering liquids containing solids. However, they are inferior to venturis for this purpose.

The Pitot Tube

All the head meters considered so far measure mean velocities. In contrast, the pitot tube measures point velocities. The principle of the pitot tube is illustrated in Figure 7–7. At point 1, a small amount of liquid is brought to a standstill. The pressure exerted at this point consists of the static pressure plus the additional pressure required to bring the liquid to rest. The head at point 1 is thus the pressure head plus the velocity head $v^2/2g$, where v is the point linear velocity in this region. The pressure exerted at point 2 is the static pressure only. The head at point 2 is thus the pressure head only. If points 1 and 2 are sufficiently close for frictional head losses to be negligible, then the difference in head Δh between the two points measures the velocity head $v^2/2g$.

Therefore the point velocity v in ft/sec is given by the equation

$$v = \sqrt{2g\Delta h} \qquad\qquad (7\text{–}18)$$

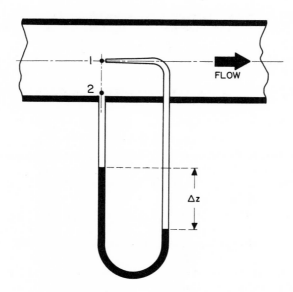

Figure 7-7.   Pitot tube.

where g is the gravitational acceleration 32.2 ft/sec² and Δh is the difference in head between points 1 and 2 measured in ft of liquid. The latter is the same liquid as that flowing through the pipeline.

In practice, a pitot tube usually consists of two concentric tubes parallel to the liquid flow. The inner tube points into the flow and transmits the combined pressure and velocity heads. The outer tube is perforated with small holes which are perpendicular to the direction of flow. Thus the annular space transmits only the pressure head.

Pitot tubes are not widely used for process measurements.[3] Although they are inexpensive and have negligible permanent pressure losses, they are highly sensitive to fouling. Furthermore, the required alignment is critical. The mean velocity in the pipe can be calculated from a single measurement only if the velocity distribution across the pipe is known.

Differential Pressure Measurement

The traditional instrument for measuring the pressure differential across the various primary elements discussed above is the U-tube manometer. This is shown schematically in Figure 7–8. Liquid from the high pressure tap of the flowmeter transmits pressure to arm 1 of the manometer. Similarly, liquid from the low pressure tap of the flowmeter transmits pressure to arm 2 of the manometer. The liquid in arm 1 of the manometer is separated from the liquid in arm 2 by an immiscible liquid of a higher density. The most common liquid used is mercury. Let the densities of the process liquid and the mercury be ρ and ρ_m lb/cu ft, respectively.

In Figure 7–8, consider the heights of the mercury in the two arms of the manometer. Let the lower mercury level a arbitrarily have a vertical height $z_a = 0$. Thus the higher mercury level b has a vertical height $z_b = \Delta z$ where Δz ft is the vertical distance between the two mercury levels.

At equilibrium, no flow occurs in the manometer. Consider the pressures at levels a and b in the two arms of the manometer.

Let the pressures at level b in the manometer be P_1 and P_2 poundals/sq ft in arm 1 and arm 2, respectively.

Thus the pressures at level a in the manometer are calculated to be

$$(P_1 + \Delta z \rho g) \text{ poundals/sq ft in arm 1}$$

and

$$(P_2 + \Delta z \rho_m g) \text{ poundals/sq ft in arm 2}$$

However, the pressures at level a in the two arms of the manometer must be equal since a continuous column of mercury connects the two points.

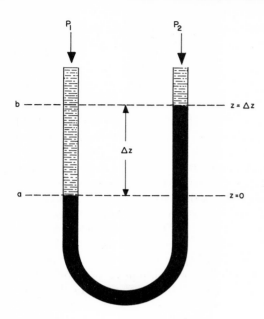

Figure 7-8.   U-tube manometer.

 Process liquid

Liquid with a high density which is immiscible with the process liquid

Therefore,

$$P_1 + \Delta z \rho g = P_2 + \Delta z \rho_m g$$

which can be written as

$$P_1 - P_2 = \Delta z (\rho_m - \rho) g \qquad (7\text{-}19)$$

where $P_1 - P_2$ is the required pressure differential across the flowmeter in poundals/sq ft.

If the pressures P_1 and P_2 are in psi, Equation (7–19) becomes

$$144 \, (P_1 - P_2) \, g_c = \Delta z (\rho_m - \rho) g$$

which can be rewritten as

$$P_1 - P_2 = \left[\frac{(\rho_m - \rho) g}{144 g_c} \right] \Delta z \qquad (7\text{-}20)$$

Alternatively, the required pressure differential across the flowmeter may be expressed as the difference in head Δh measured in ft of process liquid where

$$\Delta h = 144(P_1 - P_2)g_c/\rho g = \Delta z(\rho_m - \rho)/\rho \qquad (7\text{--}21)$$

In Equation (7–21), $P_1 - P_2$ is the pressure differential in psi. If the manometer is replaced by a pressure gauge, the differential pressure may be read directly in psi.

Modified versions of the simple manometer shown in Figure 7–8 are also in common use. For small pressure differences, the manometer may be inclined at some angle ϕ to the vertical. In this case, the distance between the interfaces in the two arms of the manometer is increased to $\Delta z/\cos \phi$. Alternatively, an inverted manometer may be employed. This allows a metering liquid of lighter density than the process liquid to be used.

In some applications, bellows and diaphragm-type units have replaced the traditional visual manometer for the measurement of differential pressures. Differential converters are also used. In these units, the differential pressure across a primary element is balanced by an air pressure acting in a weight beam system.

MECHANICAL AND ELECTROMAGNETIC FLOWMETERS

Area Flowmeters

The most common instrument in this class is the rotameter. In head flowmeters, the constriction area is fixed and the pressure drop varies as the flow rate alters. In the rotameter, the pressure drop is held constant and the constriction area varies as the flow rate alters. A schematic drawing of a rotameter is shown in Figure 7–9. It normally consists of a vertical tapered glass tube in which a float is free to move up or down. The float is subjected to the downward action of gravity and the upward force of the flowing liquid. The float maintains a steady position when these forces are balanced. This position is a function of the liquid velocity in the tube. The latter is marked with a scale which is calibrated for a given liquid to give flow velocity at each scale reading.

Rotameters are seldom used in pipe sizes larger than 2 inches since their cost becomes prohibitive. Furthermore, the flow rate must be read at the instrument rather than on a control panel. However, transmitters are available which convert the float position into usable pneumatic or electrical signals. The principle advantage of the rotameter is its 10 to 1 linear scale.

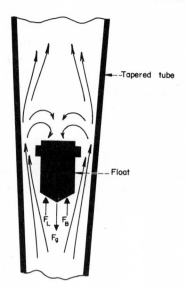

Figure 7-9.   Rotameter.

Positive Displacement Flowmeters

Unlike the liquid flowmeters so far discussed, positive displacement flowmeters are largely unaffected by viscosity and density changes. Positive displacement flowmeters are widely used as flow totalizers for accounting purposes. They operate by discharging measured volumes of liquid. The flow rate may be obtained by timing this discharge over a convenient time interval. Auxiliary equipment is required to do this.

A typical positive displacement of liquid flowmeter is the rotary disk meter shown in Figure 7–10. A pivoted disk is contained inside a cylindrical measuring chamber. Liquid entering the measuring chamber causes the disk to wobble. The disk, in turn, forces liquid out of the discharge side of the chamber. A counter measures the number of wobbles in a given time; from this information the volumetric flow rates can be obtained.

Rotary disk meters cannot be used to measure low flow rates since substantial amounts of liquid bypass the flow sensitive components.[5] Piston and oval gear meters are used to measure low liquid flow rates.

Positive displacement flowmeters are particularly vulnerable to dirt or foreign matter in the process liquid.

Velocity Flowmeters

Modern velocity flowmeters usually consist of a nonmagnetic casing, a bladed rotor freely suspended in the liquid flow path with its axis of rotation in line with the flow, and an electromagnetic pickup. The most commonly used rotors are propellers and turbines. The rotor, which is suspended on ball bearings, turns in the liquid flow stream at a rate proportional to the flow rate. The rotating propeller or turbine cuts through the lines of force of an electric field produced by an adjacent induction coil. The electrical pulse output from the induction coil pickup is amplified and fed to readout instruments or recorders to give either total flow or flow rate. Figure 7–11 shows a typical turbine flowmeter. Flow straighteners are commonly used on the upstream side of the rotor. In addition, it is recommended that a straight pipe section, ten diameters in length, should be installed on the upstream side of the flowmeter. Similarly, a straight pipe section, five diameters in length, should be installed on the downstream side of the flowmeter.

Figure 7-10.   Rotary disk meter. (*Courtesy Rockwell Mfg. Co.*)

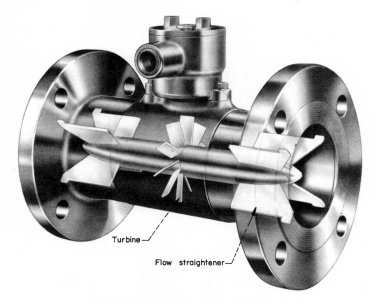

Figure 7-11. Turbine flowmeter. (*Courtesy Rockwell Mfg. Co.*)

Alternatively, the rotor in a velocity flowmeter may be mechanically linked to the readout instrument. Propeller units are widely used in this way for direct totalization.

If qualitative flow indication is required, the equipment used is of comparatively simple design. A variety of sight flow indicators are available which register flow or no flow conditions by means of a moving turbine, bob or flapper positioned in the liquid stream. Figure 7–12 illustrates this type of indicator.

Electromagnetic Flowmeters

The flowmeters considered so far all require the use of some kind of restriction in the flow line. These restrictions lead to additional frictional head losses in the systems. The electromagnetic flowmeter does not suffer from this disadvantage. The unit consists of a straight length of non-magnetic pipe containing no bends or obstructions through which the liquid flows. Thus, frictional head losses are no greater than those occurring in a similar length of straight pipeline. The nonmagnetic pipe is normally lined with electrically insulating material. Two small electrodes, diametrically opposite each, other are sealed in flush with its interior surface. A magnetic field is provided by coil windings mounted on the outside of the

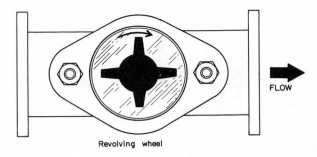

Revolving wheel

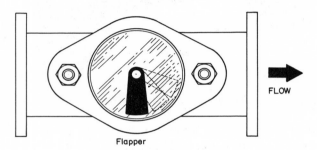

Flapper

Figure 7-12. Sight flow indicators.

nonmagnetic pipe. When a conductor is moved in a magnetic field, a voltage is induced in it directly proportional to the number of magnetic lines of force cut by the conductor in unit time. In this case, the flowing liquid is the conductor. A voltage which is directly proportional to the liquid velocity is induced in the liquid. This is detected by the electrodes. Usually an alternating magnetic field is used. Thus, the voltage which appears across the flowmeter electrodes will, in this case, be alternating.

The output from the electrodes is amplified and then transmitted to either readout instruments or recorders. Electromagnetic flowmeters can only be used to meter liquids having some electrical conductivity. All hydrocarbons are excluded. These units are unaffected by variations in liquid viscosity, density or temperature. They are especially suitable for metering liquids containing suspended solids. Entrained gases or heavy fouling of the walls will cause errors.[3] Electromagnetic flowmeters are unaffected by turbulence or variations in velocity profile. They can thus be mounted in any position in the overall system regardless of the proximity of valves, bends, fittings, etc. Their principal disadvantage is the high initial cost.

Mass Flowmeters

All the flowmeters so far considered measure volume or volumetric rate. Since mass is the product of volume and density, these flowmeters can be adapted to measure mass or mass rate if the liquid density is measured and the flow and density signals are coordinated.

In recent years, direct reading mass flowmeters have been developed in which the sensing element is simultaneously affected by density and flow velocity. These operate on the angular momentum principle. The sensing element consists of a cylindrical impeller and turbine both containing tubes through which the liquid flows. A synchronous motor drives the impeller at a constant speed through a magnetic coupling. The angular momentum given to the liquid by the impeller is proportional to the mass flow rate. The liquid leaving the impeller enters the cylindrical turbine which removes all the angular momentum from the liquid stream. The resulting torque on the turbine is proportional to the mass flow rate. This torque is transferred to a gyro-integrating mechanism via a magnetic coupling. The rotation of the gyroscope is registered by a cyclometer which totalizes the mass flow of liquid.

DESIGN CONSIDERATIONS AND CALCULATIONS

Orifice Plate Calculations

EXAMPLE

A liquid of density 70 lb/cu ft is pumped by a gear pump through a 4 inch schedule 40 horizontal pipeline at a rate of 200 U.S. gpm. A 2.0 inch diameter orifice with a discharge coefficient C_d of 0.60 is inserted in the line. Calculate the pressure drop in psi, the head loss in ft of liquid and the power loss in hp across the orifice plate. Estimate the differential height in a vertical mercury manometer connected across the orifice plate. The density of mercury is 13.6 g/cc.

The inside diameter of a 4 inch schedule 40 pipe is 4.026 inches and the inside cross-sectional area is 0.08840 sq ft; 1 cu ft = 7.48 U.S. gal, 1 lb = 454 g and 1 cu ft = 28,316 cc.

The mean linear velocity in the pipeline u_1 ft/sec is related to the pressure drop $(P_1 - P_2)$ psi and the head loss Δh ft across the orifice by the equations

$$u_1 = C_d \sqrt{\frac{2g[144\ (P_1 - P_2)\ g_c/\rho g]}{[1 - (d_o/d_1)^4]}} \tag{7-11}$$

and

$$u_1 = C_d \sqrt{\frac{2g\Delta h}{[1 - (d_o/d_1)^4]}} \qquad (7\text{--}15)$$

respectively.

(1) Calculate the mean linear velocity in the pipe u_1 in ft/sec. Since 1 cu ft = 7.48 U.S. gal, 200 U.S. gpm = $200/(7.48 \times 60)$ = 0.446 cu ft/sec. Divide the liquid volume flow 0.446 cu ft/sec by the cross-sectional area 0.08840 sq ft of the 4 inch schedule 40 pipe to obtain the mean linear velocity u_1 in ft/sec. Therefore,

$$u_1 = \frac{0.446}{0.0884} = 5.05 \text{ ft/sec}$$

(2) Evaluate the ratio d_o/d_1 and the value of the dimensionless expression $[1 - (d_o/d_1)^4]$.

$$d_o/d_1 = \frac{2.0}{4.026} = 0.496, \ (d_o/d_1)^4 = 0.0606$$

Therefore, $[1 - (d_o/d_1)^4] = 0.9394$.

(3) Calculate the pressure drop across the orifice plate. Rewrite Equation (7–11) as

$$\frac{u_1^2}{C_d^2} [1 - (d_o/d_1)^4] = 2g[144(P_1 - P_2)g_c/\rho g]$$

and then as

$$(P_1 - P_2) = \frac{u_1^2}{C_d^2}[1 - (d_o/d_1)^4]/2g(144g_c/\rho g)$$

and calculate the value of $(P_1 - P_2)$ in psi. The ratio g_c/g is numerically almost unity, $g = 32.2 \text{ ft/sec}^2$ and $\rho = 70 \text{ lb/cu ft}$. Therefore,

$$(P_1 - P_2) = \frac{(5.05)^2}{(0.60)^2} \times 0.9394/(64.4 \times 144/70)$$

$$= \left(\frac{5.05}{0.60}\right)^2 \times \frac{0.9394 \times 70}{64.4 \times 144} = 0.501 \text{ psi}$$

the pressure drop across the orifice plate.

(4) Calculate the head loss across the orifice plate. Rewrite Equation (7–15) as

$$\Delta h = \frac{u_1^2}{C_d^2}[1 - (d_o/d_1)^4]/2g$$

and calculate the value of Δh in ft. Therefore,

$$\Delta h = \left(\frac{5.05}{0.60}\right)^2 \times \frac{0.9394}{64.4} = 1.03 \text{ ft}$$

the head loss across the orifice in ft of process liquid.

(5) Calculate the power loss across the orifice plate. The mass flow rate W in lb/sec is the product of the liquid density in lb/cu ft and the volumetric flow rate in cu ft/sec. Therefore, $W = 70 \times 0.446 = 31.22$ lb/sec. Since 1 hp $= 550$ ft lb/sec. the power loss across the orifice plate is $\Delta h W/550 = 0.06$ hp.

(6) Estimate the differential height in a vertical mercury manometer connected across the orifice plate. The density of mercury is 13.6 g/cc. In lb/cu ft this becomes $13.6 \times 28,316/454 = 847$ lb/cu ft.

Rewrite Equation (7–21) as $\Delta z = \Delta h \rho/(\rho_m - \rho)$ where Δz is the differential height in ft of mercury of density $\rho_m = 847$ lb/cu ft and Δh is the head loss across the orifice in ft of process liquid of density $\rho = 70$ lb/cu ft. Therefore $\Delta z = 1.03 \times 70/(847 - 70) = 0.0927$ ft, the differential height in the mercury manometer, which is more conveniently written as 1.12 inches.

Scale Error Calculations

The most common instrument scales are the square root and the linear. The former is used with all head flowmeters and the latter with rotameters, velocity flowmeters and electromagnetic flowmeters. Other scales, e.g., logarithmic, are also used, but in this case, the sensing element is specially designed to produce a signal other than its normal output.

Buzzard[1] defines per cent flow rate error Δe as

$$\Delta e = \frac{\text{absolute flow rate error}}{\text{flow rate}} \times 100 = \frac{\Delta Q}{Q} \times 100 \qquad (7\text{–}22)$$

Let Δs be the indicator or recorder error. Since,

$$\frac{\text{absolute flow rate error}}{\text{indicator error}} = \frac{\Delta Q}{\Delta s} \cong \frac{dQ}{ds}$$

Equation (7–22) can be rewritten as

$$\Delta e = \frac{100 \, \Delta s \, dQ}{Q \, ds} \qquad (7\text{–}23)$$

Consider the linear scale. In this case

$$Q = k_1 s \qquad (7\text{-}24)$$

where k_1 is a constant of proportionality between the flow rate Q and the scale reading s.

Differentiate Equation (7–24) to give

$$\frac{dQ}{ds} = k_1 \tag{7–25}$$

Combine Equations (7–23) and (7–25) to give

$$\Delta e = \frac{100 \; \Delta s \; k_1}{Q} \tag{7–26}$$

If the maximum flow rate is written as $Q = 100$ and the maximum scale reading is written as $s = 100$, then Equation (7–26) becomes

$$\Delta e = \frac{100 \; \Delta s}{Q} \tag{7–27}$$

for a linear instrument scale.

Consider the square root scale. In this case

$$Q = k_2 \sqrt{s} \tag{7–28}$$

where k_2 is also a constant.

Differentiate Equation (7–28) to give

$$\frac{dQ}{ds} = \frac{k_2}{2 \sqrt{s}} \tag{7–29}$$

Combine Equations (7–28) and (7–29) to give

$$\frac{dQ}{ds} = \frac{k_2{}^2}{2Q} \tag{7–30}$$

Substitute Equation (7–30) in Equation (7–23) to give

$$\Delta e = \frac{50 \; \Delta s \; k_2{}^2}{Q^2} \tag{7–31}$$

If the maximum flow rate is written as $Q = 100$ and the maximum scale reading is written as $s = 100$, the constant k_2 in Equation (7–28) has a value of 10 and Equation (7–31) becomes

$$\Delta e = \frac{5000 \; \Delta s}{Q^2} \tag{7–32}$$

for a square root instrument scale.

EXAMPLE

Assume that the flowmeter is inherently accurate at all points to 0.5 per cent of the full range,[1] i.e., $\Delta s = 0.5$. Calculate the per cent flow rate error Δe, using a linear scale, from Equation (7–27) for flow rates of 10, 25, 50 and 100 per cent of maximum flow.

(1) Calculate Δe in the equation

$$\Delta e = \frac{100 \, \Delta s}{Q} \tag{7–27}$$

for a flow rate 10 per cent of maximum flow. Since Equation (7–27) was derived on the basis that $Q_{max} = 100$, in this case $Q = 10$. Therefore, $\Delta e = 100 \times 0.5/10 = 5$ per cent is the error in the flow rate measurement.

(2) Calculate the error in the flow rate measurement to be $\Delta e = 100 \times 0.5/25 = 2$ per cent for a flow rate 25 per cent of the maximum.

(3) Calculate $\Delta e = 1$ per cent and $\Delta e = 0.5$ per cent for flow rate 50 and 100 per cent of the maximum, respectively.

EXAMPLE

Repeat the previous example for the case of a square root scale. The appropriate equation to use is Equation (7–32). Again assume $\Delta s = 0.5$.

(1) Calculate Δe in the equation

$$\Delta e = \frac{5000 \, \Delta s}{Q^2} \tag{7–32}$$

for a flow rate 10 per cent of maximum flow. Since Equation (7–32) was derived on the basis that $Q_{max} = 100$, in this case $Q = 10$. Therefore,

$$\Delta e = \frac{5000 \times 0.5}{100} = 25 \text{ per cent}$$

is the error in the flow rate measurement.

(2) Calculate the error in the flow rate measurement to be $\Delta e = 5000 \times 0.5/(25)^2 = 4$ per cent for a flow rate 25 per cent of the maximum.

(3) Calculate the error in the flow rate measurement to be $\Delta e = 5000 \times 0.5/(50)^2 = 1$ per cent for a flow rate 50 per cent of the maximum.

(4) $\Delta e = 0.25$ per cent for a flow rate 100 per cent of the maximum.

The two previous examples show that the square root scale is more accurate than the linear scale at flow rates near the maximum of the scale, but less accurate at flow rates substantially lower than the maximum of the scale.

COMPARISON OF LIQUID FLOWMETERS

A straight comparison of liquid flowmeters is impossible. The best flow-meter to use depends on the particular application. Factors which affect flowmeter selection are: (1) the liquid flow rate; (2) the variation in liquid flow rate; (3) temperature and pressure; (4) the presence of solids or gases in the liquid; (5) corrosiveness and erosiveness of the liquid; (6) liquid viscosity and density; (7) variation in liquid viscosity and density; (8) electrical conductivity of the liquid; (9) the accuracy and type of readout required, e.g., rate, totalization, local or at a distance, etc.

The Orifice Meter

The conventional concentric hole orifice is probably the most widely used liquid flowmeter. Among its advantages are its simple construction, easy installation and replacement. It has no moving parts, it is inexpensive, and a large amount of operating data is available for it.

On the other hand, its calibration is sensitive to erosion and corrosion, it has a nonlinear scale, and disturbances in the flow pattern can lead to substantial errors. Furthermore, it is affected by viscosity changes, and solids in the liquid tend to collect at the orifice plate. Other disadvantages of the orifice meter are the restriction in the flow line and the high permanent pressure losses.

Costs do not vary much with line size. An orifice plate with a manometer readout indicator costs about $120. The same orifice with a differential pressure gauge indicator costs about $200.[7]

Other Head Flowmeters

Like the orifice, the other head flowmeters suffer from the disadvantage of a nonlinear scale. Thus head flowmeters are unsuitable for measuring flow rates which vary widely because of the large inaccuracies at the lower end of the scale.

Venturis and nozzles both measure greater flow rates than the same size orifice plate. Moreover, both these units are superior to orifice plates in their ability to handle liquids containing suspended solids and in their substantially lower permanent pressure losses. Venturis are accurate to about 0.75 per cent.

Mechanical and Electromagnetic Flowmeters

Rotameters have the advantages of a linear scale, visible indication of flow and good ability to handle liquids containing solids. They have the disadvantage of being affected by viscosity and density changes. Furthermore, they have to be used vertically. Their accuracy is in the range 0.5 to 2.0 per cent. A 2 inch line size rotameter with stainless steel fittings costs about $270.[7] Approximate maximum pressure and temperature limits are 500 psi and 300°F, respectively.

Positive displacement meters have the advantage of being unaffected by viscosity and density changes. A typical cost for a 4 inch line size rotary disk unit with a bronze or galvanized iron body is $650.[7] Rotary disk meters are accurate to about 1 per cent.

Turbine flowmeters are available with accuracies as high as 0.25 per cent. A typical cost for a 2 inch line size unit is $1600 with a recorder. Approximate maximum pressure and temperature limits for turbine meters are 5000 psi and 500°F, respectively.

Electromagnetic flowmeters have the advantage of no restrictions in the flow line. A typical cost for a 4 inch line size unit is $1800 with a recorder. Approximate maximum pressure and temperature limits for electromagnetic flowmeters are 1500 psi and 500°F, respectively.

Angular momentum mass flowmeters are priced at $3000 and upward.

NOMENCLATURE

A_1 cross-sectional flow area of pipe, sq ft
A_o cross-sectional flow area of orifice hole, sq ft
A_2 smallest cross-sectional area of flow, sq ft
C_d discharge coefficient (dimensionless)
d_o orifice hole diameter, ft
d_1 inside pipe diameter, ft
d_2 diameter of smallest cross-sectional area of flow, ft
g gravitational acceleration, 32.2 ft/sec^2
g_c conversion factor, 32.174 lb$_m$ ft/lb$_f$ sec^2
hp   horsepower
k flow coefficient (dimensionless)
P pressure, psi or poundals/sq ft
psi   pounds per square inch
u mean linear velocity of liquid inside pipe, ft/sec
v linear velocity of liquid at a point in a pipe, ft/sec
W mass flow rate of liquid, lb/sec
α_1 factor in Equation (7–1), (dimensionless)
α_2 factor in Equation (7–1), (dimensionless)
ρ density of liquid, lb/cu ft
Δh difference in head across orifice, ft
Δz difference in vertical height, ft
ϕ angle of inclination of manometer to vertical

REFERENCES

1. Buzzard,W., *Chem. Eng.*, **66**, No. 5 (1959).
2. Coulson,J. M., and Richardson,J. F., "Chemical Engineering," Vol. 1, p. 110, New York, The Macmillan Co., 1964.
3. Driskell,L. R., *Chem. Eng.*, **70**, No. 5 (1963).
4. Foust, A. S., Wenzel, L. A., Clump, C. W., Maus, L., and Anderson, L. B., "Principles of Unit Operations," p. 23, New York, John Wiley & Sons, Inc., 1964.
5. Keller, G. D., *Chem. Eng.*, **71**, No. 20 (1964).
6. Larian, M. G., "Fundamentals of Chemical Engineering Operations," p. 49, Englewood Cliffs, N. J., Prentice-Hall, Inc., 1958.
7. Liptak,B. G., *Chem. Eng.*, **69**, No. 6 (1962).
8. Ziemke,M. C., and McCallie,B. G., *Chem. Eng.*, **71**, No. 19 (1964).

CHAPTER 8

Transport of Slurries in Pipelines

A liquid containing solid particles in suspension is called a slurry. It is common practice to transport solid materials by mixing them with a liquid and pumping the resultant slurry through a pipeline. Water is the most widely used carrier liquid. Slurries can be divided into two classes:[10] settling and nonsettling.

Nonsettling Slurries

When a high concentration of finely divided solid particles is suspended in a liquid, the resultant slurry may be nonsettling. Alternatively, the solid particles may settle so slowly that the slurry may be considered nonsettling for all practical purposes.

Nonsettling homogeneous slurries exhibit the same flow behavior as true liquids. They may either be Newtonian or non-Newtonian, although the latter are more common. Thus nonsettling homogeneous slurries can be pumped through a pipeline either in laminar or turbulent flow.

Examples of nonsettling slurries are finely crushed limestone or clay in water and finely crushed coal in either water or oil.

A number of nonsettling slurries have Bingham plastic characteristics. In this case, when the force applied to the pipe cross-section is less than the yield point, the mixture is elastically compressed and liquid is squeezed out to the periphery of the plug.[15] This liquid provides lubrication between the plug and the pipe wall. For a given velocity through a pipe, plug flow provides a lower frictional head loss than either laminar or turbulent flow. It has been found that plug flow is the most economical and practical way of transporting coal slurries through pipelines.[15]

Other examples of nonsettling slurries are milk, which behaves as a thixotropic liquid, and liquid detergent slurries, which are largely pseudo-plastic. Excessive shear can cause liquid detergent slurries to settle.

Settling Slurries

Settling slurries contain larger solid particles at lower concentrations than nonsettling slurries. In contrast to the latter, the solid particles in

291

settling slurries do not alter the viscosity of the conveying liquid. Thus settling slurries are two-phase heterogeneous mixtures in which the liquid and the solid particles exhibit their own characteristics. A common example of a settling slurry is finely divided sand in water.

In contrast to nonsettling slurries, settling slurries cannot be transported in laminar flow. Turbulence must be present in the pipeline to prevent the solid particles from settling. Turbulent flow is characterized by the presence of eddy currents emanating in all directions. In horizontal flow, the eddy momentum vector perpendicular to the axis of the pipe enables the solid particles to be suspended in the liquid.[10]

For settling slurries, a minimum velocity exists below which the solid particles will settle out in a horizontal pipeline. In addition, there is a velocity which results in the minimum pressure drop across the pipeline. These two velocities have approximately the same value.[13] Thus settling slurries should be transported through pipelines at velocities which just prevent the solid particles from settling out.

Alternatively, solid particles can be transported in liquids by the process of saltation.[1] In this case, the solid particles are not suspended but bounce and roll along the bottom of a horizontal pipe.[9] Saltation results if the solid particles are large or dense and the liquid flow velocity is low.

Heterogeneous slurry systems are characterized by the settling velocities of the solid particles.

Settling Velocity, Particle Size and Drag Coefficient

The resistance to motion of a solid particle in a liquid is a function of the viscosity μ and density ρ of the liquid, the density ρ_s of the solid particle, and the relative velocity v between the solid particle and the liquid.

From dimensional analysis, the following equation can be derived for the retarding force F on a solid particle falling through a liquid:

$$F = C_d A \rho \frac{v^2}{2} \tag{8-1}$$

In Equation (8-1), C_d is the dimensionless drag coefficient and A is the projected area of the solid particle.

The retarding force on a solid particle moving relative to a liquid is usually made up of skin friction and form drag. As a result of skin friction, the liquid immediately in contact with the solid particle is at rest. Form drag results from the thickening of the boundary layer and its subsequent separation from the solid particle. This gives rise to eddies in the wake of the solid particle with a consequent dissipation of energy. At low velocities, no separation of the boundary layer from the surface of the solid occurs and the entire force on the particle is due to skin friction.

Drag coefficient data are available for various kinds of particles in the form of dimensionless plots of C_d vs Reynolds number N_{Re} where, in this case, $N_{Re} = \rho v d_s / \mu$.

Consider the forces on a spherical solid particle of diameter d_s falling through a liquid. The appropriate equation can be written as

$$\frac{\pi d_s^3}{6}(\rho_s - \rho)g - C_d\left(\frac{\pi d_s^2}{4}\right)\rho\frac{v^2}{2} = \frac{\pi d_s^3}{6}(\rho_s - \rho)\frac{dv}{dt} \qquad (8\text{--}2)$$

where $\pi d_s^2/4$ is the projected area of the spherical particle and dv/dt is its acceleration.

When the particle reaches its terminal falling velocity v_t, i.e., when acceleration has ceased, Equation (8–2) can be written as

$$\frac{\pi d_s^3}{6}(\rho_s - \rho)g - C_d\left(\frac{\pi d_s^2}{4}\right)\rho\frac{v_t^2}{2} = 0 \qquad (8\text{--}3)$$

Equation (8–3) can be rearranged in the form

$$\frac{4}{3}\left(\frac{\rho_s - \rho}{\rho}\right) = \frac{C_d v_t^2}{g d_s} \qquad (8\text{--}4)$$

In the case of the streamline flow of a spherical particle in a liquid, i.e., for $N_{Re} < 1$, the dimensionless drag coefficient C_d is related to the Reynolds number N_{Re} by the equation

$$C_d = \frac{24}{N_{Re}} \qquad (8\text{--}5)$$

Combine Equation (8–5) with Equation (8–4) and rearrange to give

$$v_t = \frac{d_s^2(\rho_s - \rho)g}{18\mu} \qquad (8\text{--}6)$$

Equation (8–6) is known as Stokes' law for spherical particles moving in steady state flow in the laminar flow region.

Equation (8–4) can also be written in the form

$$v_t = \left(\frac{g d_s}{C_d}\right)^{1/2}\left[\frac{4}{3}\left(\frac{\rho_s - \rho}{\rho}\right)\right]^{1/2} \qquad (8\text{--}7)$$

where v_t is the terminal falling velocity of the spherical particle. For non-spherical particles, an analogous equation can be written as follows:

$$v_t = \left(\frac{\psi g d_s}{C_d}\right)^{1/2}\left[\frac{4}{3}\left(\frac{\rho_s - \rho}{\rho}\right)\right]^{1/2} \tag{8-8}$$

where ψ is a dimensionless shape coefficient for the particle and d_s is the diameter of a sphere having the same volume as the particle. The dimensionless shape coefficient ψ is the ratio of the cross-sectional area of a spherical particle of diameter d_s to the largest cross-sectional area of the nonspherical particle. The value of ψ cannot be greater than unity.

Condolios and Chapus[1] have defined an apparent drag coefficient C_d' as

$$C_d' = \left(\frac{C_d g d_s}{\psi v_t}\right)\left[\frac{3}{4}\left(\frac{\rho}{\rho_s - \rho}\right)\right] \tag{8-9}$$

where C_d is the true drag coefficient of the particle. The apparent drag coefficient C_d' characterizes a Froude number of decantation.[1]

From Equation (8–6) it is seen that in the Stokes region of flow, i.e., $N_{Re} < 1$, the terminal falling velocity v_t of a particle is proportional to the square of its diameter and inversely proportional to the liquid viscosity. In the turbulent region of particle flow $N_{Re} > 1000$, the dimensionless drag coefficient C_d is constant. From Equation (8–8), it is seen that in this region, the terminal falling velocity v_t of a particle is proportional to the square root of its diameter and independent of the liquid viscosity. This relationship is known as Rittinger's law. Particles obeying this law are always transported by saltation.

On the basis of a particle specific gravity of 2.65, particles up to 0.2 mm in diameter obey Stokes' law when settling in water. On the same basis, particles with diameters over 2.0 mm obey Rittinger's law.[1] Particles in between these limits settle out according to laws which are between those of Stokes and Rittinger.

For a number of particles of a given size and density, the settling velocity is reduced as the concentration increases. The latter results in an increase in the drag coefficient.[6]

Minimum and Standard Velocities for Settling Slurries

Below the minimum velocity, the turbulence in a horizontal pipe is insufficient to maintain all of the particles in a settling slurry in suspension. At the minimum velocity, a concentration gradient exists from the top to the bottom of a horizontal pipe. Howard[8] measured this concentration gradient for a sand-water mixture flowing in a horizontal pipe at velocities above the minimum. As the flow velocity is increased, a point is reached where the concentration gradient disappears, i.e., the flow becomes homogeneous. Spells[14] called this second limiting velocity the standard velocity. He also called the flow region between the minimum and the standard velocities the heterogeneous flow region.

Spells[14] also defined an equivalent true liquid as a liquid having the same density as the slurry and the same velocity as the transporting liquid.

The density ρ_m of the slurry mixture is related to the volume fraction x_v of the solids in the slurry by the equation

$$x_v = \frac{\rho_m - \rho}{\rho_s - \rho} \tag{8-10}$$

where ρ_s and ρ are the densities of the solid particles and the transporting liquid, respectively.

The weight fraction x_w of the solids in the slurry, i.e., weight of solids divided by the weight of mixture, is related to the volume fraction x_v by the equation

$$x_w = \frac{x_v \rho_s}{\rho_m} \tag{8-11}$$

Equations (8-10) and (8-11) can be rearranged to give the density ρ_m of the slurry mixture in terms of the volume fraction and weight fraction, respectively, as follows:

$$\rho_m = x_v(\rho_s - \rho) + \rho \tag{8-12}$$

and

$$\rho_m = \frac{\rho}{\left[1 - \dfrac{x_w(\rho_s - \rho)}{\rho_s}\right]} \tag{8-13}$$

In the heterogeneous flow region, the frictional head losses in a horizontal pipe are substantially greater than for the equivalent true liquid.[14] At the standard velocity, the frictional head losses in a horizontal pipe become identical with those for the equivalent true liquid.

Spells[14] analyzed the experimental data of a number of investigators for aqueous slurries of sands, boiler ash and lime flowing in horizontal pipes. He obtained the following empirical equation:

$$\left(\frac{u_1^2}{gd_s}\right)\left(\frac{\rho}{\rho_s - \rho}\right) = 0.0251\left(\frac{\rho_m u_1 d_i}{\mu}\right)^{0.775} \tag{8-14}$$

In Equation (8–14), u_1 is the mean minimum linear liquid velocity in a horizontal pipe of inside diameter d_i; ρ ρ_s and ρ_m are the densities of the liquid, the solid particles and the slurry mixture, respectively; d_s is the nominal particle diameter; g is the gravitational acceleration, and μ is the liquid viscosity.

In Equation (8–14), the term (u_1^2/gd_s) is a dimensionless Froude number and the term $(\rho_m u_1 d_i/\mu)$ is a dimensionless Reynolds number. The Froude and Reynolds numbers represent the ratio of the applied to the opposing gravitational and viscous forces, respectively.

Spells[14] also obtained the equation

$$\left(\frac{u_2^2}{gd_s}\right)\left(\frac{\rho}{\rho_s - \rho}\right) = 0.074\left(\frac{\rho_m u_2 d_i}{\mu}\right)^{0.775} \tag{8–15}$$

where u_2 is the mean standard linear liquid velocity in a horizontal pipe.

Equations (8–14) and (8–15) can be rearranged as follows to give the mean minimum and standard linear liquid velocities:

$$u_1 = \left[0.0251 gd_s\left(\frac{\rho_m d_i}{\mu}\right)^{0.775}\left(\frac{\rho_s - \rho}{\rho}\right)\right]^{1/1.225} \tag{8–16}$$

and

$$u_2 = \left[0.0741 gd_s\left(\frac{\rho_m d_i}{\mu}\right)^{0.775}\left(\frac{\rho_s - \rho}{\rho}\right)\right]^{1/1.225} \tag{8–17}$$

where the various terms are in consistent absolute units.

Equations (8–14), (8–15), (8–16) and (8–17) are based on experimental data for solid particle diameters in the range 0.06 to 0.6 mm and pipe diameters of 1 to 12 inches. Equations (8–16) and (8–17) can be used to estimate the minimum and standard velocities for slurries flowing in horizontal pipelines as follows:

EXAMPLE

Consider a sand-water mixture flowing in a 10 inch schedule 40 horizontal steel pipeline of internal diameter 10.02 inches. The volume fraction x_v of the solids in the slurry is 0.25. The sand particles have a nominal diameter of 0.1 mm and a density of 146.0 lb/cu ft. The transporting water can be taken to have a density of 62.4 lb/cu ft and a viscosity of 1.0 cp. Calculate the minimum and standard velocities from Equations (8–16) and (8–17), respectively. Calculate the Reynolds numbers for the equivalent true liquid at the minimum and standard velocities.

(1) Calculate the density ρ_m of the slurry mixture from Equation (8–12):

$$\rho_m = x_v(\rho_s - \rho) + \rho = x_v\rho_s + (1 - x_v)\rho$$

Therefore,

$$\rho_m = 0.25 \times 146.0 + (1 - 0.25)\,62.4 = 83.3 \text{ lb/cu ft}$$

(2) Calculate the dimensionless term $\left(\dfrac{\rho_s - \rho}{\rho}\right)$ to be

$$\left(\frac{146.0 - 62.4}{62.4}\right) = 1.34$$

(3) Calculate the term $(\rho_m d_i/\mu)$ to be

$$\frac{(83.3 \text{ lb/cu ft}) \, (10.02 \text{ inch}) \, (1 \text{ ft/12 inch})}{(1 \text{ cp}) \, (0.000672 \text{ lb/ft sec/cp})} = 1.037 \times 10^5 \text{ sec/ft}$$

(4) Calculate $(\rho_m d_i/\mu)^{0.775}$ to be 7800.

(5) Calculate the term $g d_s$ to be
$(32.2 \text{ ft/sec}^2) \, (0.1 \text{ mm}) \, (1 \text{ inch/25.4 mm}) \, (1 \text{ ft/12 inch}) = 1.056 \times 10^{-2} \text{ ft}^2/\text{sec}^2$

(6) Calculate the term

$$\left[0.0251 g d_s \left(\frac{\rho_m d_i}{\mu}\right)^{0.775} \left(\frac{\rho_s - \rho}{\rho}\right) \right]$$

in consistent absolute units to be

$$(0.0251 \times 1.056 \times 10^{-2} \times 7800 \times 1.34) = 2.775$$

(7) Calculate the minimum velocity u_1 from Equation (8–16) to be

$$u_1 = (2.775)^{1/1.225} = 2.3 \text{ ft/sec}$$

(8) Calculate the standard velocity u_2 from Equation (8–17) to be

$$u_2 = (8.16)^{1/1.225} = 5.5 \text{ ft/sec}$$

(9) The Reynolds number N_{Re} for the equivalent true liquid at the minimum velocity u_1 is

$$N_{\text{Re}} = \frac{\rho_m u_1 d_i}{\mu}$$

Calculate this to be

$$N_{\text{Re}} = \frac{(83.3 \text{ lb/cu ft}) \ (2.3 \text{ ft/sec}) \ (10.02 \text{ inch}) \ (1 \text{ ft/12 inch})}{(1 \text{ cp}) \ (0.000672 \text{ lb/ft sec/cp})}$$

$$= 238{,}000$$

(10) The Reynolds number N_{Re} for the equivalent true liquid at the standard velocity u_2 is

$$N_{\text{Re}} = \frac{\rho_m u_2 d_i}{\mu}$$

Calculate this to be

$$N_{\text{Re}} = \frac{(83.3 \text{ lb/cu ft}) \ (5.5 \text{ ft/sec}) \ (10.02 \text{ inch}) \ (1 \text{ ft/12 inch})}{(1 \text{ cp}) \ (0.000672 \text{ lb/ft sec/cp})}$$

$$= 570{,}000$$

It should be noted that these Reynolds numbers are far greater than the critical value of 2100 which normally marks the transition from laminar to turbulent flow for liquids in pipes. Clearly for slurry flow, the critical Reynolds number has no meaning.

Equation (8–15) can also be rearranged to enable the pipe size to be calculated for a given standard velocity.

Hughmark[9] also analyzed the experimental data of a number of investigators for aqueous slurries of various materials. He made the following observations:

(1) The standard velocity is independent of pipe size in the diameter range 0.5 to 3.0 inches.

(2) The standard velocity is independent of particle size in the diameter range 0.0145 to 0.08 inch.

(3) For slurries having a distribution of particle sizes, the mean particle diameter should be taken as the diameter of the particle whose surface area is equal to the average surface area of all the particles.

Condolios and Chapus[2] observed the deposit of solids from a slurry in a horizontal pipe. They noted that from the moment particles start to settle and the deposit builds up, the flow velocity u_f in the free part of the pipe increases and adjusts itself according to the equation

$$\frac{u_1}{\sqrt{gd_i}} = \frac{u_f}{\sqrt{4gr_h}} \qquad (8\text{–}18)$$

where r_h is the hydraulic radius of the cross-sectional area available for flow. In Equation (8–18), u_f is the new minimum velocity for the flow region above the deposit.

Pressure Gradients for Settling Slurries

For sand-water mixtures flowing above the minimum velocity in horizontal pipes, Durand and Condolios[5] found the following equation to fit the experimental data:

$$\frac{i - i_w}{x_v i_w} = 180\left[\left(\frac{u^2}{gd_i}\right)(C_d)^{1/2}\right]^{-3/2} \tag{8–19}$$

where i and i_w are the head losses per unit length of pipe for the mixture and for clear water, respectively, x_v is the volume fraction of solids in the mixture, u is the mean linear liquid velocity in the pipe, d_i is the inside diameter of the pipe, g is the gravitational acceleration and C_d is the dimensionless drag coefficient for the solid particles.

Condolios and Chapus[2] rewrote Equation (8–19) in the more general form

$$\frac{i - i_w}{x_v i_w} = 180\left[\left(\frac{u^2}{gd_i}\right)(C_d')^{1/2}\right]^{-3/2} \tag{8–20}$$

where C_d' is the apparent drag coefficient defined by Equation (8–9).

Condolios and Chapus[2] found Equation (8–20) to be valid for sand-water mixtures of different grain sizes if the apparent drag coefficient is defined by the equation

$$(C_d')^{1/2} = y_1(C_{d1}')^{1/2} + y_2(C_{d2}')^{1/2} + \cdots + y_n(C_{d3}')^{1/2} \tag{8–21}$$

where y_1, y_2, etc., are the weight fractions of various sizes of sand graded within as narrow bands as practicable.

Condolios and Chapus[2] found that the presence of fines in a coarse slurry decreases the frictional head losses in a horizontal pipe to a much greater extent than might be expected from their relative proportion in the solids.

Figure 8–1 shows a typical head loss plot for fine sand-water slurries flowing in a horizontal pipe. The frictional head loss in ft of water per ft of pipe is plotted against the mean linear liquid velocity in ft/sec on log-log coordinates for various sand concentrations expressed as the volume fraction x_v. The plot represents the experimental data of Condolios and Chapus[2] for water containing sand of nominal diameter 0.44 mm.

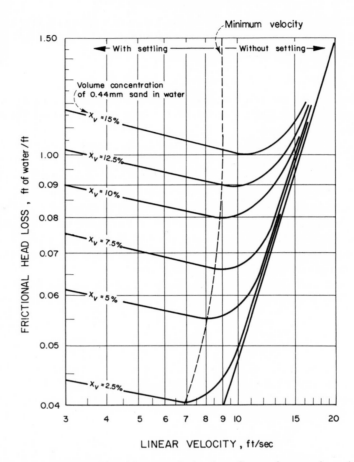

Figure 8-1. Frictional head loss vs velocity for a fine sand-water slurry in a
horizontal pipe (lines of Condolios and Chapus[2]).

Figure 8–1 shows that for the higher velocities, the frictional head losses
approach those for clear water. As the flow velocity is decreased, the frictional head losses are reduced. The reduction in head loss is greatest
for clear water and least for the slurry of highest solids concentration.
Below the minimum velocity for a given slurry concentration, the frictional head loss no longer decreases with a reduction in flow velocity. In
fact, below this point, the frictional head loss has a tendency to rise as
the flow velocity is reduced. The rise in this region is much greater for
coarse sand than for fine sand. The plot for coarse sand-water slurries
also differs from Figure 8–1 in that at high velocities, the frictional head

losses no longer approach those for clear water. In this case, the curve for each slurry concentration approaches its own straight line. Each of these straight lines is parallel to the clear water line but is offset upward by an amount depending on the concentration of solids in the slurry.

The use of a homogeneous non-Newtonian slurry as the conveying medium in place of clear water shows great promise as a means of substantially reducing the frictional head losses in the transport of coarse materials.[2]

So far, the transport of slurries through horizontal pipes only has been considered. Durand[4] measured pressure drops of sand-water slurries in vertical pipes. Worster and Denny[16] made similar measurements in vertical pipes for coal-water and gravel-water slurries. From both investigations, it was concluded that the pressure drops for the slurries were the same as for clear water flowing at the same mean linear liquid velocity, provided that allowance was made for the static head of solids in the vertical pipe.

Newitt, Richardson and Gliddon[12] also carried out experiments in vertical pipes. They used aqueous slurries of pebbles, zircon, manganese dioxide, perspex and various kinds of sand in 1 inch and 2 inch diameter pipes. Their results were satisfactorily correlated by the following equation:

$$\frac{i - i_w}{x_v i_w} = 0.0037 \left(\frac{g d_i}{u^2} \right)^{1/2} \left(\frac{d_i}{d_s} \right) \left(\frac{\rho_s}{\rho} \right)^2 \tag{8-22}$$

In Equation (8–22), u is the mean velocity in ft/sec defined as:

$$u = \frac{\text{volumetric flow rate of slurry}}{\text{cross-sectional area of pipe}} \tag{8-23}$$

The solid particles hydraulically conveyed in a vertical pipe travel at a mean velocity which is lower than the mean velocity of the transporting liquid. This results from the tendency of the solid particles to settle. Thus the volume fraction x_v in Equation (8–22) refers to the delivered concentration which is less than the volume fraction in the vertical pipeline.

Also in Equation (8–22), d_i and d_s are the inside pipe and nominal particle diameters, respectively, in ft and ρ_s and ρ are the densities of the solid particles and the transporting liquid, respectively, in lb/cu ft. In this case, water was used as the transporting liquid.

Particles of slurries conveyed in vertical pipes are subjected to forces which cause them to rotate and move toward the axis of the pipe. This phenomenon which is most pronounced with large velocity gradients is known as the Magnus effect.

In the transport of settling slurries in horizontal pipes, a minimum liquid velocity must be exceeded to prevent solids from settling on the bottom of the pipe. In vertical pipes, this problem does not arise, since the slurry will always be conveyed provided the liquid velocity exceeds the settling velocity of the particles.

Power Requirements for Transporting Settling Slurries

The horsepower required to transport aqueous slurries per mile of horizontal pipe at a pumping efficiency of 60 per cent can be calculated from the following equation:[6]

$$\text{hp/mile} = 997iQ \qquad (8\text{--}24)$$

In Equation (8–24), i is the frictional head loss in ft of water per ft of pipe and Q is the slurry throughput in cu ft/sec.

Alternatively, Equation (8–24) can be written in terms of inside diameter as

$$\text{hp/mile} = 782id_i^2u \qquad (8\text{--}25)$$

where u is the mean slurry velocity in ft/sec and d_i is the inside pipe diameter in ft.

Stepanoff[15] has pointed out that the true criterion of the economy of hydraulic transport of solids is the conveyance efficiency. He defines this as the weight of solids delivered per unit power expended.

Condolios and Chapus[2] have given the following approximate horsepower requirements for the aqueous slurry transport of 100 tons/hr of materials of the same density such as gravel, sand or cement slurry:

   6 hp/ton/mile for gravel particles larger than 2 mm in diameter,
   2.2 hp/ton/mile for sand particles of mean diameter 0.4 mm with a
        size range 0.15 to 0.7 mm,
   0.12 hp/ton/mile for raw cement particles of mean diameter 0.045
        to 0.050 mm with a size range 0.002 to 0.100 mm.

These figures show that it requires about fifty times more horsepower to transport gravels than it does raw cement under the same conditions.

Pumping of Settling Slurries

Stepanoff[15] has pointed out that only 10 per cent of existing pipeline systems used for transporting solids in water employ reciprocating pumps. The rest use single-stage centrifugal pumps. It has been estimated that the wear of major parts of centrifugal pumps used to transport slurries varies directly with the cube of the speed.[15] Thus most centrifugal pumps in existing slurry pipelines operate at low rotational speeds.[15]

Centrifugal pumps are capable of handling stones with sizes of up to half the smallest impeller width.[3] Thus the larger the centrifugal pump, the bigger is the size of the solid particles that can be transported.

Consider the transport of a settling solid-water slurry with a centrifugal pump. The presence of solids in the water increases the average or apparent specific gravity of the mixture. However, since the impeller of a centrifugal pump applies energy only to the water in an aqueous slurry, the pump will operate along the same total head vs capacity curve as for clear water.[15]

In some installations, the solids are introduced on the discharge side of the pump. In this case, a standard pump designed to handle liquids can be used.

Commercial Applications

As early as 1850, aqueous slurries containing gold-bearing gravels were transported through pipelines in California. In 1914, Bell in England installed a 1750 ft long 8 inch diameter pipeline for the transport of coal slurry. Since 1850, many pipelines have been installed to convey a wide range of products. Typical of modern installations is a 72 mile long pipeline which conveys 700 tons/day of gilsonite from Utah to Colorado.[7]

The cost of preparing the slurry for pumping and of separating the solids from the liquid at the terminal often exceeds the actual cost of transportation.[11] The transport of coal-water slurries is an attractive application since burners are now available which can be fed directly with the coal slurry.

NOMENCLATURE

A projected area of a solid particle, sq ft

C_d drag coefficient (dimensionless)

C_d' apparent drag coefficient (dimensionless)

d_i inside pipe diameter, ft

d_s diameter of a solid particle, ft

F force on a solid particle, poundals/sq ft

g gravitational acceleration, 32.2 ft/sec^2

hp   horsepower

i frictional head loss per unit length of pipe, ft of liquid/ft

N_{Re} Reynolds number (dimensionless)

Q volume flow rate, cu ft/sec

r_h hydraulic radius, ft

t time, seconds

u mean linear velocity inside a pipe, ft/sec
v relative velocity between a solid particle and a liquid, ft/sec
x_v volume fraction of solids in a slurry
x_w weight fraction of solids in a slurry
y weight fraction in a solid
μ viscosity, lb/ft sec
ρ density, lb/cu ft
ψ shape coefficient in Equation (8–8), (dimensionless)

REFERENCES

1. Condolios, E., and Chapus, E. E., *Chem. Eng.*, **70**, No. 13 (1963).
2. Condolios, E., and Chapus, E. E., *Chem. Eng.*, **70**, No. 14 (1963).
3. Condolios, E., and Chapus, E. E., *Chem. Eng.*, **70**, No. 15 (1963).
4. Durand, R., *Houille Blanche*, **8**, 124 (1953).
5. Durand, R., and Condolios, E., Centenary Congr. Mineral Industry, France, 1955.
6. Ellis, H. S., Redberger, P. J., and Bolt, L. H., *Ind. Eng. Chem.*, **55**, 18 (1963).
7. Henderson, J. H., Am. Inst. Chem. Engrs., Denver, Colorado, 1962.
8. Howard, G. W., *Proc. Am. Soc. Civil Engrs.*, **64**, 1377 (1938).
9. Hughmark, G. A., *Ind. Eng. Chem.*, **53**, 389 (1961).
10. Lowenstein, J. G., *Chem. Eng.*, **66**, No. 1 (1959).
11. Nardi, J., *Chem. Eng.*, **66**, No. 15 (1959).
12. Newitt, D. M., Richardson, J. F., and Gliddon, B. J., *Trans. Inst. Chem. Engrs.*, **39**, 93 (1961).
13. Perry, J. H., "Chemical Engineer's Handbook," 19–4, New York, McGraw-Hill Book Co. Inc., 1963.
14. Spells, K. E., *Trans. Inst. Chem. Engrs.*, **33**, 79 (1955).
15. Stepanoff, A. J., *Mech. Eng.*, **86**, No. 9 (1964).
16. Worster, R. C., and Denny, D. F., *Proc. Inst. Mech. Engrs.*, **169**, 563 (1955).

CHAPTER 9

Prevention of Heat Losses from Pipelines

Frequently liquids flowing through pipelines must be maintained at a temperature above ambient. This may be necessary either to avoid freezing or to prevent the liquid from becoming too viscous to pump economically. A common industrial problem is how best to prevent heat losses and thus maintain the liquid at an elevated temperature.

Although only liquid transport is considered in this text, the following discussion holds true for the general case of fluid transport.

Heat Losses from a Pipe

The rate of heat loss Q/A in Btu/hr sq ft from each square foot of a pipeline is given by the equation

$$Q/A = \frac{\Delta T_m}{1/U} \tag{9-1}$$

where ΔT_m is the log mean temperature difference driving force in °F between the process fluid and the atmosphere. Since U is the overall heat transfer coefficient or conductance in Btu/hr sq ft °F, $1/U$ is the resistance to heat transfer.

Equation (9–1) can be rewritten in the more conventional form

$$Q = UA\Delta T_m \tag{9-2}$$

In order to keep the heat loss Q Btu/hr to a minimum, either the conductance term U or the driving force term ΔT_m must be made as small as possible.

Prevention of Heat Losses

The oldest method of reducing heat losses is to surround the pipeline with sufficient insulation to make the conductance U very small. The alternative method is to supply heat energy to balance the heat losses and to make the driving force ΔT_m substantially zero. The latter method is increasing in popularity as a wide variety of sophisticated equipment becomes available. The heat energy can be supplied either indirectly by a carrier fluid such as steam, hot water or an organic liquid or directly by electrical heating. The carrier fluid may be transported either through a jacket surrounding the pipe or by a trace line adjacent to the pipe. There are various methods of electrically heating a pipe. The two most common are resistance and induction heating.

The different methods used to minimize heat losses from pipelines will be considered individually before discussing their comparative advantages and disadvantages.

INSULATION

The heat loss from an insulated pipe is largely determined by the thickness and thermal conductivity of the insulation and the temperature difference between the process fluid and the atmosphere. Insulation is a valid method of maintaining the temperature of a process fluid in a pipeline only if the fluid is flowing. In the case of safety showers, the water is not flowing for most of the time and eventually the water reaches the atmospheric temperature irrespective of the insulation over the pipe.

Resistance to Heat Transfer

The overall resistance to heat transfer from the pipe to the atmosphere can be expressed in terms of heat transfer areas by the following equation:[5]

$$\frac{1}{U_i} = \frac{1}{h_i} + \frac{x_{12}}{k_{12}}\frac{A_i}{A_{m1}} + \frac{x_{23}}{k_{23}}\frac{A_i}{A_{m2}} + \frac{1}{h_a}\frac{A_i}{A_a} \qquad (9\text{--}3)$$

which can be rewritten in terms of pipe diameters by the equation

$$\frac{1}{U_i} = \frac{1}{h_i} + \frac{x_{12}}{k_{12}}\frac{d_i}{d_{m1}} + \frac{x_{23}}{k_{23}}\frac{d_i}{d_{m2}} + \frac{1}{h_a}\frac{d_i}{d_a} \qquad (9\text{--}4)$$

| overall resistance | process fluid resistance | pipe wall resistance | insulation resistance | atmospheric resistance |

where U_i is the overall heat transfer coefficient in Btu /hr sq ft °F based on the inside area of the pipe A_i sq ft, h_i is the heat transfer film coefficient in Btu/hr sq ft °F for the process fluid inside the pipe, k_{12} is the thermal conductivity in Btu/hr sq ft °F/ft of the pipe wall, and k_{23} is the thermal conductivity in Btu/hr sq ft °F/ft of the insulating material. h_a is the heat transfer film coefficient in Btu/hr sq ft °F for the air adjacent to the insulation surrounding the pipe, and x_{12} and x_{23} are the thicknesses of the pipe wall and the insulation, respectively, in ft. A_{m1} and A_{m2} are the mean heat transfer areas in sq ft in the pipe wall and insulation, respectively, A_a is the heat transfer area in sq ft between the insulation and the atmosphere, d_i is the inside diameter of the pipe in ft, and d_{m1}, d_{m2} and d_o are the diameters in ft corresponding to the heat transfer areas A_{m1}, A_{m2} and A_o, respectively.

Temperature Distribution over Insulation

In Equation (9–4), the process fluid and pipe wall resistance terms are usually small compared with the insulation and atmospheric resistance terms. The various resistance terms determine the temperature distribution between the process fluid and the outside of the insulation. Frequently more than one insulating material is used. The insulating material on the outside may have an upper temperature use limit substantially below the insulating material on the inside. In order to decide whether this outside insulating material can be used, the temperature distribution in the system must be estimated.

EXAMPLE

A process fluid at a temperature of 300°F is transported through a 1½ inch schedule 80 steel pipe having an inside and an outside diameter of 1.50 and 1.90 inches, respectively. The pipe is surrounded by a 1½ inch thickness of insulator A on the outside of which is a 0.06 inch thickness of insulator B. The thermal conductivities of steel, insulator A and insulator B are taken to be 25.9, 0.132 and 0.094 Btu/hr sq ft °F/ft, respectively. Insulator B is not recommended for use at temperatures greater than 150°F.

Determine the temperature of insulator B when the atmospheric temperature is 80°F.

Consider a radius r in the cross section of the insulated pipe system shown in Figure 9–1.

The heat transfer rate at this radius can be written as

$$Q = -kA_r \frac{dT}{dr} \tag{9–5}$$

where A_r is the heat transfer area at radius r. The negative sign is used in Equation (9–5) since the temperature gradient dT/dr is negative. For a pipe of length ℓ,

$$A_r = 2\pi r\ell \tag{9–6}$$

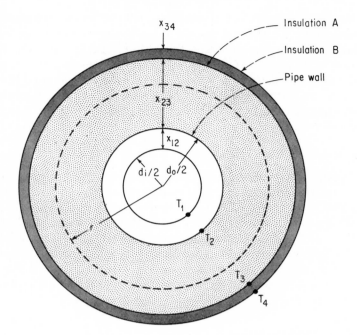

Figure 9-1.   Cross section of double layer insulated pipe.

Combine Equations (9–5) and (9–6) to give

$$-kr\,\frac{dT}{dr} = \frac{Q}{2\pi\ell} = C_1 \tag{9–7}$$

where C_1 is a constant.

Equation (9–7) can be integrated to give

$$-T_r = \frac{C_1}{k}\log_e r + C_2 \tag{9–8}$$

where C_2 is an additional constant. T_r is the temperature at a radius r.

Let k_{12}, k_{23} and k_{34} be the thermal conductivities of the pipe of thickness x_{12}, the insulation A of thickness x_{23} and the insulation B of thickness x_{34}.

Equation (9–8) can be applied over any of the three thicknesses.

Let the temperatures at the inside and outside radius of the pipe thickness x_{12} be T_1 and T_2 °F, respectively, and the temperatures at the outside radii of the insulation A and the insulation B be T_3 and T_4 °F, respectively.

For the pipe thickness x_{12}, the inside and outside radii are $d_i/2$ and $d_o/2$, respectively. The inside and outside radii for the insulation A thickness x_{23} are $d_o/2$ and

$[(d_o/2) + x_{23}]$, respectively. The corresponding radii for the insulation B thickness x_{34} are $[(d_o/2) + x_{23}]$ and $[(d_o/2) + x_{23} + x_{34}]$, respectively.

Equation (9–8) can be rewritten in terms of the temperature limits of each thickness as follows:

$$T_1 - T_2 = \frac{C_1}{k_{12}} \log_e (d_o/d_i) \tag{9-9}$$

for the pipe thickness x_{12};

$$T_2 - T_3 = \frac{C_1}{k_{23}} \log_e \left[\frac{(d_o + 2x_{23})}{d_o} \right] \tag{9-10}$$

for the insulation A thickness x_{23};

$$T_3 - T_4 = \frac{C_1}{k_{34}} \log_e \left[\frac{(d_o + 2x_{23} + 2x_{34})}{(d_o + 2x_{23})} \right] \tag{9-11}$$

for the insulation B thickness x_{34}.

Equations (9–9) and (9–10) can be combined to give

$$\frac{T_1 - T_2}{T_2 - T_3} = \frac{k_{23} \log_e (d_o/d_i)}{k_{12} \log_e [(d_o + 2x_{23})/d_o]} \tag{9-12}$$

and Equations (9–10) and (9–11) can be combined to give

$$\frac{T_2 - T_3}{T_3 - T_4} = \frac{k_{34} \log_e [(d_o + 2x_{23})/d_o]}{k_{23} \log_e [(d_o + 2x_{23} + 2x_{34})/(d_o + 2x_{23})]} \tag{9-13}$$

The rate of heat transfer Q Btu/hr between the outside wall of the insulation B at temperature T_4 °F and the atmosphere at temperature T_a °F is given by the equation

$$Q = h_a A_a (T_4 - T_a) \tag{9-14}$$

where h_a is the heat transfer film coefficient for the atmospheric air in Btu/hr sq ft °F. From Equation (9–7)

$$Q = 2\pi \ell C_1 \tag{9-15}$$

Therefore Equation (9–14) can be rewritten as

$$2\pi \ell C_1 = h_a 2\pi \ell \left[\frac{(d_o + 2x_{23} + 2x_{34})}{2} \right] (T_4 - T_a) \tag{9-16}$$

since

$$A_a = 2\pi \ell [(d_o/2) + x_{23} + x_{34}]$$

Equation (9–16) can be rewritten as

$$T_4 - T_a = \frac{2C_1}{h_a(d_o + 2x_{23} + 2x_{34})} \tag{9-17}$$

which when combined with Equation (9–11) gives

$$\frac{T_3 - T_4}{T_4 - T_a} = \left[\frac{h_a(d_o + 2x_{23} + 2x_{34})}{2k_{34}}\right] \log_e \left[\frac{(d_o + 2x_{23} + 2x_{34})}{(d_o + 2x_{23})}\right] \tag{9-18}$$

(1) Calculate T_3 in terms of T_4 using Equation (9–18):

$$d_o = \frac{1.90}{12} = 0.158 \text{ ft}$$

$$2x_{23} = \frac{2 \times 1.5}{12} = 0.25 \text{ ft}$$

$$2x_{34} = \frac{0.12}{12} = 0.01 \text{ ft}$$

Therefore

$$d_o + 2x_{23} + 2x_{34} = 0.418 \text{ ft}$$

and

$$d_o + 2x_{23} = 0.408 \text{ ft}$$

Therefore,

$$\log_e \left[\frac{(d_o + 2x_{23} + 2x_{34})}{(d_o + 2x_{23})}\right] = \log_e 1.0245 = 0.0242$$

In Equation (9–18), h_a can be taken as 2 Btu/hr sq ft °F. Since $k_{34} = 0.094$ Btu/hr sq ft °F/ft and $T_a = 80°F$, Equation (9–18) can be written as

$$\frac{T_3 - T_4}{T_4 - 80} = \frac{2 \times 0.418 \times 0.0242}{0.188} = 0.108$$

Therefore,

$$T_3 = 1.108T_4 - 8.61°F$$

and

$$T_4 = 0.903T_3 + 7.77°F$$

(2) Calculate T_2 in terms of T_3 using Equation (9–13):

$$\log_e \left[\frac{(d_o + 2x_{23})}{d_o}\right] = \log_e 2.582 = 0.9487$$

Since $k_{34} = 0.094$ and $k_{23} = 0.132$ Btu/hr sq ft °F/ft, Equation (9–13) can be written as

$$\frac{T_2 - T_3}{T_3 - T_4} = \frac{0.094 \times 0.9487}{0.132 \times 0.0242} = 27.9$$

or $T_2 = 28.9T_3 - 27.9T_4$. Therefore, from step (1):

$$T_2 = 28.9T_3 - 27.9(0.903T_3 + 7.77) = 3.7T_3 - 217°F$$

(3) Calculate T_2 in terms of T_3 from Equation (9–12):

$$\log_e (d_o/d_i) = \log_e 1.267 = 0.2365$$

Since $k_{23} = 0.132$ and $k_{12} = 25.9$ Btu/hr sq ft °F/ft and $T_1 = 300°F$, if h_i in Equations (9–3) and (9–4) is large, Equation (9–12) can be written as:

$$\frac{300 - T_2}{T_2 - T_3} = \frac{0.132 \times 0.2365}{25.9 \times 0.9487} = 0.00127$$

or $1.00127T_2 = 300 + 0.00127T_3$. Therefore, $T_2 = 299.6 + 0.00127T_3$. From step (2):

$$T_2 = 3.7T_3 - 217°F$$

Substitute this value of T_2 into the previous equation to give $3.7T_3 = 517$ and

$$T_3 = 140°F$$

Therefore the maximum temperature of insulator B is 10°F below the recommended upper use limit of 150°F.

Effectiveness of Insulation

For only one thickness of insulation, the appropriate heat transfer equations are

$$T_1 - T_2 = \frac{C_1}{k_{12}} \log_e (d_o/d_i) \tag{9–9}$$

$$T_2 - T_3 = \frac{C_1}{k_{23}} \log_e \left[\frac{(d_o + 2x_{23})}{d_o} \right] \tag{9–10}$$

$$T_3 - T_a = \frac{2C_1}{h_a(d_o + 2x_{23})} \tag{9–19}$$

and

$$Q = h_a A_a(T_3 - T_a) \tag{9–20}$$

where the outside heat transfer area $A_a = 2\pi\ell \left[(d_o/2) + x_{23}\right]$.

The temperatures T_2 and T_3 can readily be calculated from Equations (9–9), (9–10) and (9–19) by the method used in the previous example if T_1, T_a, d_i, d_o, x_{23} and h_a are known. The heat transfer rate Q can then be calculated from Equation (9–20).

Alternatively, Equations (9–9), (9–10) and (9–19) may be added together to give

$$T_1 - T_a = C_1 \left\{ \frac{1}{k_{12}} \log_e (d_o/d_i) + \frac{1}{k_{23}} \log_e \left[\frac{(d_o + 2x_{23})}{d_o} \right] \right.$$

$$\left. + \frac{2}{h_a(d_o + 2x_{23})} \right\}$$

which can be rewritten as

$$\frac{Q}{\ell} = 2\pi(T_1 - T_a) \left\{ \frac{1}{k_{12}} \log_e (d_o/d_i) + \frac{1}{k_{23}} \log_e \left[\frac{(d_o + 2x_{23})}{d_o} \right] \right.$$

$$\left. + \frac{2}{h_a(d_o + 2x_{23})} \right\}^{-1} \qquad (9\text{–}21)$$

since $C_1 = Q/2\pi\ell$.

Equation (9–21) gives the heat loss in Btu/hr for each foot of an insulated pipe in terms of the temperature of the inside wall of the pipe T_1 °F and the temperature of the atmosphere T_a °F. The heat transfer film coefficient for the process fluid is usually sufficiently large so that the temperature of the process fluid can be assumed to be the same as the inside wall temperature T_1 °F. For an additional layer of insulation of thickness x_{34} ft and thermal conductivity k_{34} Btu/hr sq ft °F/ft, an analogous equation to Equation (9–21) can be written as

$$\frac{Q}{\ell} = 2\pi(T_1 - T_a) \left\{ \frac{1}{k_{12}} \log_e (d_o/d_i) + \frac{1}{k_{23}} \log_e \left[\frac{(d_o + 2x_{23})}{d_o} \right] \right.$$

$$\left. + \frac{1}{k_{34}} \log_e \left[\frac{(d_o + 2x_{23} + 2x_{34})}{d_o + 2x_{23}} \right] + \frac{2}{h_a(d_o + 2x_{23} + 2x_{34})} \right\}^{-1} \quad (9\text{–}22)$$

The heat transfer film coefficient h_a between the outside surface of an insulated or an uninsulated pipe and the atmosphere depends on the surface temperature. The use of Equations (9–21) and (9–22) to calculate the heat loss has the disadvantage that the surface temperature is not estimated as part of the calculation.

For the case of no insulation, the appropriate heat transfer equations are

$$T_1 - T_2 = \frac{C_1}{k_{12}} \log_e (d_o/d_i) \tag{9-9}$$

$$T_2 - T_a = \frac{2C_1}{h_a d_o} \tag{9-23}$$

and

$$Q = h_a A_a (T_2 - T_a) \tag{9-24}$$

where the outside heat transfer area $A_a = 2\pi \ell d_o/2 = \pi \ell d_o$.

The temperature T_2 can easily be calculated from Equations (9-9) and (9-23) if T_1, T_a, d_i, d_o and h_a are known. The heat transfer rate Q can then be calculated from Equation (9-24).

EXAMPLE

A process fluid at a temperature of 300°F is transported through a 1½ inch schedule 80 steel pipe having an inside and an outside diameter of 1.50 and 1.90 inches, respectively. The atmospheric temperature is 80°F. Estimate the surface temperature and calculate the rate of heat loss per unit length of pipe.

Estimate the surface temperature and calculate the rate of heat loss per unit length of pipe when the pipe is insulated by a 1½ inch thickness of insulator A. The following assumptions are made. The thermal conductivities of steel and insulator A are 25.9 and 0.132 Btu/hr sq ft °F/ft, respectively. Temperature T_1 in Equation (9-9) is substantially 300°F.

(1) Divide Equation (9-9) by Equation (9-23) to give

$$\frac{T_1 - T_2}{T_2 - T_a} = \frac{h_a d_o}{2k_{12}} \log_e (d_o/d_i) \tag{9-25}$$

(2) Solve Equation (9-25) for T_2. In Equation (9-25),

$$h_a = 2 \text{ Btu/hr sq ft °F}$$

$$d_o = \frac{1.90}{12} = 0.158 \text{ ft}$$

$$k_{12} = 25.9 \text{ Btu/hr sq ft °F/ft}$$

$$\log_e (d_o/d_i) = 0.2365 \text{ from the previous example}$$

$$T_1 \cong 300°F$$

$$T_a = 80°F$$

Therefore,

$$\frac{300 - T_2}{T_2 - 80} = \frac{2 \times 0.158 \times 0.2365}{2 \times 25.9} = 0.00144$$

Therefore,

$$T_2 = 299.7°F$$

$$= 300°F$$

which shows that substantially no temperature gradient exists across the pipe wall.

(3) Write Equation (9–24) as

$$\frac{Q}{\ell} = h_a \pi d_o (T_2 - T_a)$$

and solve for Q/ℓ

$$\frac{Q}{\ell} = 2 \times \pi \times 0.158(300 - 80)$$

$$= 218 \text{ Btu/hr}$$

the rate of heat loss per unit length of uninsulated pipe.

(4) Divide Equation (9–10) by Equation (9–19) to give

$$\frac{T_2 - T_3}{T_3 - T_a} = \frac{h_a(d_o + 2x_{23})}{2k_{23}} \log_e \left[\frac{(d_o + 2x_{23})}{d_o}\right] \qquad (9\text{–}26)$$

(5) Solve Equation (9–26) for T_3. In Equation (9–26),

$$h_a = 2 \text{ Btu/hr sq ft °F}$$

$$d_o + 2x_{23} = 0.408 \text{ ft}$$

$$k_{23} = 0.132 \text{ Btu/hr sq ft °F/ft}$$

$$\log_e \left[\frac{(d_o + 2x_{23})}{d_o}\right] = 0.9487 \text{ from the previous example}$$

$$T_a = 80°F$$

$$T_2 = 300 + 0.00127 T_3 \cong 300°F \text{ from the previous example.}$$

Therefore,

$$\frac{300 - T_3}{T_3 - 80} = \frac{2 \times 0.408 \times 0.9487}{2 \times 0.132}$$

$$= 2.93$$

Therefore, $T_3 = 136°F$.

(6) Write Equation (9–20) as

$$\frac{Q}{\ell} = h_a \times 2\pi[(d_o/2) + x_{23}](T_3 - T_a)$$

and solve for Q/ℓ.

$$\frac{Q}{\ell} = 2 \times 2\pi \times 0.204(136 - 80)$$

$$= 143.6 \text{ Btu/hr}$$

the rate of heat loss per unit length of insulated pipe.

This example shows that for a 1½ inch schedule 80 steel pipe, a 1½ inch thickness of insulator A of thermal conductivity 0.132 Btu/hr sq ft °F/ft reduces the heat loss to 66 per cent of the heat loss from the noninsulated pipe when the process fluid and atmospheric temperatures are 300°F and 80°F, respectively.

Heat Transfer Film Coefficient to Atmosphere

In the two previous examples, the heat transfer film coefficient h_a between the outside of the insulation or pipe and the atmosphere has been taken as 2 Btu/hr sq ft °F. In practice, the value of h_a varies depending on a number of factors.

Heat transfer from the surface of an insulated or an uninsulated pipe to air occurs by both convection and radiation. In still air, radiant heat transfer may be noticeably greater than convective heat transfer. For example, a bare pipe in still air with a surface temperature of 400° F has a 68 per cent heat loss by radiation and 32 per cent by convection.[7]

The rate of heat loss Q Btu/hr from an insulated or an uninsulated pipe can be written as

$$Q = h_a A_a (T_s - T_a) \tag{9–27}$$

where T_s is the surface temperature in °F of the insulated or uninsulated pipe in contact with the atmosphere.

The heat transfer film coefficient h_a between the insulated or uninsulated pipe and the atmosphere can be written as

$$h_a = h_c + \epsilon h_r \qquad (9\text{--}28)$$

where h_c and h_r are the heat transfer film coefficients for convection and radiation, respectively, and ϵ is the emissivity of the surface. Values for h_a in Btu/hr sq ft °F are plotted in Figure 9–2 as a function of surface temperature T_s °F and the outside diameter in inches of an insulated or an uninsulated pipe. The values for h_a in Figure 9–2 are based on a surface emissivity $\epsilon = 0.90$ and an ambient air temperature $T_a = 70$°F. Although the surface emissivity may be as little as 0.039 for highly polished aluminum pipe, a value $\epsilon = 0.90$ is representative of the more common industrial pipe and insulation surfaces. The surface emissivities of oxidized iron and steel, asbestos, soft gray and hard glossy rubber, shiny and dull black lacquer, white enamel paint, gypsum, lime plaster, black matte shellac, rough red brick and smooth glass are all in the range 0.87 to 0.92 at approximately 70°F.[25]

Table 9–1 gives the effectiveness of insulation for various insulation thicknesses, thermal conductivities and pipe temperatures using h_a values read from Figure 9–2. For materials which have an emissivity considerably different from $\epsilon = 0.9$, e.g., galvanized pipe, where $\epsilon = 0.23$ to 0.28, Equation (9–28) must be used to calculate h_a. In Equation (9–28), h_c and h_r can be calculated by methods described by a number of authors.[11, 16, 26]

An additional factor affecting the heat transfer film coefficient h_a between the surface of an insulated or an uninsulated pipe and the atmosphere is the air velocity across the pipe surface. In still air, the term h_c in Equation (9–28) results from natural convection. When the air around the pipe is set in motion, forced convection heat transfer takes place which is greater than natural convection heat transfer. In high winds, the heat loss from a pipe may be substantially greater than in still air. This is shown in Figure 9–3.

The proximity of a pipe to other heat sources also affects the heat loss. It is common practice to run pipes in groups or banks. The masking effect reduces the heat loss. Cremer and Davies suggest the approximate masking effect factors given in Table 9–2.

The heat loss from pipes near walls or ceilings is about 20 per cent less than for freely exposed pipes.

Selection of Insulation

A thermal insulator is any material which effectively restricts the flow of heat caused by a temperature gradient. Over the years a large variety of

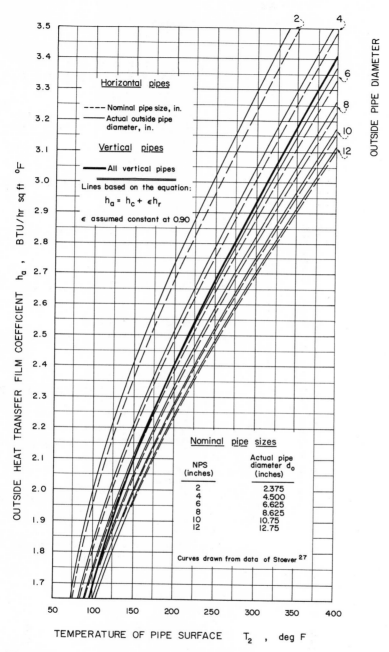

Figure 9-2.   Outside heat transfer coefficient as a function of pipe surface
temperature and outside diameter.

TABLE 9-1. Percentage of Bare Pipe Heat Loss as a Function of Pipe Diameter and Inside Pipe Wall Temperature for Various Insulation Thicknesses and Thermal Conductivities[a]

Thermal Conductivity of Insulation k_{23} (Btu/hr sq ft °F/ft)	Nominal Pipe Size (in.)	Inside Wall Temperature of Pipe T_1 (°F)								
		100			200			300		
		Insulation Thickness z_{23} (in.)								
		1	2	3	1	2	3	1	2	3
0.01	2	8.2	5.2	4.7	5.9	3.8	3.0	4.8	3.0	2.4
	3	8.0	4.7	4.3	5.7	3.5	2.7	4.7	2.8	2.2
	4	7.8	4.6	3.9	5.6	3.4	2.6	4.6	2.7	2.1
	5	7.7	4.5	3.8	5.5	3.3	2.5	4.5	2.6	2.0
	6	7.5	4.4	3.6	5.4	3.1	2.3	4.4	2.6	1.9
	8	7.3	4.3	3.3	5.3	3.1	2.2	4.4	2.5	1.8
	10	7.3	4.2	3.0	5.3	3.0	2.2	4.4	2.5	1.8
0.05	2	33	22	20	25	17	14	21	14	12
	3	31	21	17	24	15	13	20	13	10
	4	31	20	15	24	14	11	19	13	9
	5	30	19	15	23	14	11	19	13	9
	6	29	19	15	22	14	11	18	12	9
	8	29	19	14	22	13	10	18	11	8
	10	28	18	14	22	13	10	18	11	8

0.10	2	56	43	36	43	32	27	36	26	22
	3	52	37	31	41	28	23	34	23	20
	4	51	34	28	40	26	21	33	22	19
	5	48	33	27	39	25	20	32	21	18
	6	47	33	27	37	25	20	31	21	17
	8	47	33	26	36	24	19	31	20	16
	10	46	32	25	36	24	18	30	20	15

Heat Loss from Bare Pipe (Btu/hr/ft)

	Inside Wall Temperature of Pipe T_1 (°F)		
	100	200	300
2	36.2	216	464
4	63.1	372	817
6	91.0	537	1160
8	113	681	1460
10	137	831	1800

[a] Ambient temperature taken as 70°F.

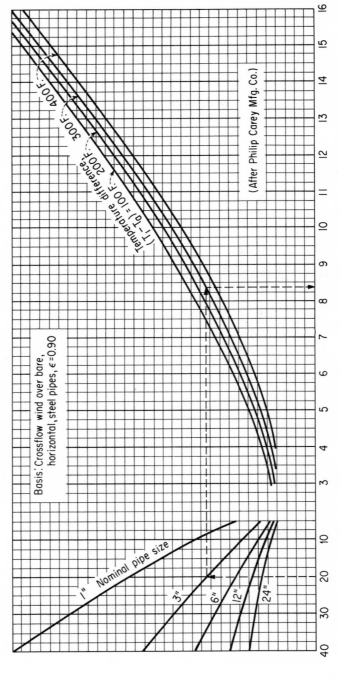

Figure 9-3. Effect of air velocity on heat loss. (*Courtesy Philip Carey Mfg. Co.*)

320

TABLE 9-2.   Masking Effects for Decreased Heat Losses in Horizontal Pipe Banks[7]

Number of Pipes	Heat Loss from Each Pipe (fraction of single pipe losses)	Total Heat Loss from Pipe Bank (fraction of single pipe losses)
2	0.95	1.90
4	0.85	3.40
6	0.75	4.50
8	0.65	5.20

Pipes near walls or ceilings—deduct 20% of the heat losses from fully exposed pipes.

insulating materials have become available. Hence the selection of the best insulator for a specific application can be a source of uncertainty. The selection of an insulator depends on the following factors:

Thermal Requirements. The insulator should not deteriorate at the maximum use temperature. This temperature may be calculated for a particular pipeline system as described in the section on the temperature distribution over insulation. Two other important thermal properties of insulators are thermal conductivity and surface emissivity. The thermal conductivity of the insulator must be sufficiently low to restrict the heat loss to an acceptable limit. The heat loss from the surface of an insulator takes place by both convection and radiation. The radiant heat loss may be a substantial proportion of the total heat loss. The emissivity of the insulation surface determines the radiant heat loss. McAdams[17] gives tables of emissivity for various insulation materials. An additional thermal property to consider in the selection of an insulator is the coefficient of thermal expansion.

Chemical Requirements. Insulating materials should resist attack by chemicals which may come in contact with them. Alternatively, the insulation may be jacketed with a chemically resistant material. Since jacketing is an additional expense, it is preferable to find the best insulation material for the application.

Mechanical Requirements. Insulating materials should resist any mechanical shock, vibration or abrasion to which they may be subjected. The adaptability of the insulating material to conform to any unusual pipeline shapes is an additional consideration.

Moisture Resistance Requirements. For pipelines subject to moisture, e.g., outdoor installations, the insulation material should not deteriorate under wet conditions.

Cost Considerations. An insulator may fulfill all of the above requirements but have too high an initial cost. However, length of life is also an important consideration. A low cost insulator which is difficult to install and requires frequent replacement can, through labor costs, become an expensive item. Aries and Newton,[2] Chilton,[6] Littleton,[14] and Mills[20] present data for use in estimating the materials and installation costs of thermal insulators.

TABLE 9-3 (A).   Characteristics of

Insulating Material	Composition	Mechanical Strength Properties	Moisture Resistance	Available Forms
Asbestos felts (40 laminations/inch)	Asbestos fiber formed into sheets separated by spongy cellular nodules	Moderate compressive strength, moderate tensile strength	Moderate	Blankets, blocks, curved sections, cloths
Asbestos (corrugated, 4 plies/inch)	Asbestos felts	Low compressive strength, moderate tensile strength	Poor	Corrugated asbestos felts laminated into sections, half sections, and sheets
Calcium silicate (hydrous)	Calcium silicate with long asbestos fibers	High flexural strength, moderate compressive strength	Good	Molded shapes, blocks, sections, half sections
Diatomaceous earth (with asbestos)	Diatomaceous earth with long asbestos fibers and bonding material	Moderate compressive strength, low flexural strength	Fair	Molded sections and half sections, blocks, segments
Glass (cellular)	Inorganic glass, cellular structure	High compressive strength, moderate tensile strength, low abrasion resistance	Excellent	Rigid pipe section and half section covers, segments, shapes
Glass felts	Fine glass fibers	Low compressive strength, soft, flexible	Good	Blanket rolls
Hair felt (100% cattle hair)	Cattle hair, chemically cleaned and felted	9 lb/cu ft: very spongy, easily torn; 17 lb/cu ft: firm and fair tensile strength	Poor	Blanket rolls
Magnesia (85%)	85% hydrated magnesium carbonate and 15% asbestos	Moderate compressive strength, low flexural and tensile strength	Fair	Molded forms, half sections, sections, segments
Mineral wool felts	Bonded mineral wool fibers	Soft, low compressive and tensile strength	Fair	Semi-rigid blanket
Mineral wool (with binders)	Mineral fibers blended with binders	Moderate flexural strength, low compressive strength	Excellent	Molded into blocks and slabs
Polystyrene (expanded, cellular)	Polystyrene foamed with air cells	High compressive strength, low tensile strength	Excellent	Molded blocks, sections, half sections
Polyurethane (expanded, cellular)	Foamed diisocyanate and polyester resin	Fair compressive strength	Good	Molded blocks, sections, half sections

Rigid Thermal Insulating Materials

Advantages	Disadvantages	Temperature Range (°F)		Thermal Conductivity[a] k (Btu/hr sq ft°F/ft)	
		Min.	Max.	70°F	Equation $(T = 70 \rightarrow T_{max}$ °F$)$
Ideal for rough usage and excessive vibration	Softens when penetrated by water	100	700	0.032	$k = 0.032 + 0.000032T$
Lightweight, easily installed on straight pipes, good for steam traced lines	Requires protective covering in outdoor service, will not hold up under mechanical abuse	100	300	0.041	$k = 0.041 + 0.000035T$
Easily prefabricated in the field, high flexural strength, low shrinkage at high temperature	Inflexible	100	1200	0.031	$k = 0.031 + 0.000028T$
Excellent handling characteristics, good for high temperatures	Inflexible, not suitable for nonflush installations	22	1900	0.055	$k = 0.055 + 0.000035T$
Easily fitted, incombustable, excellent moisture protection, low vapor diffusity, good low temperature service	Must be protected against abrasion	—400	800	0.0325	$k = 0.0325 + 0.000042T$
Lightweight, flexible, easily installed over valves and curved pipe sections, good low temperature service	Requires covering to protect against mechanical abuse, easily torn	—300	600	0.021	$k = 0.021 + 0.00005T$
Excellent shaping characteristics, easily installed, moderate low temperature service	Requires protection from mechanical abuse, easily torn, vapor diffusity high	—150	200	9 lb/cu ft: 0.022 17 lb/cu ft: 0.024	$k = 0.022 + 0.00002T$ $k = 0.024 + 0.000075T$
Easily cut and fitted, moderate strength	Inflexible, is not self supporting, softens when wet, dusty	Atmos.	600	0.034	$k = 0.034 + 0.0000287$
Easily fitted	Inflexible, will not resist mechanical abuse	—400	250	0.0273	$k = 0.0273 + 0.000044T$
Excellent expansion and contraction properties	Soft, will not stand mechanical abuse	Atmos.	1700	0.0325	$k \cong$ constant $\cong 0.0325$
Lightweight, easily fitted, vapor resistant	Will not withstand fire, limited high temperature service	—400	175	0.022	$k = 0.022 + 0.000066T$
Lightweight, low thermal conductivity, vapor resistant, wide selection of properties	Will not withstand fire unless protected by outside covering	—400	230	0.0142	$k = 0.0142 + 0.00001T$

TABLE 9-3 (A). —(continued)

Insulating Material	Composition	Mechanical Strength Properties	Moisture Resistance	Available Forms
Vegetable cork	Granulated cork bonded with natural cork resin	Moderate compressive strength, moderate tensile strength	Good	Molded sections, half sections, slabs and shapes
Wool felt	Rag felt bonded into sheets	Moderate compressive and tensile strength	Fair	Molded sections and half sections, blankets
Aluminum foil (7 air spaces/2.5 in.)	Aluminum	Easily torn or crushed	Good (if properly sealed)	Foils and prefabricated forms

ᵃ T = Operating temperature − 70°F, i.e., for asbestos felts (40 laminations/in.) at 170°F.

Thermal conductivity, $k = 0.032 + 0.000032\,T$ $= 0.032 + (100)\,(0.000032)$

                    $= 0.032 + (170 - 70)\,(0.000032)$ $= 0.0352$ Btu/hr sq ft °F/ft.

TABLE 9-3 (B). Characteristics of Loose Fill Insulating

Insulating Material	Composition	Mechanical Strength Properties	Moisture Resistance	Available Forms
Asbestos fiber	Asbestos (loose)	Fibers are relatively fragile	Poor-fair	Loose filler
Asbestos (long fiber and binder)	Long asbestos fibers blended with a binder	Medium hard finish surface	Fair	Dry mix powder
Asbestos (with mineral wool)	Long asbestos fibers blended with mineral wool and binders	Fairly soft surface finish, fair compressive strength	Poor	Dry mix powder
Diatomaceous earth (loose powder, fine particles)	Diatomaceous earth, fine particles 20 lb/cu ft	Moderate compressive strength	Poor	Loose powder
Diatomaceous earth (loose powder, course particles)	Diatomaceous earth, coarse particles, 17 lb/cu ft	Moderate compressive strength	Poor	Loose powder
Glass (loose fibers)	Fine glass fibers (loose)	Low tensile strength, flexible	Good	Loose fillers
Magnesia (85%)	85% magnesium carbonate and 15% asbestos	Soft, little mechanical strength	Fair	Dry mix powder

Advantages	Disadvantages	Temperature Range (°F)		Thermal Conductivity[a] k (Btu/hr sq ft°F/ft)	
		Min.	Max.	70°F	Equation $(T = 70 \rightarrow T_{max}$ °F)
Excellent resistance to vibration, easily fitted and formed	Limited temperature range, will not withstand fire unless fireproofed	—250	200	0.025	$k = 0.025 + 0.000033\,T$
Low cost, easily cut and fitted	Will not withstand fire	32	225	0.030	$k = 0.030 + 0.00002\,T$
Lightweight, incombustible, weather resistant	Corrosion possible, efficiency decreases if reflective surface becomes dull, installation moderately expensive	Atmos.	1100	0.025	$k = 0.025 + 0.000052\,T$

Materials and Insulating and Finishing Cements

Advantages	Disadvantages	Temperature Range (°F)		Thermal Conductivity[a] k (Btu/hr sq ft°F/ft)	
		Min.	Max.	70°F	Equation $(T = 70 \rightarrow T_{max}$ °F)
Lightweight, low conductivity, easily applied in spaces	Material will pack down, fibers have little strength, requires retaining walls	Atmos.	1200	0.092	$k = 0.092 + 0.000134\,T$
Hard finish, high grade finishing and insulating cement, good for valves, fittings, joints	Will not withstand mechanical abuse, poor compressive strength	Atmos.	1000	0.100	$k = 0.10 + 0.000035\,T$
Good adhesion and cohesion properties, good trowling characteristics	Water will soften the dried cement	100	1800	0.058	$k = 0.058 + 0.000064\,T$
High temperature service, easily applied in spaces	Will pack down, requires retaining walls	100	1600	0.038	$k = 0.038 + 0.00003\,T$
High temperature service, easily applied in spaces	Will pack down, requires retaining walls	100	1600	0.032	$k = 0.032 + 0.000024\,T$
Extremely lightweight, easily applied in spaces, may be used over valves, etc.	Will pack down, little mechanical strength	—300	600	0.010	$k = 0.010 + 0.00008\,T$
Fairly good insulating qualities, fair trowling characteristics	Soft exterior not suitable for finishing cement	Atmos.	600	0.050	$k = 0.050 + 0.00004\,T$

Types of Insulation

Insulating materials may be classified into four groups[18] according to physical structure:

(1) *Fibrous*. These materials consist of strands or fibers which are either used as loose fillers or bonded together with low conductance binders. Typical materials in this group are asbestos, glass wool, felted hair wool, mineral wool and slag wool. These are available as blankets, cements and semirigid or rigid shapes.

(2) *Granular*: These materials consist of small nodules which contain hollow air spaces. The static air contributes to the over-all resistance to heat flow. Typical materials in this group are diatomaceous earth and 85 per cent magnesia. These are available as segments, blocks and molded shapes.

(3) *Cellular*: These materials are unique in that they consist of a rigid framework of individual cellular chambers, sealed from each other. The development of synthetic plastic foams has greatly increased the number of materials in this group. Cellular foams are also available in glass and silica.

(4) *Metallic*: These insulators consist of sheets of reflective metal separated by air spaces. The effectiveness of insulation increases with the number of reflective sheets used. Aluminum is the most commonly used material. Stainless steel foil is used where the atmosphere is sufficiently corrosive to justify the increased cost.

Table 9–3 lists some of the more common insulating materials together with their important physical characteristics.

Most Economical Thickness of Insulation

The total annual cost of insulation is the sum of the cost of the heat energy lost and the fixed charges for the insulation. The latter is made up of maintenance costs and depreciation. A plot of costs as a function of insulation thickness has the form shown in Figure 9–4. The total annual cost of insulation decreases to a minimum and then increases as the insulation thickness is increased. The minimum in Figure 9–4 occurs at the most economical insulation thickness.

An alternative method of finding the most economical insulation thickness is to use the following equation given by Stoever.[27]

$$\psi_i = \frac{2}{d_{ii}} \left[\sqrt{\frac{tC_h k_{23}(T_s - T_a)}{fC_i \times 10^6}} - \frac{k_{23}}{h_a} \right] \qquad (9\text{--}29)$$

where ψ_i is a dimensionless factor which is plotted in Figure 9–5 as a function of the ratio of the outside to the inside diameter of the insulation d_{io}/d_{ii}.

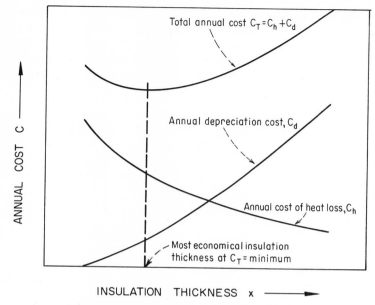

Figure 9-4.   Most economical insulation thickness.

In Equation (9–29), t is the operating time of the equipment in hr/yr, C_i is the installed cost of the insulation in \$/cu ft, C_h is the annual cost of the heat loss in \$/million Btu and f is the fraction of the installed cost of the insulation depreciated annually.

The most economical insulation thickness x_{23} is found as follows. Calculate ψ_i in Equation (9–29). From Figure 9–5 read the corresponding value of the ratio d_{io}/d_{ii}. Calculate the most economical thickness x_{23} from the equation

$$x_{23} = \frac{d_{io} - d_{ii}}{2} \qquad (9\text{–}30)$$

Critical Insulation Thickness—A Special Case

The purpose of insulation is to decrease heat flow. The extent to which it does this depends on the magnitude of the term

$$\frac{1}{k_{23}} \log_e \left[\frac{(d_o + 2x_{23})}{d_o} \right]$$

in Equation (9–21). If the thermal conductivity of the insulation k_{23} is small, the above term is large and the heat loss is small. Since the heat transfer area per unit length on the outside surface of the insulation is $\pi(d_o + 2x_{23})$, an increase in the insulation thickness x_{23} increases the area available for heat loss. The smaller the thermal conductivity k_{23} and the greater the thickness x_{23}, the lower is the surface temperature T_s and hence the lower is the temperature difference driving force $(T_s - T_a)$ between the insulation and the atmosphere. Since the heat transfer film coefficient h_a

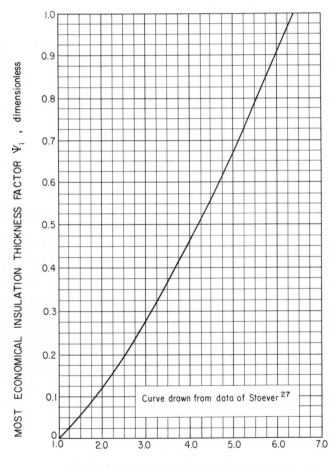

Figure 9-5.   Most economical insulation factor vs ratio of outer-to-inner diameter of insulation.

between the surface and the atmosphere decreases with increasing diameter, an increase in insulation thickness x_{23} decreases h_a.

It is possible, in certain cases, for the heat loss from an insulated pipe to exceed the heat loss from an uninsulated pipe. In these systems, the insulator has a relatively high thermal conductivity k_{23} and its resistance to heat flow is insufficient to compensate for the additional heat loss resulting from the increased area. Figure 9–6 shows plots of heat loss as a fraction of the bare pipe heat loss vs insulation thickness for a $\frac{1}{4}$ inch schedule 80 steel pipe covered with insulation having thermal conductivities k_{23} in the range 0.05 to 0.20 Btu/hr sq ft °F/ft. The inside pipe wall temperature and the outside air temperature were assumed to be 300°F and 70°F, respectively. For a $\frac{1}{4}$ inch schedule 40 pipe, $d_o = 0.540$ inch and $d_i = 0.302$ inch. The thermal conductivity of the steel pipe k_{12} was taken as 25.9 Btu/hr sq ft °F/ft and the heat transfer film coefficient h_a between the surface and the atmosphere was assumed to be 2.0 Btu/hr sq ft °F throughout to simplify the calculations.

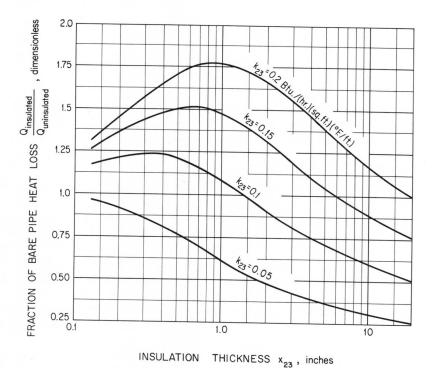

Figure 9-6. Critical insulation thickness for a small diameter pipe.

For an insulation thermal conductivity $k_{23} = 0.15$ Btu/hr sq ft °F/ft, the heat loss increases to a maximum value of 150 per cent of the bare pipe heat loss at an insulation thickness $x_{23} = 0.63$ inch, after which it decreases with further increase in insulation thickness. Twenty inches of insulation reduce the heat loss to only 76 per cent of the bare pipe heat loss.

The critical insulation thickness x_c, i.e., the thickness which gives the maximum heat loss, can also be determined by differentiating Equation (9–21) with respect to thickness x_{23} and setting dQ/dx_{23} equal to zero. This gives

$$x_c = \frac{12k_{23}}{h_a} - \frac{d_o}{2} \qquad (9\text{–}31)$$

From Equation (9–31), the critical insulation thickness is calculated to be $x_c = 0.63$ inch for an insulation thermal conductivity $k_{23} = 0.15$ Btu/hr sq ft °F/ft an h_a value of 2.0 Btu/hr sq ft °F and $d_o = 0.540$ inch. Thus the calculated value agrees with the value obtained from the graph.

To avoid the problem of insulation giving an increased heat loss, the following rule should be followed: Make

$$\frac{12k_{23}}{h_a} < \frac{d_o}{2}$$

since in this case x_c in Equation (9–31) is negative and a practical critical insulation thickness does not exist. This can be attained by choosing an insulator with a sufficiently low thermal conductivity k_{23}.

Installation of Pipeline Insulators

Incorrectly installed insulation can give inadequate performance and involve the additional expense of premature replacement.

Since most insulators are adversely affected by moisture (plastic and glass foams are an exception), it is common practice to cover the insulator with a waterproof jacket. A typical example is shown in Figure 9–7 for an outdoor pipeline insulated with corrugated asbestos sections. The insulation is directly applied over the pipe. Care should be taken to tightly butt each section to reduce the possibility of water seepage. The sections are held in place by flat aluminum straps and a layer of asphalt-coated felt is applied with about a 2 or 3 inch overlap. The outer felt covering is then secured with wire bands placed 6 to 12 inches between centers.

Other common methods of waterproofing an outdoor pipeline are waterproof canvas and metallic jackets. The choice of jacket material depends on location, company safety requirements and economics.

For most indoor installations, a light canvas jacket coated with sizing and a final coat of paint or shellac provides adequate protection against moisture. For additional protection on indoor pipes, a lightweight corrugated aluminum jacket can be used as shown in Figure 9–8. This is secured

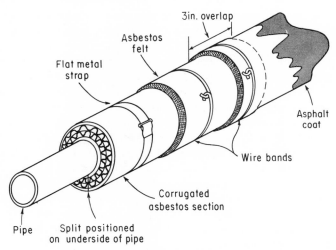

Figure 9-7.   Outdoor insulated pipe with moisture protection.

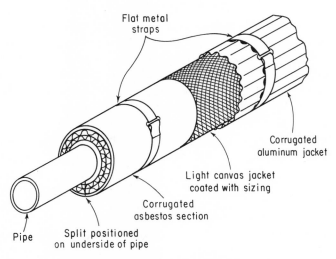

Figure 9-8.   Indoor insulated pipe with moisture protection.

by flat aluminum bands placed about 12 inches apart. The corrugated aluminum should overlap at the joints to insure a good seal.

Unless preshaped forms are available, rigid pipe insulation cannot be applied to flanges, valves, elbows and other curved surfaces. For these, insulating tape or rope wound around the fitting is commonly used. This is covered with insulating cement, and a final coat of paint is applied. Hard surface cements are commonly used to provide some resistance to mechanical damage. In the case of pipes insulated with felts and other flexible coverings, these are also used around the fittings.

Frequently, low thermal conductivity insulators are not capable of withstanding high temperatures. Insulators that can withstand high temperatures usually have only moderately low thermal conductivities. High temperature pipes can be efficently insulated by using a combination of the two types as shown in Figure 9-1. The pipe is first covered with a high temperature–moderate thermal conductivity insulator A. Over this is placed a moderate temperature–low thermal conductivity insulator B. Although the method is very effective, it is costly in both materials and labor. A typical combination is to use diatomaceous earth as the inner insulator A and 85 per cent magnesia as the outer insulator B. For moderate temperature service, it is common practice to place the pipe to be insulated inside a larger pipe made of polyvinyl chloride (PVC) and to fill the intermediate space with polyurethane foam.

HEATING SYSTEMS FOR PIPELINES

For big temperature differences between the process fluid and the ambient air, large and expensive insulation thicknesses are required to reduce heat losses to an acceptable minimum. An alternative way of maintaining the temperature of a process fluid in a pipeline is to supply additional heat to balance the heat losses. The systems used to supply heat can be conveniently divided into fluid and electrical heating systems. Further subdivisions of these two classes are shown in Figure 9-9.

Pipeline heating systems are not used to raise the temperature of the process fluid in the pipeline but simply to maintain it at a constant temperature.

Fluid Heating Systems

Fluid heating systems can be divided into liquid and vapor systems. Some common liquids used are hot water, mineral oils and organic liquids such as "Therminols" and "Dowtherms." By far the most commonly used vapor is steam. Organic vapors are also used.

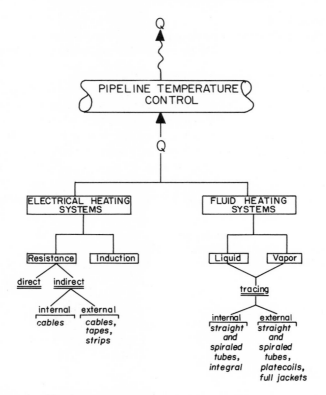

Figure 9-9.   Heating systems for maintaining pipeline temperatures.

In liquid systems, the heat transferred is from sensible heat. The faster the liquid is pumped through the system, the less is its change in temperature over the heat transfer surface and the more uniform is the heating. In vapor systems, the heat transferred is from latent heat. Since all the heat transfer takes place at the saturation temperature, the heat transfer surface can be at a more uniform temperature. Although these two heating methods are quite different, the same equipment is used for both. This is listed under tracing in Figure 9–9.

Pipeline Tracing Methods

The choice of a particular tracing method depends on the following factors:

(1) Characteristics of the process liquid in the pipeline,
(2) Heat load,

(3) Heating fluid,

(4) Pipeline geometry: number of bends, valves, fittings, etc.,

(5) Whether the pipeline is to be installed or is already in existence.

Tracing can be classified as either external or internal.

External Tracing. This includes jackets, platecoils and tubing. These do not come into intimate contact with the process fluid in the pipeline. For small heat loads, a single tube or pipe is run parallel to, and in contact with, the pipeline. In this case, the tracing is usually held in place with wire loops positioned at 1 ft intervals as shown in Figure 9–10(A). For higher heat loads, additional trace lines can be used as shown in Figure 9–10(B). For still higher heat loads, the tracer tube can be wound around the pipeline as shown in Figure 9–10(C). The greater the heat load, the smaller is the

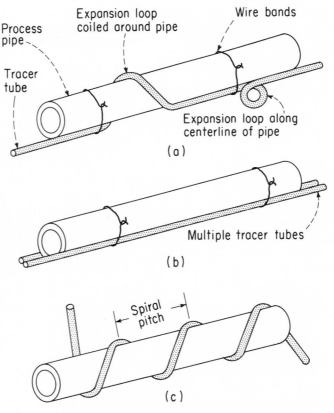

Figure 9-10.   External trace tubing.

distance between spirals, i.e., the smaller the pitch. For long tracer lines, expansion loops should be provided at suitable intervals. Two types of expansion loops are shown in Figure 9–10(A).

External tracing with tubing is commonly used on pipelines containing numerous irregularities such as bends, valves and other fittings. Several turns of tubing are wound around the main body and bonnet of a valve to provide an uninterrupted supply of heat to all parts of the valve. A valve traced by tubing is shown in Figure 9–11. For pipelines with numerous valves and fittings, insufficient tracing of these areas can seriously reduce the capability of the tracing system to maintain a desired temperature. The trace lines are usually flexible tubing such as type K copper. This is used up to approximately 150 psig and 366°F. For higher temperatures and pressures, schedule 80 steel pipe is used. External tubular tracing systems have a very low efficiency. Heat transfer takes place by conduction from the trace tubing to the pipeline. The contact area between the trace tubing and the pipeline is extremely small compared with the total surface area available. A large portion of the usable heat energy carried by the heating fluid is lost to the surrounding atmosphere. Some of this heat which is

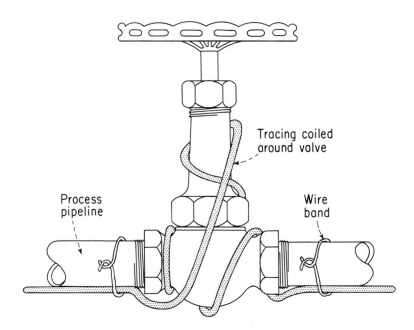

Figure 9-11.   Valve traced with tubing.

transferred to the atmosphere by convection and radiation raises the temperature of the air in the vicinity of the pipeline. The resultant decrease in temperature difference driving force between the pipe surface and the atmosphere has some influence in reducing the heat loss from the pipeline. However, this is a far less efficient way of transferring heat than by conduction through the metal.

Trace tubing has a tendency to separate from its surface contact with the pipeline, reducing heat transfer area and hence efficiency even further. Hot spots occur at the points where wire bands are used to hold the tracer in position. At these points, the tracer tubing is pressed against the pipeline. For pipelines carrying heat sensitive fluids, hot spots are undesirable. The danger of hot spots can be reduced by placing thin strips of asbestos paper between the trace tubing and the pipe at each of the wire band locations.[3]

Several methods may be used to increase the efficiency of external tubular tracing systems. The bare tracer-pipeline system can be covered with insulation. This raises the temperature of the entrapped air. Although less of the available heat is lost to the atmosphere, the efficiency remains relatively low since heat transfer continues to take place primarily by convection rather than by conduction.

The inherent fault in external tubular tracing is the poor contact between the trace tubing and the pipeline. This reduces even further the small area available for conductive heat transfer. This area can be increased by the use of a heat transfer cement. These cements are available from a number of manufacturers and are applied directly as a paste. The cement bonds itself to both the trace tubing and the pipeline, substantially increasing the heat transfer area available for conduction. Heat transfer cements are particularly effective in increasing the efficiency of tracing around valves and fittings. The maximum temperature possible with cemented trace tubing may, for certain systems, be double that with uncemented trace tubing under the same operating conditions.[22] Maximum temperature can be reached five to ten times faster with cement than without cement.[22] The efficiency of cemented trace tubing can be further increased by covering the tracer-pipeline system with insulation. Rigid insulation sections are recommended and are installed as shown in Figure 9–12.

Heat transfer cements are nearly always used with external platecoil tracing. Cements not only increase the heat transfer but have the additional advantage of securing the platecoil to the pipeline.

The most effective way of externally tracing a pipe is to jacket the pipeline. The process line is located inside a larger pipe and the heating fluid passes through the annulus between the two pipes. For flanged pipes, the jacket should be welded to the pipe at a point before the flange-to-pipe

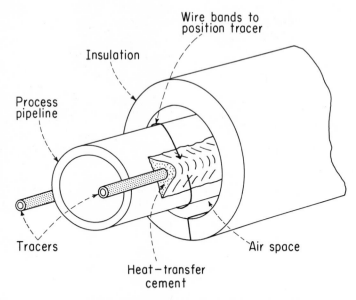

Figure 9-12.   Cemented trace tubing covered with insulation.

weld. If both welds are at the flange, the danger of product contamination exists. Jackets are more efficient than tubular tracing or platecoils since the entire process pipeline is surrounded by the heating fluid. Heat transfer in jacketed systems occurs primarily by conduction and is capable of close control. This is an advantage when the pipeline is being used to transport heat sensitive liquids. Heat losses may be reduced and the system efficiency increased by covering the jacket with insulation.

Jacketed valves, tees, elbows, pumps, etc., are available. These can be used in conjunction with either jacketed pipe or tube traced pipe. Jacketed fittings are much neater than fittings traced with tubing. Furthermore, with heating fluids at high pressures and temperatures, the trace tubing must be steel and not copper. Steel pipe is not easily formed around fittings. Jacketed fittings are also used in certain cases with copper trace tubing. An example of a jacketed fitting is the jacketed elbow shown in Figure 9–13.

Internal Tracing. Internal tracing differs from external tracing in that the trace line is located inside the process pipeline. In contrast to external tracing, internal tracing comes into intimate contact with the process fluid in the pipeline. External tracing functions by reducing the temperature difference driving force which in turn reduces the heat losses. On the other hand, internal tracing does not reduce heat losses but simply compensates

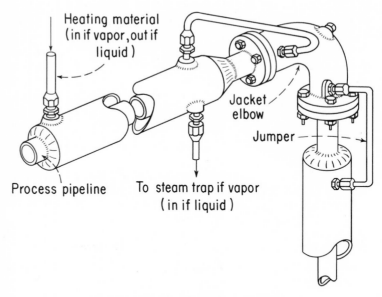

Figure 9-13.   Jacketed pipe and elbow.

for them by supplying additional heat to the process fluid. When the process fluid is in laminar flow, heat transfer takes place by conduction through the process fluid film and by natural convection to the bulk of the fluid. When the process fluid is in turbulent flow, heat transfer from the tracing to the fluid takes place largely by forced convection.

The most elementary form of internal tracing is a single tube running through the center of the process pipeline. Since heat is transferred to the process fluid over the entire outside surface area of the trace tube, internal tracing is usually more efficient than external tracing under comparable conditions. Larger diameter trace tubing may be used to provide a greater heat transfer area where higher heat loads are required. However, this reduces the available cross-sectional flow area for the process fluid. An alternative method of providing a greater heat transfer area is to use internal coils. Expansion coils can be used with straight trace tubing[4] as shown in Figure 9–14. These prevent damage to both the trace tubing and the process pipeline which may result from differential expansion. It is important to use expansion coils with the more rigid types of internal traces, e.g., steel pipe and stainless steel tubes. At valves and fittings, internal tubular tracing must be interrupted and brought out of the process pipe. This can then be connected to either tubular traced or jacketed fittings. Figure 9–11 shows a tubular traced valve and Figure 9–13 a jacketed elbow. Product leaks are common at the points where the internal tubular tracing is brought out of the process pipe. These can be particularly damaging when the pipeline is insulated. Internal tubular tracing is not recommended for use in pipelines carrying fluids at high pressures, especially gases.

Pipelines containing internal tubular tracing are difficult to clean. Scale and encrusted product can build up to the point where heat transfer is reduced below the system requirements. In this case, it would be necessary to increase the temperature of the heating fluid to compensate for the decreased heat conductance.

Another form of internal tracing is the integrally traced aluminum alloy pipe shown in Figure 9–15. This tracing provides a relatively unrestricted passage for the process fluid compared with internal tubular tracing. During manufacture, the pipe is extruded with the additional channel. Integrally traced aluminum pipe is easily joined by first welding the main channel with 4043 weld wire and then joining the trace channels with a welded trace cap. Tees and cross-overs are fabricated in the same way. Although direct welding is the recommended method of joining integrally traced pipe, flanged sections are also available in standard sizes. These are convenient for joining to valves and fittings. Flanged joints require a jumper tube to connect the trace channels as shown in Figure 9–15. Integrally traced elbows are available. These can be joined to the straight sections either by direct welding or by flanges. Alternatively, straight sections can be bent to form elbows during installation. One manufacturer claims that bends may be

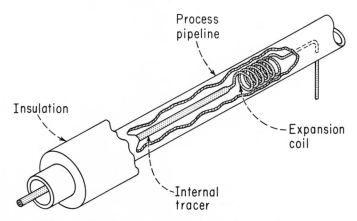

Figure 9-14.   Internal trace tubing with expansion coils.

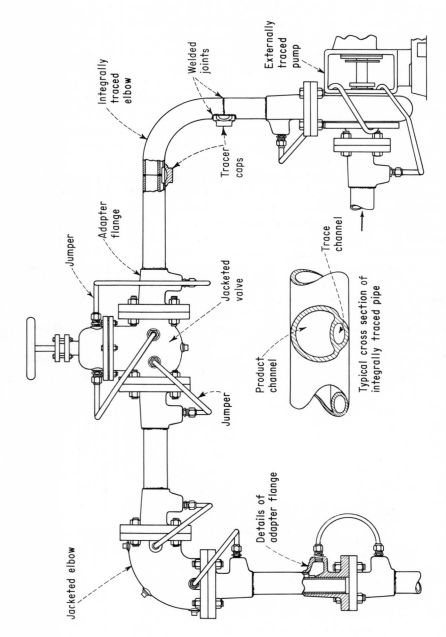

Figure 9-15. Uses of integrally traced aluminum pipe. (*Courtesy Aluminum Co. of America*)

formed ranging from a 5 inch radius bend for a 1 inch line to a 48 inch radius bend for an 8 inch line. The available integrally traced elbows range from a 3 inch radius bend for a 1 inch line to a 24 inch radius bend for an 8 inch line.[1] Thus where space is limited, the preformed elbows are preferred. Figure 9–15 illustrated the various methods of connecting integrally traced pipe to valves and other fittings.

The thermal conductivity of aluminum is somewhat lower than that of copper but is much greater than iron and steel. At 212°F, $k = 119$ Btu/hr sq ft °F/ft for aluminum compared with 218, 30 and 26 Btu/hr sq ft °F/ft for copper, cast iron and steel, respectively.

Integrally traced aluminum pipe can be insulated and then weatherproofed with an outer jacket of aluminum. Since dissimilar metals are not present, the problem of galvanic corrosion does not exist in this case.

Whether internal or external tracing of pipelines is used, the methods for tracing valves and fittings are the same.

Steam Heating

Steam is widely used as a heating fluid for process line tracing. Its principal disadvantage is the high pressure involved when high temperature is required. In addition, there is the danger of frozen lines in cold weather, when outside systems are not in use. Although steam systems are more expensive to install and maintain than some of the more recently developed electrical systems, they remain as popular as ever. Moreover, the cost of steam is lower than for an equivalent amount of electrical energy. However, this may not be the case in the future.

Steam can be used in either internal or external trace lines. In steam systems, the main source of heat (approximately 70 per cent) is the latent heat of condensation.[19] The sensible heat from the hot condensate is therefor about 30 per cent of the total heat supplied. This condensate must be removed smoothly for a steam tracing system to function efficiently. In addition, the steam must be supplied at the required pressure and distributed with the minimum loss of this pressure. The over-all system can therefore be divided into (1) the steam supply and distribution network and (2) the means of removal for spent steam and condensate.

Steam Supply and Distribution

Modern industrial steam generating plants are capable of supplying steam at pressures well above that required in most tracing systems. For example, main lines may carry 600 psig steam, whereas tracers are ordinarily supplied with steam in the range 10 to 200 psig. In fact, steam in the range 15 to 30 psig is frequently used.

Since the full main line pressure is normally not required for plant use, a network of reduced pressure lines is used. The available steam pressure is frequently greater than that required in trace lines. A pressure reducing station shown in Figure 9–16 is used to lower the pressure to the required value.

Pressure reducing stations consist of a primary line containing the pressure regulator and a bypass line. The latter can be used if the regulator requires repairs or cleaning. A screen strainer is located immediately before the regulator. This traps any dirt or scale carried over from the high pressure line. The pressure reducing station is connected to the top of the main steam line. This reduces the possibility of condensate carry-over as well as dirt or scale carry-over. Pressure gauges are positioned on the high and low pressure sides of the regulator. Three valves are used in the system, one on either side of the pressure regulator and the third in the bypass line. The latter should be a globe valve to facilitate efficient throttling of the steam when the regulator is inoperative.[15]

The low pressure steam from the pressure reducing station can be used to feed a header from which individual steam trace lines can be taken. The trace lines should be taken from the top of the header to avoid carry-over. The use of a header lowers both the initial and the maintenance cost of a system, since only one pressure reducing station need be used with a number of trace lines. Each trace line should have a separate valve to enable it to be isolated without affecting the rest of the system. These valves should be tagged and located in groups to facilitate identification and maintenance. On long trace lines, intermediate valves can be used to permit a partial shutdown for repairs.

A steam tracing system is shown in Figure 9–16. The steam supply and condensate removal components are shown shaded and black, respectively. The diameter of the supply header must be large enough so that steam can be fed continuously to the tracers. Table 9–4 gives the required diameters of the header for various numbers of $\frac{1}{2}$ inch diameter trace lines.[3, 4]

The size and number of trace lines depend on the steam pressure, heat load, trace line material, method of tracing, type of insulation, ambient conditions, etc. However, trace lines with diameters below $\frac{1}{4}$ inch are

TABLE 9-4.   Steam Supply Header Diameters for ½ Inch Tracers

Number of External Tracers	Diameter of Header, NPS (in.)
2–3	$\frac{3}{4}$
4–6	1
7–12	$1\frac{1}{2}$

impractical, since the pressure drops are too high. Also, for diameters greater than $\frac{1}{2}$ inch, the tubing becomes too inflexible for winding around valves and fittings. Generally, $\frac{1}{4}$ inch tubing is used for tracing smaller diameter process lines. For larger diameter process lines, $\frac{3}{4}$ inch and $\frac{1}{2}$ inch diameter trace lines are used.

If a heat transfer cement is to be used, the manufacturer can give the trace line size for the most efficient use of the product.

Condensate Removal Systems

For efficient steam heating, the condensate liquid should be removed from the trace lines. To avoid a poor quality or "wet" steam, condensate should also be removed from the main supply line and the headers as shown in Figure 9–16.

The buildup of condensate and noncondensable gases in a steam line reduces heat transfer. The causes for this are as follows:[9]

(1) Condensate forms pools at the low points in a system. These inhibit the flow of steam and thus reduce heat transfer.

(2) The water condensate is a poor heat conductor. Thus the water pools and films restrict heat flow.

(3) Entrapped air or gas reduces the partial pressure and hence the temperature of the steam. Furthermore, air has a heat capacity approximately half that of steam. Thus the heat carried by the steam is reduced. Golding[9] predicts the loss of steam temperature in air-steam mixtures as shown in Table 9–5.

Steam Traps. The removal of condensate, air and noncondensable gases from steam lines is effected through steam traps. These trap steam in the line and allow the gases and condensate to escape. A wide variety of steam traps are available. A classification of steam traps is given in Figure 9–17.

TABLE 9-5. Temperature Loss Due to Air in Steam

	Steam Pressure (psig)				
	10	25	50	75	100
Per Cent Air (by Volume)	Temperature of Air-Steam Mixture (°F)				
0	240	267	298	320	338
10	236	263	291	313	330
20	228	254	283	305	322
30	221	246	275	296	312

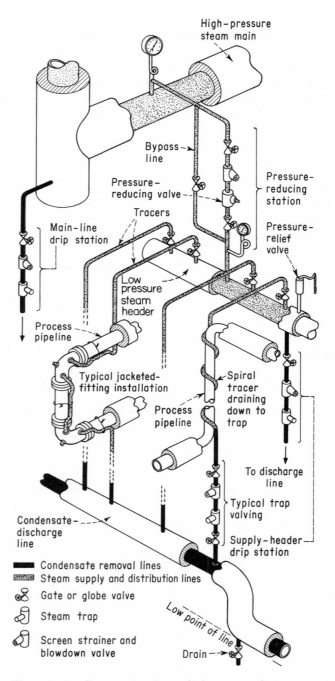

High-pressure steam main

Bypass line

Pressure-reducing valve

Tracers

Main-line drip station

Pressure-reducing station

Pressure-relief valve

Low pressure steam header

Process pipeline

Typical jacketed-fitting installation

Spiral tracer draining down to trap

Process pipeline

To discharge line

Typical trap valving

Condensate-discharge line

Supply-header drip station

■ Condensate removal lines

▨ Steam supply and distribution lines

⚥ Gate or globe valve

⏀ Steam trap

⏁ Screen strainer and blowdown valve

Low point of line

Drain

Figure 9-16. Components of a typical steam tracing system.

344

The advantages and disadvantages of various steam traps are listed in the various manufacturers' bulletins. The personal preferences of plant engineers in the selection of steam traps differ widely.

The amount of condensate produced in a system determines the required capacity of the steam trap. Steam traps are available over a wide range of capacities. The thermostatic types are capable of handling the biggest loads. The layout of the system determines the number of steam traps. Long trace lines with numerous bends and other areas where condensate can collect must be more heavily trapped than comparatively straight trace lines.

In general, steam traps should be installed at the low points of a system. If impulse traps are used, one trap may be used with multiple tracers on the same process pipeline.[15] In this case, each trace line should have a check valve prior to the steam trap to prevent back-flow between trace lines. Trace lines from more than one process pipeline should never be drained at a common trap. All lines should gently slope to the low point of the system to facilitate drainage. This is particularly important in outdoor installations to prevent freezing. To avoid freezing inside steam traps, these should preferably be installed on vertical lines to allow drainage by gravity. If this is not possible, the discharge line should slope as much as possible. To facilitate drainage in trace lines, spiral tracing should only be used on

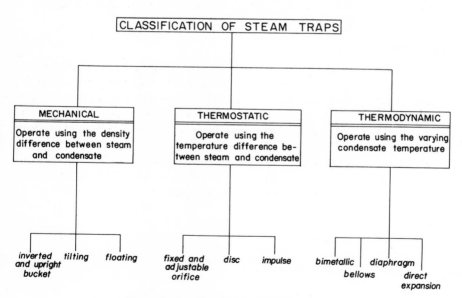

Figure 9-17. Classification of steam traps.

vertical pipelines. Each section of jacketed pipe should have a steam trap at the lower end of the pipe. All steam lines should be drained in the direction of steam flow to avoid "hammer" and possible damage to traps, etc. Steam traps can be protected against damage from foreign bodies by locating a fine screen strainer immediately prior to the trap. Combination strainer and blow-off valves are available which facilitate cleaning the strainer screen and checking the line.

Condensate Discharge Lines. It is common practice to drain steam traps into a condensate return or disposal line. The size of this line depends on the number of traps and the total condensate discharge rate. Approximate sizes are given in Table 9–6.[4]

TABLE 9-6.   Main Condensate Discharge Line Diameters for ½ Inch Tracers

Number of Traps Draining Single Tracer Lines	Diameter of Discharge Line, NPS (in.)
1–4	1
5–9	1½
10–15	2

A typical arrangement of valves in the vicinity of a trap is shown in Figure 9–16. These allow the partial shutdown of lines discharging into a common condensate line.

Electrical Heating Systems

There are various electrical methods of supplying heat to a pipeline. The two most common are resistance heating and induction heating. In the former, heat is produced by the direct application of a voltage to a resistor. Induction heating systems work on the principle that disturbances in the molecular structure of materials caused by a varying magnetic field produce heat.

At present, electrical heating is not as common as steam heating. Electrical heating is likely to become more popular in the future as electricity costs are reduced and more sophisticated equipment becomes available.

Resistance Heating

The basic rate equation

$$\text{flow rate} = \frac{\text{driving force}}{\text{resistance}} \tag{9-32}$$

describes the flow of an electrical current through a conductor.

Ohm's law is written as

$$I = \frac{E}{R} \qquad (9\text{-}33)$$

where I is the current or flow rate of electricity, E is the applied voltage or electrical driving force and R is the resistance opposing the flow of the electrical current. Usually I is expressed in amperes, E in volts and R in ohms.

The conversion of electrical energy into heat energy in a resistor is known as the I^2R effect. This energy rate is expressed in watts when I is in amperes and R is in ohms (1 watt = 3.415 Btu/hr). Thus the heat energy available per unit time from resistance heating can be written as

$$Q = 3.415 I^2 R = \frac{3.415 E^2}{R} \qquad (9\text{-}34)$$

where Q is in Btu/hr, I in amperes, E in volts and R in ohms.

Equation (9–34) can be rewritten as

$$\frac{Q}{\ell} = 3.415 I^2 \left(\frac{R}{\ell} \right) \qquad (9\text{-}35)$$

and

$$\frac{Q}{\ell} = \frac{3.415 E^2}{R\ell} \qquad (9\text{-}36)$$

in terms of the heat transfer per unit length of the resistor. For a pipe Q/ℓ is normally expressed as Btu/hr/ft.

Equation (9–36) can be more conveniently written in the form

$$\frac{Q}{\ell} = 3.415 \left(\frac{E}{\ell} \right)^2 \left(\frac{\ell}{R} \right) \qquad (9\text{-}37)$$

where E/ℓ in volts/ft is the electrical driving force of the resistor and R/ℓ is the resistance in ohms/ft of the resistor.

Direct Resistance Heating of Pipelines

One method of maintaining pipeline temperatures is to pass an electric current through the pipeline itself. The heat generated by the I^2R effect is then used to compensate for the heat losses in the system. Current is supplied by DC generators or from standard transformers. Since the pipe carries a live current, a safety hazard exists. Thus low voltages in the range 40 to 60 volts are used.[12] These necessitate the use of high amperage transformers and generators.

The amount of electrical energy required to maintain the temperature in a pipeline depends on the following factors:

(1) Temperature of the fluid to be maintained,
(2) Ambient temperature,
(3) Pipe diameter and length,
(4) Electrical resistance of the pipe,
(5) Thickness and thermal conductivity of insulation around the pipe.

The required amperage and voltage are calculated as follows:

(1) Calculate the rate of heat loss per ft of pipe as described in the section entitled "Effectiveness of Insulation" for both insulated and uninsulated pipes. This heat rate Q/ℓ must be balanced by the Q/ℓ in Equations (9–35) and (9–36) for the pipeline temperature to be maintained.

(2) Find the electrical resistance of the pipeline in ohms from tables. Table 9–7 gives the resistances in ohms/ft of schedule 40 pipes made of various materials for diameters in the range ½ to 6 inches NPS.

(3) Calculate the amperage from Equation (9–35). The normal range of current is from 300 to 500 amperes.[13]

(4) Calculate the voltage per ft of pipe E/ℓ either from Equation (9–37) or from the amperage and the resistance of the pipe in ohms/ft using Ohm's law.

(5) Obtain the voltage over the whole length of pipe by multiplying E/ℓ found from step (4) by the length of pipe.

EXAMPLE

A 2 inch schedule 40 steel pipe carries a liquid at 300°F. The total length of pipeline is 3000 ft. The pipe is covered with a 1 inch thickness of insulation having a thermal conductivity of 0.01 Btu/hr sq ft °F/ft. It is desired to maintain the 300°F process liquid temperature using a direct resistance heating. The ambient temperature is 70°F. Calculate the required voltage and amperage.

(1) The rate of heat loss per ft of bare 2 inch schedule 40 pipe for a pipe temperature of 300°F and an ambient temperature of 70°F is read from Table 9–1 to be

$$\frac{Q}{\ell} = 464 \text{ Btu/hr ft}$$

TABLE 9-7. Electrical Resistance of Pipelines[12]

Pipe Diameter NPS (in.)	Pipeline Material			
	Wrought Iron	Steel	Copper Tubing	Cast Iron (class A)
	Resistance R (ohms/ft of pipe at 60°F[a])$\times 10^5$			
$\frac{1}{2}$	26.0	19.8	8.24	—
$\frac{3}{4}$	20.2	14.9	4.45	—
1	13.8	10.0	3.40	—
$1\frac{1}{2}$	8.42	6.18	2.08	—
2	6.25	4.60	1.33	—
4	—	—	—	9.20
6	—	—	—	6.00

[a] Multiply tabular values by 10^{-5} to obtain resistance in ohms/ft of pipe, e.g., resistance of 2 in. steel pipe is 4.60×10^{-5} ohms/ft. The change in resistance with temperature of the pipe may be disregarded.

For a 1 inch thickness of insulation having a thermal conductivity of 0.01 Btu/hr sq ft °F/ft, Table 9–1 gives, for this case, the heat loss as 4.8 per cent of the bare pipe heat loss. Therefore, for the insulated pipe

$$\frac{Q}{\ell} = 464 \times \frac{4.8}{100} = 22.3 \text{ Btu/hr ft}$$

(2) The electrical resistance of 2 inch schedule 40 steel pipe is found from Table 9–7 to be 4.6×10^{-5} ohms/ft.

(3) Equation (9–35) can be written as

$$I^2 = \left(\frac{Q}{\ell}\right) \div 3.415\left(\frac{R}{\ell}\right)$$

which is solved for this case to give

$$I^2 = \frac{22.3 \times 10^5}{3.415 \times 4.6} = 14.2 \times 10^4$$

Therefore, $I = 377$ amperes.

(4) Ohm's law can be rewritten as

$$\frac{E}{\ell} = I\left(\frac{R}{\ell}\right)$$

where E/ℓ is the volts/ft of pipe.

Therefore, in this case

$$\frac{E}{\ell} = 377 \times 4.6 \times 10^{-5} = 1.74 \times 10^{-2} \text{ volt/ft}$$

(5) The length of pipeline is 3000 ft; therefore, the voltage E across the whole pipeline is

$$E = 1.74 \times 10^{-2} \times 3000$$

$$= 52 \text{ volts}$$

The total electrical power requirements for the 3000 ft pipeline are 19.6 kW which give 66,900 Btu/hr of heat.

Indirect Resistance Heating of Pipelines

The principle of indirect resistance heating is the same as for direct resistance heating, i.e., the I^2R heating effect of an electric current in a resistor is used to compensate for the heat losses from a pipeline. In direct resistance heating, the pipe itself is used as the resistor. For indirect resistance heating, the electric current is passed through a resistor which is completely insulated from the pipeline. Commonly used resistors for indirect resistance heating are heating cables, heating tapes and a recently developed continuous length heating strip. The maximum operating temperature of a cable, tape or strip is determined by the melting point of either the resistor material or the insulation. In most cases, the insulation has the lower melting point and is therefore the limiting factor.

Heating Cables. For relatively low temperature service, electrical resistors insulated with plastics and other organic materials may be used. The power outputs are restricted to the range 5 to 10 watts/ft.[23] Mineral-insulated cables are used for higher heat loads. Commonly known as MI cables, they consist of two bare resistance wires encased in a copper jacket. The intervening space is filled with a refractory insulating material such as magnesium oxide which separates and insulates the two resistance wires from each other and from the copper jacket. The two wires are joined together at one end of the cable and connected to the power supply at the other. Thus a closed circuit is formed as shown in Figure 9–18. MI cables do not involve any significant safety hazard since the copper jacket functions as an electrical ground. Hence the possibility of electrical shock is greatly reduced.[24] MI cables are relatively flexible and may be bent over moderately irregular piping systems. However, bends should not be less than five times the cable diameter.[24] If a bend is made with a smaller diameter, the wires may get pinched together or the copper jacket damaged.

The maximum working temperature for an MI cable is 475°F, since the copper jacket oxidizes above this temperature. Some manufacturers recommend a safe maximum temperature of 350°F. This allows for power surges which could damage the cable if it were operating at the upper temperature limit.

Great care should be taken when splicing lengths of MI cable. A junction box is required and the splice area should be made airtight. This is also the case with standard cable. Failure to make the splice area airtight is the cause of many cable "burn-outs." Thus splicing is only recommended when absolutely necessary.

Staihar[24] cites the use, by the United States Air Force, of cable heating to keep utility pipelines warm at the North Pole. Ambient temperatures were as low as −50°F and wind velocities as high as 100 mph.

Many of the problems associated with external fluid tracing are also encountered with MI cable. It is common practice to run MI cable parallel to the outer surface of the pipe. The line contact between the cable and the pipe wall provides only a very small area for heat conduction to occur. As in the case of steam tracing, an outer covering over the pipe and tracer decreases the heat losses. However, heat transfer still takes place primarily by convection and radiation. Heat transfer cements can be used to increase the conductive heat transfer area. The use of a cement together with an outer covering of insulation over the pipeline and tracer provides the most efficient system. This method is illustrated in Figure 9–12 for steam tracing.

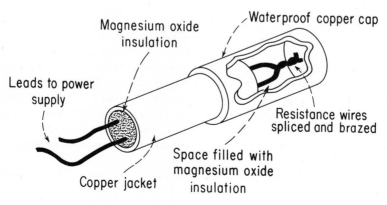

Figure 9-18.   Heating cable construction.

Occasionally, MI cable is run internally through the center of the process line in direct contact with the process liquid. This is considered poor practice in view of the possibility of cable "burn-out." Replacement of a defective cable involves the expense and trouble of dismantling the pipeline.

The power requirements for MI cables are calculated in the same way as for direct resistance heating. However, the resistance of the MI cable is used in Equation (9–34) in place of the pipeline resistance. The resistance data for MI and other cables can be obtained from the various manufacturers.

Heating Strips and Tapes. To overcome the problem of the small heat transfer areas associated with heating cables, resistance heating strips and tapes having comparatively large widths were developed. Heating strips and tapes have the additional advantage over cables of being extremely flexible.

The only heating strip available[8] consists of two copper bus-strips separated by a high resistance graphite-silica sheet. This assembly is sandwiched between two layers of asbestos sheet on the outside of which is a sheath of an inert organic insulator such as "Teflon." Since this heating strip is $3\frac{1}{2}$ inches wide and only 1/32 inch thick, it possesses both flexibility and a large heat transfer contact area.

The use of the tape is limited to straight runs of pipe and bends occurring in one plane, on which it is laid flat and fastened in place at 1 ft intervals. The heating strip generates heat at a constant rate over its entire length. This is possible because the graphite-silica sheet behaves as a large number of identical resistance wires connected in parallel between two parallel copper electrodes. Hence the heat output of each resistance wire is the same regardless of the length of the strip for a constant voltage across the copper bus-strips.

Two kinds of strip are available: one with a design power rating of 16 watts/ft and the other with a design power rating of 5.3 watts/ft. Actual power outputs are at least 20 per cent greater than these values which are used in design calculations. For the 16 watts/ft strip, any combination of lengths totaling 100 ft can be used in a single circuit. Individual lengths are connected using crimp-type terminals and jumper cables. The jumpers may be equipped with quick-disconnects to facilitate dismantling sections of traced pipe. A total of 600 ft of the 16 watts/ft strip or 1500 ft of the 5.3 watts/ft strip may be controlled by a single thermostat and power supply as shown in Figure 9–19.

The power and operating requirements of the strip are calculated as follows:

(1) Obtain the rate of heat loss per ft of unheated pipe in Btu/hr ft either from Table 9–1 or by direct calculation as described in the section

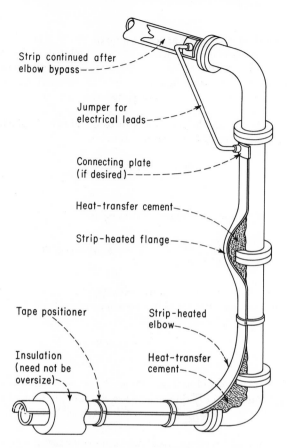

Figure 9-19.   Methods of installing heating strip.
(*Courtesy Electro-Trace Corp.*)

entitled "Effectiveness of Insulation" for both insulated and uninsulated pipes.

(2) Divide the value obtained in step (1) by 3.415 to get the rate of heat loss per ft of unheated pipe in watts/ft.

(3) Calculate the fraction of the time for which the appropriate heating strip is operating. The heating strip operates at a constant power output. Thus if the rate of heat loss per ft of pipe in watts/ft is less than the constant power rating for the strip, intermittent operation is necessary. This is effected by using a thermostat. If the rate of heat loss per ft of pipe is greater than the power rating for the strip, either parallel heating strips can be used or the strip can be wound as a spiral around the pipe.

EXAMPLE

A 2 inch schedule 40 steel pipe carries a liquid at 300°F. The total length of pipeline is 200 ft. The pipe is covered with a 1 inch thickness of insulation having a thermal conductivity of 0.01 Btu/hr sq ft °F/ft. It is desired to maintain the 300°F process liquid temperature using heating strip. The ambient temperature is 70°F. Find the quantity of heating strip required and the fraction of the time for which the strip is operating.

(1) From a previous example, the rate of heat loss per ft of unheated pipe for the above specifications and conditions was found to be

$$\frac{Q}{\ell} = 22.3 \text{ Btu/hr ft}$$

(2) The rate of heat loss per ft of unheated pipe is

$$\frac{22.3 \text{ Btu/hr ft}}{3.415 \text{ Btu/hr watt}} = 6.54 \text{ watts/ft}$$

(3) For the strip having a design power rating of 16 watts/ft, the fraction of time during which the heating strip would be operating is therefore

$$\frac{6.54}{16.00} = 0.409$$

Thus the thermostat would activate the strip for 24½ minutes in every hour to maintain the pipeline at 300°F. Since there are 200 ft of pipe, two strips are required to conform with the recommended 100 ft maximum length per strip.

In contrast to heating strips, heating tapes operate in a similar manner to cables. The total electrical resistance of a tape is the resistance per ft multiplied by the length of the tape. The calculation of power requirements for tapes is the same as for cables. Heating tapes are usually very flexible and may be used to trace pipeline systems with extreme irregularities. Heating tapes are laid flat on the pipe and fastened at 1 ft intervals with electrical tape.

The efficiency of a heating tape may be increased by using heat transfer cement and an outer convering of insulation. For high heat loads, parallel tapes can be used or the tape can be wound as a spiral around the pipe. This increases the heat transfer area available per ft of pipe.

If only a single tape is used parallel to the pipe, the risk of "burn-out" for high heat loads is much greater than with a number of parallel tapes or with a spirally wound tape.

Induction Heating

The principle of resistance heating is the conversion of electrical energy to heat energy in a resistor through the I^2R effect. Induction heating also operates on the I^2R principle. However, in this case, the heating current is induced and flows along the outer layer of the pipe. Coils of wire carrying an alternating current encircle the pipeline at regular intervals. Up to pipe temperatures of about 300°F, the coils are placed next to the pipe with a small air space between the two. At higher temperatures, insulation is placed between the coils and pipe. The alternating current in the coils generates a rapidly changing magnetic field. This in turn induces a current in the pipeline in the same way as in a transformer. However, the pipe material must be ferromagnetic. Since the induced current flows in the outer layer of the pipe, the heat produced is often called the "skin effect."[21] This heat then travels by conduction to the bulk of the pipe material.

The induced current is a function of the frequency of the alternating current in the coils, the number of turns in the coil, the air gap between the coils and pipe, and the spacing between the coils on the pipe.

The only manufacturer of pipeline induction heating equipment[28] supplies standard systems for pipes of 1 to 8 inches NPS operating at 60 cycles/sec and at 110, 220 or 440 volts. The coils are placed around the pipeline at 1 ft intervals. A polyvinyl chloride outer jacket is fitted over the entire assembly and the intervening space is filled with polyurethane foam. Each individual coil is completely sealed except for the points where the electrical leads emerge. The coils are preset to operate in series at the available voltage. For a 110 volt supply, each circuit could consist of ten 11 volt coils. For a 220 volt supply, each circuit could consist either of ten coils rated at 22 volts each or 20 coils rated at 11 volts each. A typical installation is shown in Figure 9–20.

Individual coils may be equipped with crimp-type connectors to facilitate installation in the plant. Figure 9–21 illustrates methods of connecting coils and "jumping" flanges, etc. Alternatively, entire sections of pipe may be prewound to form a continuous induction coil. In this case, the pipe is first covered with a 1 inch thickness of rigid insulation over which the wire is coiled. A polyvinyl chloride outer jacket is fitted over the entire assembly and the intervening space is filled with polyurethane foam. Recommended methods for installing prewound pipe sections are illustrated in Figure 9–22.

Induction heating systems require very little maintenance. Since the heating current is induced in the pipeline, the coil windings do not become excessively hot. Thus the coils have a long life. If a short circuit develops in one of the coils and the circuit remains intact, the system will continue

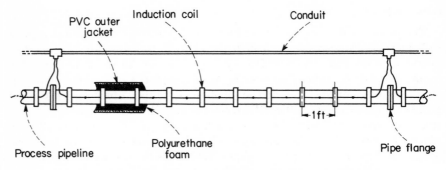

Figure 9-20. Typical induction coil heating system for pipelines.
(Courtesy Trans Continental Electronics Corp.)

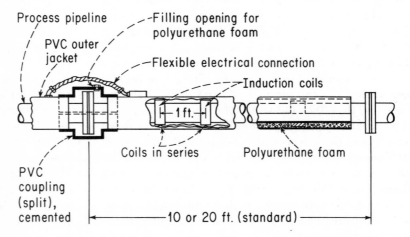

Figure 9-21. Construction details of an induction coil heating system for pipelines.
(Courtesy Trans Continental Electronics Corp.)

to operate with only a slight decrease in heating capacity. If a break occurs in a coil, as with resistance heating, the system ceases to function.

Induction heating systems are capable of providing very tight temperature control. However, since induction heating depends on the magnetic properties of the pipeline material, this must be ferromagnetic. Thus nonferromagnetic materials such as 316 stainless steel cannot be induction heated. However, the problem can be overcome by using lined pipes. If an iron pipe is lined with a nonferromagnetic material, a heating current can be induced in the iron and the heat transferred through the liner by conduction.

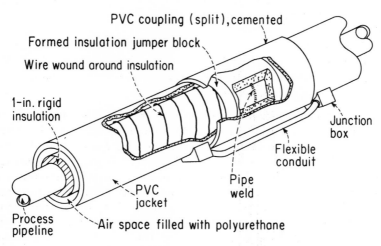

PVC coupling (split), cemented

Formed insulation jumper block

Wire wound around insulation

1-in. rigid insulation

Junction box

Flexible conduit

Process pipeline

PVC jacket

Pipe weld

Air space filled with polyurethane

Figure 9-22.   Prewound induction heated pipe. (*Courtesy Trans Continental Electronics Corp.*)

COMPARISON OF SYSTEMS FOR PREVENTING HEAT LOSSES FROM PIPELINES

Tables 9–8 and 9–9 list some advantages and disadvantages of electrical and fluid heating systems, respectively. Cost considerations have been omitted from these Tables.

It is very difficult to make valid generalizations about cost comparisons.[10] However, the trend is moving in favor of electrical systems.

Costs for heat loss prevention systems vary widely, depending on a number of factors. Some of the factors affecting cost are as follows:

(1) The pipe size and length;

(2) The geometry of the pipeline and the number of pumps, valves, fittings, etc., in the systems;

(3) Whether the pipeline is buried or above ground—for buried pipes, ground conditions are a factor;

(4) Process fluid temperature to be maintained;

(5) Whether the process fluid flows continuously or intermittently;

(6) The susceptibility of the process fluid to damage by hot spots;

(7) Degree of temperature control required;

(8) Climatic conditions;

(9) Corrosiveness of the atmosphere;

(10) Utility supplies available in the plant;

(11) Cost of utilities;

(12) Engineering design time required;

(13) Auxiliary equipment required;

(14) Maintenance required;

(15) Labor costs;

(16) Skilled manpower available and trade union regulations;

(17) The ease with which pipeline or pump repairs can be made;

(18) The degree of reliability required by the process.

A large chemical company recently compared the cost of keeping safety showers from freezing in a particular location using induction heating, MI cable heating and steam heating with trace tubing, respectively. In order of lowest installed cost, the systems were listed as follows: steam tracing, MI cable heating and induction heating. In order of lowest maintenance cost, the systems were listed as follows: induction heating, MI cable heating and steam tracing. Induction heating was chosen for this particular application.

The wide variety of methods and equipment in general use for preventing heat losses in pipelines bear testimony to the fact that no one system is dominantly better and cheaper than the others for the majority of applications.

TABLE 9-8.   Advantages and Disadvantages of Electrical Heating Systems

System	Advantages	Disadvantages
Electrical Heating Systems in General	Clean. Convenient to control by thermostat. Cannot contaminate the process fluid. Uses energy only when required. Heating systems will not freeze in cold weather.	Requires dismantling thermal insulation to make repairs. Pipes must be clearly identified for safety. Local and national safety regulations must be strictly adhered to. Large heating loads require multiple tracers.
Direct Resistance Heating	Entire pipe surface uniformly heated. Not subject to burnout. Not subject to damage by mechanical abuse. Oversized insulation not required.	Voltages must be stepped down to low levels for safety, requiring bulky low voltage high current transformers. Inflexible, since the pipe is an integral part of the electrical circuit and cannot be changed. Since the leads are bulky, transformers and control equipment must be mounted close to the heated pipe, thus occupying valuable space. Accelerated galvanic corrosion.

TABLE 9-8.—(continued)

System	Advantages	Disadvantages
Induction Heating	Relatively long life for coils because of the low operating temperature. Very little maintenance required. Can withstand physical abuse. Can, if necessary, be put on the outside of pipe insulation. Entire pipe surface uniformly heated. Prewound sections of pipe are available.	Will only heat pipes made of ferromagnetic materials. Requires an expert to design the system. Each coil could weigh as much as 7 lb on the larger pipe sizes. Pipeline must be dismantled to install the coils.
Indirect Resistance Heating in General	Easy to install. Easy to replace without dismantling the pipeline.	Subject to burn-out. Must be kept dry. Entire pipe surface not subject to uniform heating.
Cables	Can be cut to any length in the field. Copper sheath reduces safety hazards. Withstands corrosive atmospheres.	Only moderately flexible. Must be kept airtight. Oversized or notched insulation required. Susceptible to damage as the pipe expands or contracts. Galvanic corrosion may be a problem. Require heat transfer cements when output is greater than 10 watts per ft of cable.
Tapes	Very flexible. Do not require oversized or notched insulation. Can be used up to 500°F. No problem with galvanic corrosion. Continuous tapes only require heat transfer cement at fittings.	Subject to damage by physical abuse. Very susceptible to burn-out.
Strips	Relatively flexible. Large conductive heat transfer area. Do not require oversized or notched insulation. No problem with galvanic corrosion. Continuous strips only require heat transfer cement at fittings if jumpers are not used.	Limited temperature range (to 300°F). long pipelines require multiple power supplies.

TABLE 9-9. Advantages and Disadvantages of Fluid Heating Systems

System	Advantages	Disadvantages
Fluid Heating Systems in General	Valves can be used to isolate sections requiring repairs without closing down the entire system. No electrical hazards. Heating fluids readily available. Flexibility in design and operation. Can withstand mechanical abuse.	Possibility of leaks which can soak the insulation and cause it to deteriorate. Possibility of leaks which can contaminate the process fluid. Hard to control since heating is not uniform along the trace length. Sometimes hard to drain the system. Heating system subject to freezing in cold weather. Large pressure drops on long trace lines.
Steam Heating Systems in General	Almost all plants have steam readily available. High available latent heat. Exhaust steam may be used. Does not require pumps to circulate through the tracing.	Requires additional equipment such as pressure reducing stations, steam traps strainers, pressure gauges, etc.
External tubular tracing	Relatively easy to trace valves and fittings. Changes in trace system easily made.	Tendency to "hot spot." Small conductive heat transfer area. Oversized or notched insulation required. Require heat transfer cements for efficient operation.
Jacketing	Relatively high conductive heat transfer area. Entire pipe surface uniformly heated. No heat transfer cement required. Little maintenance required.	Require jumpers at valves and fittings. Presents a large surface to insulate.
Internal tracing	Very efficient. Does not require oversized insulation. No heat transfer cement required.	Pipeline must be dismantled to make repairs. Available cross-sectional flow area reduced for process fluid.

NOMENCLATURE

A Area of heat transfer surface, sq ft
A_a Area of heat transfer between the insulation and atmosphere, sq ft
A_i Inside area of the pipe, sq ft
A_{ml} Mean heat transfer area in the pipe wall, sq ft

A_{m2} Mean heat transfer area in the pipe insulation, sq ft

A_o Outside area of the pipe, sq ft

A_r Area of heat transfer surface at radius r, sq ft

C_h Annual cost of the heat loss, \$/million Btu

C_i Installed cost of insulation, \$/ cu ft

C_1, C_2 Constants

d_a Maximum outside diameter, ft

d_i Inside diameter of pipe, ft

d_{ii} Inside insulation diameter, ft

d_{io} Outside insulation diameter, ft

d_{m1} Mean diameter of pipe, ft

d_{m2} Mean diameter of pipe insulation, ft

d_o Outside diameter of pipe, ft

E Applied voltage, volts

f Fraction of the installed insulation cost depreciated annually

h_a Heat transfer film coefficient for air adjacent to an insulated or uninsulated pipe, Btu/hr sq ft °F

h_c Heat transfer film coefficient for convection, Btu/hr sq ft °F

h_i Inside heat transfer film coefficient for the process fluid, Btu/hr sq ft °F

h_r Heat transfer film coefficient at radius r, Btu/hr sq ft °F

I Electrical current, amperes

k Thermal conductivity, Btu/hr sq ft °F/ft

k_{12} Thermal conductivity of the pipe wall, Btu/hr sq ft °F/ft

k_{23} Thermal conductivity of the first layer of insulating material (A), Btu/hr sq ft °F/ft

k_{34} Thermal conductivity of the second layer of insulating material (B), Btu/hr sq ft °F/ft

ℓ Pipe length, ft

Q Heat flow rate, Btu/hr

r Any radius in the cross section of insulated pipe system, ft

R Electrical resistance, ohms

T_a Ambient temperature, °F

T_r Temperature at radius r, °F

T_s Surface temperature of an insulated or uninsulated pipe in contact with the atmosphere, °F

T_1 Temperature at the inside radius of pipe thickness x_{12}, °F

T_2 Temperature at the outside radius of pipe thickness x_{12}, °F

T_3 Temperature at the outside radius of the first layer of insulating material A, °F

T_4 Temperature at the outside radius of the second layer of insulating material B, °F

t Operating time of equipment, hr/yr

U Overall heat transfer coefficient, Btu/hr sq ft °F

U_i Overall heat transfer coefficient based on the inside area of the pipe, Btu/hr sq ft °F

x_c Critical insulation thickness, ft

x_{12} Pipe wall thickness, ft
x_{23} Pipe insulating material (A) thickness, ft
x_{34} Pipe insulating material (B) thickness, ft
ΔT_m Log mean temperature difference, °F
ϵ Emissivity of the outside pipe or insulation surface
ψ_i Most economical diameter insulation thickness factor

REFERENCES

1. "A Technical Report on Unitrace Design and Installation," Aluminum Co. of America, Pittsburgh, Pa.
2. Aries, R. S., and Newton, R. D., "Chemical Engineering Cost Estimation," p. 97, New York, McGraw-Hill Book Co., Inc., 1955.
3. Beach, W. J., *Soap Chem. Specialties*, **40**, No. 7 (1964).
4. Bower, J. N., and Peterson, H. R., *Hydrocarbon Process Petrol. Refiner*, **42**, No. 3 (1963).
5. Chapman, F. S., and Holland, F. A., *Chem. Eng.*, **72**, No. 2 (1965).
6. Chilton, C. H., "Cost Engineering in the Process Industries," p. 193, New York, McGraw-Hill Book Co., Inc., 1960.
7. Cremer, H. W., and Davies, T., "Chemical Engineering Practice," Vol. 7, p. 411, New York, Academic Press, Inc., 1958.
8. "Electrowrap—Unlimited Length Strip Heating, Bulletin 115C," Electro-Trace Corp., Danbury, Conn.
9. Golding, R. C., *Modern Power and Eng.* (December 1962).
10. Hynes, L. P., *Heating, Piping and Air Conditioning*, 105 (May 1956).
11. Kern, D. Q., "Process Heat Transfer," p. 16, New York, McGraw-Hill Book Co., Inc., 1950.
12. Knowlton, A. E., "Standard Handbook for Electrical Engineers," p. 1693, McGraw-Hill Book Co., Inc., 1957.
13. *Ibid.*, p. 1695.
14. Littleton, C. T., "Industrial Piping," p. 297, New York, McGraw-Hill Book Co., Inc., 1951.
15. Long, J. F., *Petrol. Refiner*, **35**, No. 7 (1956).
16. McAdams, W. H., "Heat Transmission," p. 12, New York, McGraw-Hill Book Co., Inc., 1954.
17. *Ibid.*, p. 472.
18. Mead, W. J., "The Encyclopedia of Chemical Process Equipment," p. 959, New York, Reinhold Publishing Corp., 1964.
19. *Ibid.*, p. 898.
20. Mills, H. E., *Chem. Eng.*, **71**, No. 12 (1964).
21. "New Heater In Hand," *Chem. Week*, **92**, No. 16 (1963).
22. "Properties and Uses of Thermon Heat Transfer Cements—Engineering Data Book 502," Thermon Mfg. Co., Houston, Texas.
23. Silverman, D., *Chem. Eng.*, **71**, No. 15 (1964).
24. Staihar, Lt. N. J., *Power Eng.*, 46 (August 1964).

25. Stoever, H. J., "Applied Heat Transmission," p. 213, New York, McGraw-Hill Book Co., Inc., 1941.
26. *Ibid.*, p. 24.
27. *Ibid.*, p. 200.
28. "60 Cycle Induction Heating," Trans Continental Electronics Corp., New York, N. Y.

CHAPTER 10

Piping and Auxiliary Equipment

Process piping is usually the largest single item in the cost of a chemical plant.[12] Its cost, including valves, fittings, fabrication and installation, is of the order of one-third the total cost of the entire plant.

Most liquids pumped in the process industries are to some extent corrosive. The choice of piping material depends on the following factors: resistance to corrosion and erosion, strength at the temperature of operation, ease of installation, repair and joining, thermal conductivity and expansion, availability, cost of pipe and fittings, and the required service life. The latter is frequently determined by plant obsolescence. Thus a less expensive material with only fair resistance to corrosion may be the most economical for a particular application.

Piping Codes

The American Standards Association codes the wall thickness x in inches of circular cross-section piping by a schedule number based on the following formulas:

$$\text{schedule number} = 1000\left(\frac{P}{S}\right) \tag{10-1}$$

$$\text{schedule number} = 2000\left(\frac{x}{D_m}\right) \tag{10-2}$$

where

P = internal working pressure in psig,

S = allowable stress in psig,

D_m = mean diameter of pipe in inches.

Nominal pipe size (NPS) is a code based on the outside diameter of the pipe. NPS is not related to the schedule number or the wall thickness. It is equal to the outside diameter for diameters of 14 inches or larger.

Voluntary standards for plastic pipes have been published by the U.S. Department of Commerce.

For thermoplastic pipes, the hydrostatic design stress P_h in psig is related to the pressure rating P_r in psig by the equation

$$\frac{2P_h}{P_r} = \frac{D_i}{x} + 1 \tag{10-3}$$

where D_i is the mean inside pipe diameter in inches and x is the minimum wall thickness in inches.

Piping codes are subject to revision. Up-to-date information can be obtained from the American Standards Association, the American Society of Mechanical Engineers and the American Society for Testing Materials.

Metal Pipes and Linings

Carbon steel is the most widely used piping material. Carbon steel pipes either are seamless or are longitudinally or spirally welded. Austenitic stainless steel alloys containing 8 per cent or more of nickel and 16 per cent or more of chrominum are also widely used. These provide good resistance to corrosion. When exposed to an oxidizing environment, the chromium forms a protective oxide film.

Cast iron pipe suffers from the disadvantage of brittleness. Furthermore, if it fails under pressure, there is a hazard from flying metal splinters. Ductile cast iron pipe is 25 per cent lighter in weight than conventional cast iron and it fails under pressure by splitting in the same way as steel.[12]

Nickel, "Monel" and "Inconel" pipes can be obtained in NPS sizes from about ½ to 4 inches. "Hastelloy" cast pipes are available in the size range ¼ to 4 inches NPS. Aluminum seamless pipe is made to the same dimensions as standard and extra strong iron pipe. Aluminum-bronze alloy pipes are made in schedules 40 and 80 from ½ to 4 inches.[14] Copper and brass pipe have outside diameters equal to NPS pipe; wall thicknesses are close to that of the intermediate grade of water tubing.[14]

Lead pipe is rated by actual inside diameter and wall thickness. Lead may also be used to line standard steel pipe in the NPS size range ½ to 12 inches. Either the lead sleeve may be expanded into the steel pipe without bonding or a bonding alloy can be applied to both the lead and the steel. Alternatively, the lead may be cast in place with the pipe.

Nonmetal Pipes and Linings

Nonmetal piping used in the process industries is made from a wide variety of materials including plastics, ceramics, glass, fused silica, carbon and rubber. Of these, the most rapidly growing group is plastics.

Plastic piping has outstanding resistance to alkalis, nearly all acids and other corrosive liquids. It does not rust, scale or pit and does not require painting. In addition, it resists the growth of bacteria, algae and fungi and is nontoxic. The latter is important when the process liquid must be free from contamination. Plastic piping weighs only one-half to one-sixth as much as metal pipe. Furthermore, it is usually substantially cheaper than piping fabricated from expensive alloys. Its use, however, is limited to moderate temperature and pressure conditions.

The principal disadvantage of plastic pipes is the tendency of the plastic to deform, since a typical plastic exhibits a rapid decrease in tensile strength above a certain temperature. A further disadvantage of plastics is their ability to build up a static charge with the consequent risk of sparking.

Plastics may be either thermoplastic or thermosetting. The thermoplastics of greatest commercial importance for piping are polyethylene (PE), polyvinyl chloride (PVC), acrylonitrile-butadiene-styrene (ABS), and cellulose-acetate-butyrate (CAB).[8] Polyesters, phenolics, furans and epoxies are typical thermosets.

Thermoplastics soften with heat and reharden on cooling. Within certain temperature limits they can be heated, reshaped and cooled indefinitely. Thermosets cannot be remelted or reshaped once they are in their final state.

Polyethylene is the least expensive of the thermoplastics. It is light in weight, flexible and has very good impact properties and excellent chemical resistance. However, it is subject to attack by liquid hydrocarbons. The chief disadvantage of polyethylene is its compartively low mechanical strength and structural rigidity. Since it has a low softening temperature, it should only be used below 120°F. The newer, higher density polyethylene has better thermal and mechanical properties than the low density grade.

Polyvinyl chloride has a relatively high tensile strength and modulus of elasticity. It is stronger and more rigid than the other major thermoplastic pipe materials. Polyvinyl chloride can be used up to 150°F. Although in general its resistance to chemical attack is excellent, polyvinyl chloride is subject to damage by ketones, aromatics and some chlorinated hydrocarbons. It has good dimensional stability and weathering properties, and it does not support combustion.[9]

Acrylonitrile-butadiene-styrene is tough and has a high impact strength. It has the highest resistance to heat among the major thermoplastic pipe materials and may be used at temperatures up to 180°F. However, its design strength and resistance to chemical attack are both lower than for polyvinyl chloride.

Cellulose-acetate-butyrate is impact resistant and has the additional advantage of transparency. However, it has fairly low mechanical strength and only moderate resistance to temperature, chemicals and weathering.[9]

A number of thermoplastics exist with better thermal properties than the major materials discussed so far. Polypropylene can be used at temperatures 30 to 50°F higher than polyethylene. It is the lightest thermoplastic piping material and has a higher strength and better resistance to chemical attack than polyethylene. "Penton," a chlorinated polyether, has exceptionally high chemical resistance and can be used at temperatures up to 225°F. However, it costs three to five times as much as polyvinyl chloride. "Kynar," a polyvinylidene fluoride, can be used with liquids containing chlorine at temperatures up to 250°F. Other thermoplastics containing fluorine include "Teflon," "Kel-F" and "Halon." Since these materials are fairly expensive, they are used mainly as pipe linings.

If thermoplastics are used as pipe liners, they have a higher maximum temperature. Thus steel pipe lined with polypropylene can be used up to 230°F. Steel pipes lined with the fluoro polymers can operate at temperatures as high as 500°F. In addition, lined pipes can be used at substantially higher pressures. Pipes made entirely of thermoplastic materials are seldom employed at pressures greater than 100 psig.

Thermosetting pipes have considerably better heat resistance than thermoplastic pipes. Thermosetting materials normally consist of a resin plus reinforcements. The resin system contains additives such as curing agents, inhibitors and plasticizers. Typical reinforcements are asbestos, graphite and glass fibers. These determine the strength of a thermosetting pipe.

Polyester thermosetting plastics include a wide variety of materials. Glass is the most common reinforcing agent. Glass reinforced polyester pipes can be used at temperatures up to 275°F. They are tough and have good resistance to impact.

Polyesters are attacked by concentrated sulfuric and nitric acids, chlorine and hydrogen peroxide. They have good resistance to concentrated and dilute nonoxidizing mineral acids at atmospheric temperatures. Their aging and weathering characteristics are also good.

Phenolic asbestos pipe can be used at temperatures up to 350°F. It has good resistance to chemical attack (except against alkalis) and is nonflammable. It has the disadvantages of low tensile and impact strengths.

Furans have about the same resistance to attack by acids as phenolics, but they have superior resistance to alkalis and solvents.

Glass reinforced epoxy pipe can be used at temperatures up to 300°F. It has high impact and tensile strength, good resistance to abrasion and excellent weathering characteristics. It is far superior to polyesters in its resistance to alkalis.

Other nonmetallic materials are used at temperatures higher than the upper limits for plastics. Unarmored porcelain is recommended for temperatures up to 350°F and pressures from 50 to 200 psig depending on size.[10]

Armoring is used to hold the porcelain together if it is broken. This prevents major leakages. A double layer of resin impregnated fiber-glass cloth bonded over the porcelain is used for this purpose. For higher temperature service (up to 400°F), steel tubing is bonded over the porcelain with portland cement.

Glass piping is designed for temperatures up to 450°F and pressures up to 50 psig. It has the advantages of transparency, noncontaminating surfaces and excellent resistance to chemical attack. Glass will not withstand severe tensile stress, and its strength depends on its surface condition. Glass piping is usually made from borosilicate glass, although for severe processing conditions, aluminosilicate glass may be used.

Glass enamel pipe linings are glass-like inorganic mixtures. These are highly resistant to attack by acids and have a similar composition to borosilicate glasses. However, glass enamel linings are susceptible to attack by hot alkaline solutions. The lining is bonded to the metal pipe by fusion at temperatures higher than 1400°F. Glass lined pipes are used in the temperature range −10 to 600°F. Thermal shock is the main cause of failure.

Soft rubber hose is extensively used in chemical plants. Braided metal jacketed hose is used for higher pressures. Sulfur is added to rubber to give vulcanization. This is a chemical reaction between the long chains of the rubber polymer which produces cross-linkages. The latter determines the degree of rigidity of the material. Soft rubbers contain 2 to 5 per cent sulfur. Hard rubbers contain up to 45 per cent sulfur. Ebonite is a trade name for hard rubber.

Rubber and Ebonite lined pipes are in common use. The properties of the linings can be varied widely by changing the compounding ingredients. Rubber is susceptible to attack by mineral oils, solvents and strong oxidizing agents.

PIPELINE COMPONENTS

Fittings

Couplings and Unions. These may be used to connect small diameter pipes of 2 inches NPS or less. Couplings are short sleeves threaded internally on each end. Each length of pipe is furnished with one coupling. Figure 10–1 illustrates one type of union. Unions may have brass rings pressed into them. The rings have spherical surfaces of different radii. This insures a tight joint even if the two pipes are not perfectly aligned. Other unions have replaceable packing rings.

Flanges. These are normally used to connect pipes with diameters of 2 inches NPS or more. Figure 10–2 illustrates the various methods used to attach a flange to a pipe. These are screwed, shrunk and peened, shrunk and riveted, welded and "Van Stone."[2] The most common method of attaching a flange to a pipe is to thread the end of the pipe and screw on the flange. For severe service, the flange is shrunk onto the pipe. Alternatively, the flange may be welded to the pipe. The "Van Stone" method has the advantage that since the flange is loose, the bolt holes may be readily aligned.

Figure 10–3 illustrates the various types of flange facing. These are plain, grooved, raised, ground, male and female, and tongue and groove.[1]

The ground type of flange facing is the only one used without a gasket. Since it has a tendency to leak, it is rarely used. The gasket on the plain flange facing normally extends to the rim of the flange. The disadvantage of this arrangement is the tendency of the gasket to be tight at the outer edge and loose at the center. Grooved flange facing is used with soft packing to secure a better grip on the packing. In raised flange facing, the gasket is cut to cover only the raised face. The male and female and the tongue and groove flange facings are used at high pressures to prevent the gasket from being blown out.

Expansion Joints. These are used to make piping systems less rigid and to limit the strains which may arise from thermal expansion, pressure,

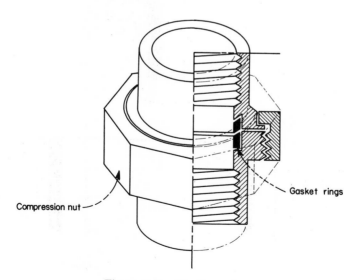

Figure 10-1. Pipeline unions.

vibration, etc. Slip joints and bellows joints are the two kinds of expansion joints commercially available. A slip joint consists of a pair of telescoping cylinders and a bellows joint consists of a series of corrugations or flexible elements. Slip joints are packed while bellows joints are packingless.

Slip joints are used at moderate process temperatures in the range 300 to 750°F.[4] Binding may be caused by corrosion or through excessive lateral forces. Alignment between the body and slip pipe of the joint prevents binding, scoring and uneven wear on the packing. Joints without built-in

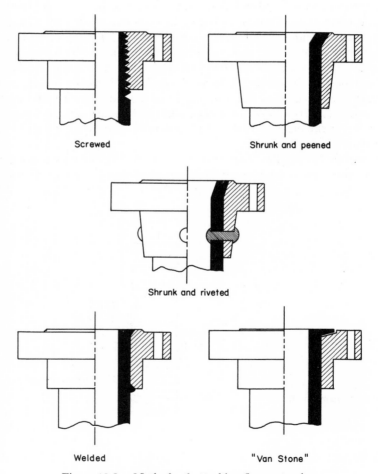

Figure 10-2.   Methods of attaching flanges to pipe.

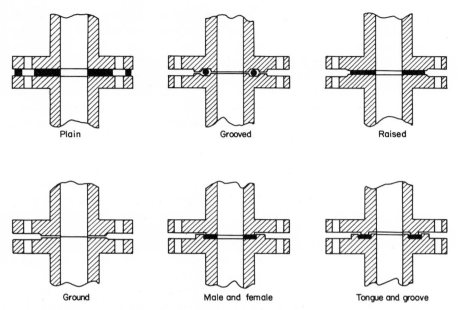

Figure 10-3. Methods of facing pipe flanges. (*Courtesy The Wm. Powell Co.*)

guides must be equipped with auxiliary alignment regulators. The packings in slip joints need to be replaced periodically. Lubrication is also a problem.

Bellows joints do not suffer from these disadvantages since there are no parts which slide against each other. However, bellows joints may fail through cyclic fatigue,[4] which could lead to a burst. Furthermore, sediment may collect in the corrugations of the joint. In addition, deep corrugations may result in a relatively high pressure drop. This can be reduced by the incorporation of an internal sleeve.

Ball or Swivel Joints. These are also used to reduce strains in piping systems due to thermal expansion, shock, vibration, etc. Ball joints provide for movement in two or more planes and can thus compensate for twisting or torsional forces. They are available in carbon steel, stainless steel and other alloys for pipe sizes up to 20 inches NPS. Gaskets are made from materials such as "Teflon" and pressure molded asbestos.

Flexible Connections. These may be obtained in metallic or nonmetallic materials. Metal flexible connections normally have a braided construction. They may have either fixed or replaceable flow liners. These may be made of stainless steel or other ferrous or nonferrous metals. Sizes up to 12 inches NPS are in common use.

In addition to compensating for thermal expansion, misalignment, shock and vibration, flexible connections allow the rapid assembly of temporary piping systems.

Rubber pipe sections reinforced with multiple plies of high strength fabric and helical steel wire are used as vibration dampeners. They do not require gaskets at end flanges. Rubber connections reduce vibrations and pipeline noises created by pumps and conducted by metal piping. They have the further advantage of eliminating metal-to-metal contact which can lead to electrolytic corrosion.

Rupture Disks. When used in pipelines, rupture disks may be located in one outlet of a tee fitting. Bigham[3] has defined rupture disks as carefully designed weak spots that let go at a predetermined pressure. Rupture disks are designed to burst at a particular temperature and pressure. In most cases, the disk will rupture at a lower pressure if used at a higher temperature.

Rupture disks are available in a wide variety of materials. Some of these are: aluminum, carbon steel, a number of stainless steels, copper, gold, "Inconel," "Monel," nickel, platinum, silver and graphite. They normally range in size from $\frac{1}{2}$ to 8 inches NPS. Larger diameter units can also be obtained. Corrosion causes a rupture disk to fail at a lower pressure. For corrosive service, a number of rupture disks can be used in series.

Strainers, Screens and Delumpers. Pipeline strainers are used to remove dirt, scale, rust, welding dross, packing shreds and miscellaneous foreign matter. They protect pumps, valves, flowmeters and other instruments from damage. Strainer bodies are made of such materials as cast iron, ductile iron, bronze, aluminum, steel and stainless steel. The screens are commonly made of stainless steel or "Monel." Most strainer screens must be periodically removed from the pipeline for cleaning. Self-cleaning line strainers are also available. The collected material is periodically discharged through a blow-off connection. Pipeline strainers are commonly available in line sizes up to 6 inches NPS.

Units are also available which break down the size of solid particles in slurries. These units are connected into the process line with flanges. A small electric motor operates an internal chopping mechanism. The units are self-cleaning and are available in pipe sizes from 4 to 24 inches NPS. They may be constructed in a wide variety of materials. The units may be designed to give any desired particle size.

Strainers and delumpers can be used to prevent pipelines and pumping systems from plugging. Cleaning out plugged piping systems can be a difficult and cumbersome job involving a substantial loss in production time.

Instruments

Instruments are used either to measure or to measure and control. A measuring instrument consists of a primary element, a means of transmission and a measuring element. Good control depends on the sensitivity of the primary element. Measurements may be either indicated by a pointer on a scale or recorded by a pen on a moving chart. The latter gives a continuous record of the value of the measurement against time. Measuring units are commonly mounted on a central control panel board at some distance away from the primary element or sensing device.

The process variables commonly measured in piping systems are flow rate, temperature, pressure, viscosity, pH, density, refractive index and turbidity.

Temperature. This cannot be measured directly. However, temperature changes can be obtained by measuring the change in property of a material in equilibrium with the process liquid. This indication may be the change in volume of a solid, liquid or gas or the emf generated at the junction of two dissimilar metals as the temperature changes.

Mercury-in-glass thermometers are the best known. They are commonly used in the range −35 to 750°F. Industrial thermometers are partial immersion units. The glass bulb is protected by a metal tube. The intervening space is filled with a heat transfer medium such as oil in order to reduce temperature lag. The length of a column of mercury is measured by a scale calibrated in units of temperature.

Bimetallic thermometers are also widely used. The primary element consists of a sheet, strip or coil of two metals having high and low coefficients of thermal expansion, respectively. As the temperature changes, the bimetallic element deflects and either the movement is indicated by a pointer on a temperature calibrated scale or chart recorder or it may be used to operate a controller.

In fluid pressure thermometers, a gas or liquid is contained in a bulb. The latter is connected via capillary tubing to a bourdon tube or a similar type of element capable of expanding with increasing pressure. As the temperature of the bulb increases, the fluid pressure increases and the bourdon tube expands. The latter may be linked either to a pointer moving over a temperature calibrated scale or chart recorder or to a controller.

The most common electrical thermometer is the thermocouple. The primary element consists of two dissimilar metal wires joined at one end. When the temperature of the junction changes, an emf is generated across the free ends or terminals which are kept at a known constant temperature. This emf can be measured by a millivoltmeter calibrated in temperature units. Copper-constantan thermocouples are widely used in liquid processing applications. Thermocouple wires are insulated by threading them through porcelain tubes. An outer protecting tube is used to cover the primary element or hot junction.

Pressure. This is a force per unit area. It is normally measured directly by balancing against a known force.

The most widely used pressure measuring device is the bourdon tube. This is a curved tube with an oval cross section. When the pressure to be measured is applied to the tube which is sealed at one end, it tends to straighten itself. The deflection of the end of the tube is communicated through a system of levers to a pointer which moves over a pressure calibrated scale.

Where the process liquid is corrosive, a diaphragm seal is used to protect the bourdon tube. The latter may be filled with oil. The pressure of the process liquid is transmitted through the diaphragm to the oil which in turn deflects the bourdon tube.

Alternatively, the pneumatic force balance seal system illustrated in Figure 10–4 may be used. This unit consists of a chamber which is divided into two parts by a thin metal diaphragm. Process liquid is admitted into the lower part of the chamber and compressed air is admitted into the upper part. The latter enters through a fixed orifice. The air pressure builds up until it equals the pressure of the process liquid. If the latter decreases, the diaphragm moves and the escape valve opening increases so that just enough air bleeds off to maintain a pressure balance across the diaphragm. The measuring instrument may be located up to 1000 ft away from the seal. However, the speed of response decreases as the distance increases.

Viscosity. A number of different types of instruments are available to continuously measure the viscosity of liquids flowing through pipelines. In one type, a portion of the process liquid stream is diverted from the main stream. This subsidiary stream, which is in viscous flow, is pumped at a known rate through a friction tube by a gear pump. The pressure difference between two reference points gives a measure of the viscosity of the process liquid in the friction tube.

In another pipeline viscometer, ultrasonic waves are applied to a thin magnetostrictive alloy steel blade. The rate at which the oscillations are damped is a measure of the viscosity of the process liquid.

pH. This is the logarithm to the base ten of the reciprocal of the hydrogen ion concentration in g/liter. For example, since the hydrogen ion concentration of pure water at 77°F is 10^{-7} g/liter, the pH is 7. The pH of a liquid is a measure of its acidity or alkalinity. A change of one pH unit represents a tenfold change in acidity or alkalinity. Thus pH must be measured with high precision.

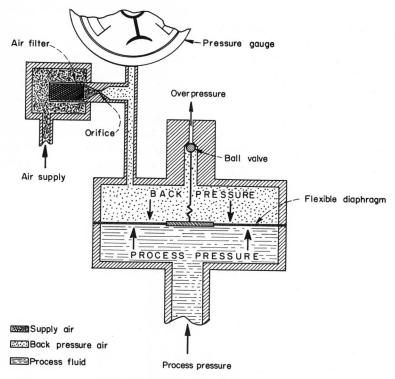

Figure 10-4.   Pneumatic force balance seal. (*Courtesy The Bristol Co.*)

The pH of a process liquid flowing through a pipeline can be measured continuously. The primary element consists of a glass electrode and a reference electrode both of which are immersed in the process liquid. The glass electrode produces an electrical potential proportional to the hydrogen ion concentration. The reference electrode completes the circuit. The potential difference between the two electrodes is directly proportional to the pH of the process liquid. The potential difference is fed to a high impedance voltmeter which is calibrated in pH units. The pH may be read on either an indicator, a recorder or a recorder-controller.

Since electrodes have a tendency to foul, they should be conveniently located to facilitate cleaning and standardization. Electrodes should not be exposed to the air for any longer than is necessary. It is good practice to wash the electrodes in water after use and to keep them covered with water until they are needed again. This can be done by locating the primary element in a small subsidiary line which operates in parallel with the main pipeline. The subsidiary line can be isolated and filled with water when the process pipeline is not in operation.

Density. Two methods are commonly used to continuously measure the density of a flowing liquid. In one method, part of the process liquid stream flows continuously through a fixed volume vessel. The liquid in the vessel is automatically weighed either by a scale or by a force balance transmitter. In the other method, part of the process liquid flows continuously through the unit illustrated in Figure 10–5. This consists of a sample chamber in which a plummet is completely submerged. A light chain is attached to the bottom of the plummet and also to the chamber wall. The plummet rises as the liquid density increases. In doing so, it supports an increasing portion

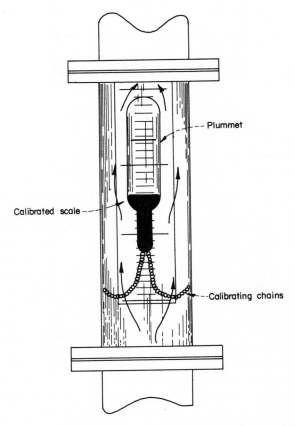

Figure 10-5.   In-line density meter. (*Courtesy Precision Thermometer and Instrument Co.*)

of the weight of the chain. The plummet reaches an equilibrium position for each value of the liquid density. Either unit can be used to indicate, record or control.

Refractive Index. Pipeline refractometers are available in sizes up to 8 inches NPS. They operate on the critical angle principle. A prism is mounted in the wall of a section of pipeline as shown in Figure 10–6. An external light beam is directed to the prism and refracted at the interface between the prism and process liquid in the pipeline. It is then directed back through a beam deflector to two photocell detectors. One photocell is located in the pure white light section. The other is located at the critical angle point where the beam changes from light to dark. The light is transmitted into the process liquid at angles smaller than the critical angle and totally reflected at angles larger than the critical angle. The latter changes with the refractive index of the process liquid. Thus the refractive index of the liquid determines the amount of light which falls on the sample photocell detector. The signal from the photocells is amplified to enable a servo motor to drive a glass restorer plate in the light beam. This returns the beam

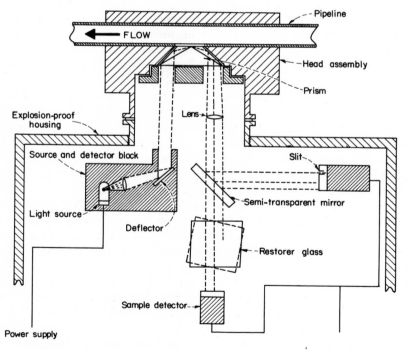

Figure 10-6.   In-line refractometer. (*Courtesy Waters Associates*)

to the optical null position. The amount of movement of the glass can provide a measure of the process liquid concentration. The unit may indicate, record or control.

Turbidity. Units are available to continuously monitor the turbidity, cloudiness or haze of a liquid flowing through a pipeline. A light source and a photoelectric scanner are located on opposite sides of a flow cell which is mounted directly in the pipeline. A change in turbidity of the process liquid affects the amount of light received by the scanner. The unit is calibrated to a relative standard which is normally process liquid with the minimum amount of turbidity. The meter is adjusted to read zero at this point. Turbidity meters can be used to indicate, record or control.

In-line Mixers

Two or more liquids can be mixed by pumping them in turbulent flow through a pipeline. Baffles may be placed in the pipeline to increase the turbulence and hence the mixing process.

Injectors are commonly used to mix two liquids in a pipeline. One of the liquids is injected through a nozzle into the flow stream of the other liquid. The jet of liquid from the nozzle entrains the liquid flowing in the pipeline. Baffles may be used to enhance the mixing process.

Alternatively, a mechanical in-line mixer may be installed in the pipeline downstream from the injector. Several types of mechanical in-line mixers are available. The type most widely used consists of a mixing chamber which houses one or more rotating agitators. The latter are usually turbines or marine propellers, depending on the axis of the agitator in relation to the axis of the pipeline. Propellers discharge axially, while the discharge from turbines is substantially radial. The mixer shown in Figure 10–7 is mounted directly along the central axis of a pipeline—in the same way as the in-line pumps discussed in Chapters 5 and 6. Flow is straight through with a minimum of restrictions.

Another type of mixer has a casing which is set at a 90° angle to the pipeline axis. This unit is normally installed at a right angle bend. In this case, it replaces the elbow required at this point. Blending of two or more components is accomplished using an axial discharge propeller in combination with a radial discharge turbine. In this unit, the turbine supplies liquid to the propeller. Under light processing conditions, the propeller gives adequate head. However, for viscous liquids and long complex lines, an auxiliary feed pump may be required. A second type of in-line mixer consists of a vibrating metallic reed in close proximity to a narrow orifice. Mixing takes place when liquid, which is forced through the orifice, impinges at high velocity on the thin metal reed, causing it to vibrate. At low

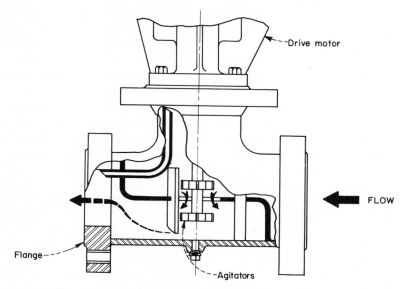

Figure 10-7. In-line mixer. (*Courtesy Mixing Equipment Co.*)

viscosities, the vibrating element is positioned very close to the orifice. As the liquid viscosity increases (up to 20,000 SSU), the vibrator is moved further away from the orifice. A pump is required with these units to insure a sufficiently high velocity at the orifice to vibrate the reed. Pressure drops are relatively high since the narrow orifice provides only a small flow area. Normally the maximum capacity of "Sonic" mixers is approximately 60 gpm at pressure drops up to 60 psi. "Sonic" mixers can only handle relatively clear liquids, since the small orifice is prone to clogging.

The in-line mixers previously described can be used to blend liquids containing foreign bodies or abrasive solids.

PIPELINE INSTALLATIONS

Pipe Joints

Two pieces of pipe may be joined either permanently or nonpermanently. Nonpermanent joints may be made with pipe fittings such as flanges, couplings, etc. The most common way of permanently joining two pipes is to fuse or weld them together.

Welded joints weigh less than nonpermanent joints and are much easier to insulate and trace. Further advantages are that they do not require maintenance and they can be made permanently leak-tight. The main disadvantage of welding is that it must be done by skilled and qualified operators. Furthermore, welding cannot be done in some hazardous areas. Additional disadvantages are that the piping system can no longer be readily dismantled, the system no longer has the stress relief provided by flanges and couplings, etc., and cheaper iron body valves cannot be welded in.

Heat welding is also used to join pipes made of thermoplastic materials such as polyethylene and polypropylene. Two pipes may be joined either by butt welding the accurately squared off pieces or by welding the outside surface of one pipe to the inside surface of a socket in the other pipe.

Thermoplastic pipes are also joined by solvent welding. A free flowing solvent cement is brushed onto the outside surface at the end of one pipe and onto the inside surface of a socket in the other pipe. The pipes are twisted slightly as one pipe is inserted into the socket of the other pipe. The solvent cement should be allowed to cure for about 15 minutes before handling the pipes. It is recommended that 24 hours should elapse before introducing full line pressure in a solvent cemented piping system.

Thermosetting pipes such as glass reinforced polyester pipes are joined by an analogous technique where an adhesive is used in place of the solvent cement. The adhesive is a mixture of the resin and the catalyst which chemically cures or sets the bond. The two materials must not be mixed until just prior to use.

Lautenbach[5] gives a detailed description of the joining of glass-fiber reinforced pipes. The most common types of joints are plain end, bell and spigot, and integral threaded. The first type of joint is made by butting two pieces of pipe together and then overwrapping the connection with successive layers of glass-fiber mats saturated with resin.

Pipe Supports

Horizontal pipes supported at intermediate points tend to sag in the regions between the supports. The extent of the sag is a function of the weight of the pipe, process liquid, insulation and any fittings included in the line.

The American Standards Association suggests the values given in Table 10–1 for the maximum spacing of hangers or supports for carbon steel pipe at a temperature of 750°F or lower. These values do not apply where there are concentrated loads between the supports.

For thermoplastic piping, the spacing of hangers should be about one-half to one-quarter of the values given in Table 10–1 for carbon steel pipe. Plastic pipes used to transport hazardous liquids at high temperatures are often continuously supported with channel iron. All fittings in plastic pipes with the exception of couplings should be supported individually. Valves should be braced to avoid damage to the pipe when the valve is turned.

In general, supports should not clamp the pipe so tightly as to resist thermal expansion. However, rigid clamping should be used for valves and other fittings located near sharp bends. Mallinson[6] describes techniques for supporting reinforced plastic pipe systems.

Glass piping should be supported so that it is free from tension. Hangers padded with a soft material should be used. The hangers are adjusted to the glass pipe and not vice versa.[7] The padding material should not adhere to the glass pipe. Common padding materials are soft asbestos and rubber.

It is preferable in glass piping systems to have the minimum number of anchor points. Since valves in glass piping systems are individually supported, they are anchor points. Right angle bends increase the flexibility of a glass piping system. There should only be one anchor point in each straight run of pipe unless an expansion joint is used.[7]

TABLE 10-1.   Suggested Maximum Spacing between Pipe Supports
for Carbon Steel Pipe

Nominal Pipe Size (in.)	Maximum Span (ft)
1	7
2	10
3	12
4	14
6	17
8	19
10	22
12	23
14	25
16	27
18	28
20	30
24	32

Basis: straight runs of standard wall and heavier pipe, maximum operating temperature of 750°F.

Vertically installed glass pipe should be hung from the top and never supported from the bottom. For underground systems, it is common practice to surround the glass pipe with a casing of a material such as polystyrene. The casing is ½ to 1 inch in thickness and will compress and absorb loads when the soil shifts to create additional pressure.

As with glass, porcelain piping should never be forced into position. It should also be free to move to reduce thermal and mechanical strains.

Pipe Bends and Loops

Changes in direction can be made in piping systems by incorporating standard elbow, tee, cross and 45° lateral fittings. These are available in most piping materials. Alternatively, straight lengths of pipe may be bent to the required curvature. The latter method can only be used with relatively small diameter pipes and with a limited number of materials.

Bends and loops may also be incorporated in a piping system to add flexibility and to relieve thermal and mechanical strains. Kiven[4] describes the various types of bends and loops commonly used in piping systems. The simplest kind of expansion loop is the U-bend. Complete circle bends are also used.

In general, the added flexibility resulting from a loop is proportional to its length. The gain in flexibility is partially offset by the stress intensification that occurs when the pipe cross-section becomes flattened into an oval shape in the bending region.

Pipe loops are inexpensive, reliable and do not require maintenance. Furthermore, they can be used with standard fittings. Pipe loops have the disadvantage that they create turbulence and increase the pressure drop in the system. They also take up space and need to be supported. For large diameter pipes, the cost of supports can be quite high. Where the available space is limited, expansion joints are used.

Thermal expansion in underground plastic pipelines is compensated by snaking the line from side to side in the trench.[11] In most cases, one cycle for each 40 ft or less is satisfactory.

Protection of Piping Systems against Waterhammer

Liquid flowing through a pipeline possesses momentum proportional to its mass and velocity. The force produced when the flowing liquid is brought to a stop is proportional to the rate of change of momentum, which in turn is inversely proportional to the time taken to stop the flow. When the liquid is suddenly brought to rest by the action of either a quick-closing valve or a check valve, a shock load or high pressure surge results. The latter is called waterhammer. The longer the pipeline and the higher the liquid velocity, the greater is the effect of the waterhammer. Waterhammer can break pipes, pumps and fittings.

Thus quick-closing valves should only be used in short pipelines. In contrast, check valves should close as quickly as possible to keep to a minimum the velocity of the back flowing liquid.

The following formula[11]

$$\Delta P = \frac{0.070u\ell}{\Delta t} \qquad (10-4)$$

gives the additional pressure ΔP in psi due to shock load for a pipeline length ℓ ft, a mean water velocity u in ft/sec, and a valve closing time of Δt seconds. Thus the waterhammer in a 100 ft long pipeline carrying water at a mean linear velocity of 5 ft/sec would be 35 psi if the valve were closed in a 1 second time interval, and 3500 psi if the valve were closed in a 1/100 second time interval. The pressures developed for process liquids other than water have a similar magnitude.

Protection of Piping Systems against Corrosion

Metals and alloys resist corrosion either because of their low position in the electromotive series with respect to hydrogen or because they build up a condition of surface passivity in the oxidizing environment. The stainless steels resist corrosion largely by building up a condition of surface passivity as a result of their chromium content. This is not really effective below 16 to 18 per cent chromium. The inclusion of nickel and molybdenum promotes passivity. Hydrochloric and sulfuric acids above certain temperatures and concentrations destroy this passivity.

Corrosion may be either localized or general. Localized corrosion can be either intergranular, electrolytic, stress or pitting. In austenitic stainless steels such as 304 or 316, intergranular corrosion takes place at the grain boundaries as a result of carbide precipitation. Electrolytic corrosion results from a current flowing between two dissimilar metals placed together in a corrosive environment. Electrolytic corrosion can also take place in the absence of dissimilar metals. Concentration differences occurring in pits or recesses can cause electrolytic corrosion. Pitting corrosion is caused by local concentrations of the corrosive media, by carbide precipitation or by stresses. Stress corrosion is the acceleration of the corrosion rate by stress. It has been observed in almost all metals and their alloys. Stress corrosion is only promoted by tensile stresses. It usually occurs in the form of rapid penetration or cracking along grain boundaries.

The corrosion rate of alloys increases as the flow rate of the corrosive media increases. Stainless steels with a high nickel content are particularly affected. The smoother the surface of the metal, the greater is the resistance to corrosion. Corrosion can be accelerated by weld projections and roughness. During welding, the metal is heated to a very high temperature over a very small area. The heated metal expands the colder surrounding metal, causing severe internal stresses. Additional stresses are created when the metal cools.

Piping systems should be designed to drain as freely and completely as possible. Flanged connections should have gaskets cut to the same diameter to avoid recesses where corrosive liquids can accumulate when the system is emptied.

The use of dissimilar metals in contact with each other should normally be avoided. However, the use of zinc, magnesium or aluminum as anodes in electrical contact with the metal to be protected is the basis of the sacrificial anode method of cathodic protection. Another way to provide cathodic protection is the impressed emf method.

The driving force for electrochemical corrosion is the potential difference between the anode and the cathode. The current leaves the anode, flows through the solution and returns to the cathode. In cathodic protection, a counter-current is used to neutralize the corroding current.

Cathodic protection has been widely applied to buried pipelines. In power systems, the anodes may consist of graphite, buried iron scrap, or an abandoned pipeline parallel to the protected line.[13] If the pipeline is coated with a material which has an electrical resistance just a few times greater than the surrounding earth, a much wider spread of current results from a single anode. In this case, a long stretch of pipeline can be protected with one installation.[13] Bituminous coatings are often used. In coated lines, the neutralizing current need only be sufficient to protect the metal at any bare spots. This is much less than the current required to protect the bare pipe.

Expendable anodes such as zinc, magnesium and aluminum are used where the soil resistance is relatively low. These anodes are located at 25 to 50 ft intervals depending on soil conditions.[13]

Erosion corrosion may be caused by certain liquids flowing at high velocities. These same liquids may not cause corrosion if motionless. It is possible that erosion corrosion results from the destruction of the passive film on metals such as stainless steel. This kind of corrosion can be reduced by keeping turbulence and impingement to a minimum.

Stress corrosion in piping systems can be minimized by reducing the obvious sources of stress such as vibrations, applied loads and excessive thermal expansion and contraction.

Color Codes for Pipelines

Color codes for pipelines have the following benefits for maintenance, operation and safety, respectively:

(1) Lines are more easily traced for repair work;

(2) Lines are easily identified by operators;

(3) Color codes permit rapid identification of pipelines during safety checks and in emergencies.

Color codes may be used in the following ways.

(1) Lines are banded at suitable intervals (usually 10 to 20 ft) with the appropriate color. The name or code of the process liquid is stenciled on the pipe near the colored band.

(2) The entire pipe is painted in the appropriate color and the process liquid is labeled every 10 or 20 ft. Easily applied pressure sensitive labels are frequently used.

A typical color code for liquids is as follows:

(1) *Nonhazardous materials:* (a) stock or raw materials—dark green, white labels (name); (b) domestic cold water—light green, black labels (DWC); (c) domestic hot water—light green, black labels (DWH).

(2) *Hazardous materials; nonflammable and nonexplosive*: all materials such as acids, caustics, etc.—yellow, black labels with product code or name.

(3) *Hazardous materials; flammable and/or explosive*: all materials such as alcohols, petroleum products, etc.—orange, black labels with product name.

NOMENCLATURE

D_i mean inside pipe diameter, inches
D_m mean diameter of pipe, inches
ℓ pipeline length, ft
P internal pipeline working pressure, psig
P_h hydrostatic design stress, psig
P_r pipe pressure rating, psig
S allowable pipeline stress, psig
u mean water velocity, ft/sec
x pipe wall thickness, inches
ΔP pressure increase in Equation (10–4), psi
Δt valve closing time in Equation (10–4), seconds

REFERENCES

1. Badger, W. L., and McCabe, W. L., "Elements of Chemical Engineering," p. 68, New York, McGraw-Hill Book Co., Inc., 1936.
2. *Ibid.*, p. 69.

3. Bigham, J. E., *Chem. Eng.*, **65**, No. 7 (1958).
4. Kiven, K., *Chem. Eng.*, **73**, No. 4 (1966).
5. Lautenbach, T., *Chem. Eng.*, **71**, No. 16 (1964).
6. Mallinson, J. H., *Chem. Eng.*, **73**, No. 2 (1966).
7. Mead, W. J., "The Encyclopedia of Chemical Process Equipment," p. 700, New York, Reinhold Publishing Corporation, 1964.
8. *Ibid.*, p. 701.
9. *Ibid.*, p. 702.
10. *Ibid.*, p. 709.
11. "Plastic Piping Handbook," Cabot Corporation, Louisville, Kentucky.
12. Riley, R. V., *Chem. & Process Eng.*, **47**, 55 (1966).
13. Speller, F. N., "Corrosion Causes and Prevention," p. 624, New York McGraw-Hill Book Co., Inc., 1951.
14. Vilbrandt, F. C., and Dryden, C. E., "Chemical Engineering Plant Design," p. 346, New York, McGraw-Hill Book Co., Inc., 1959.

APPENDIX

Design Data

TABLE A-1. Dimensions of Welded and Seamless Carbon and Alloy Steel Pipe

Nominal Pipe Size (in.)	Outside Diameter[a] (in.)	Schedule Number[b]	Wall Thickness[a] (in.)	Inside Diameter[a] (in.)	Cross-sectional Area of Flow (sq ft)	Capacity at 1 ft/sec velocity (U.S. gpm)
1/8	0.405	Stnd weight	0.068	0.269	0.00040	0.1795
		40	0.068	0.269	0.00040	0.1795
		X strong	0.095	0.215	0.00025	0.1122
		80	0.095	0.215	0.00025	0.1122
1/4	0.540	Stnd weight	0.088	0.364	0.00072	0.3232
		40	0.088	0.364	0.00072	0.3232
		X strong	0.119	0.302	0.00050	0.2244
		80	0.119	0.302	0.00050	0.2244
3/8	0.675	Stnd weight	0.091	0.493	0.00133	0.5969
		40	0.091	0.493	0.00133	0.5969
		X strong	0.126	0.423	0.00098	0.4399
		80	0.126	0.423	0.00098	0.4399
1/2	0.840	Stnd weight	0.109	0.622	0.00211	0.9470
		40	0.109	0.622	0.00211	0.9470
		X strong	0.147	0.546	0.00163	0.7316
		80	0.147	0.546	0.00163	0.7316
		160	0.187	0.466	0.00117	0.5251
		Dbl X strong	0.294	0.252	0.00035	0.1571
3/4	1.050	Stnd weight	0.113	0.824	0.00371	1.665
		40	0.113	0.824	0.00371	1.665
		X strong	0.154	0.742	0.00300	1.345
		80	0.154	0.742	0.00300	1.345
		160	0.218	0.614	0.00204	0.9170
		Dbl X strong	0.308	0.434	0.00103	0.4613

TABLE A-1.—(continued)

Nominal Pipe Size (in.)	Outside Diameter[a] (in.)	Schedule Number[b]	Wall Thickness[a] (in.)	Inside Diameter[a] (in.)	Cross-sectional Area of Flow (sq ft)	Capacity at 1 ft/sec velocity (U.S. gpm)
1	1.315	Stnd weight	0.133	1.049	0.00600	2.693
		40	0.133	1.049	0.00600	2.693
		X strong	0.179	0.957	0.00499	2.240
		80	0.179	0.957	0.00499	2.240
		160	0.250	0.815	0.00362	1.625
		Dbl X strong	0.358	0.599	0.00196	0.8784
1¼	1.660	Stnd weight	0.140	1.380	0.01039	4.663
		40	0.140	1.380	0.01039	4.663
		X strong	0.191	1.278	0.00891	3.999
		80	0.191	1.278	0.00891	3.999
		160	0.250	1.160	0.00734	3.290
		Dbl X strong	0.382	0.896	0.00438	1.966
1½	1.900	Stnd weight	0.145	1.610	0.01414	6.346
		40	0.145	1.610	0.01414	6.346
		X strong	0.200	1.500	0.01225	5.498
		80	0.200	1.500	0.01225	5.498
		160	0.281	1.338	0.00976	4.380
		Dbl X strong	0.400	1.100	0.00660	2.962
2	2.375	Stnd weight	0.154	2.067	0.02330	10.45
		40	0.154	2.067	0.02330	10.45
		X strong	0.218	1.939	0.02050	9.200
		80	0.218	1.939	0.02050	9.200
		160	0.343	1.689	0.01552	6.970
		Dbl X strong	0.436	1.503	0.01232	5.530
2½	2.875	Stnd weight	0.203	2.469	0.03322	14.92
		40	0.203	2.469	0.03322	14.92
		X strong	0.276	2.323	0.02942	13.20
		80	0.276	2.323	0.02942	13.20
		160	0.375	2.125	0.02463	11.07
		Dbl X strong	0.552	1.771	0.01711	7.680
3	3.500	Stnd weight	0.216	3.068	0.05130	23.03
		40	0.216	3.068	0.05130	23.03
		X strong	0.300	2.900	0.04587	20.59
		80	0.300	2.900	0.04587	20.59
		160	0.438	2.624	0.03755	16.85
		Dbl X strong	0.600	2.300	0.02885	12.95

TABLE A-1.—*(continued)*

Nominal Pipe Size (in.)	Outside Diameter[a] (in.)	Schedule Number[b]	Wall Thickness[a] (in.)	Inside Diameter[a] (in.)	Cross-sectional Area of Flow (sq ft)	Capacity at 1 ft/sec velocity (U.S. gpm)
3½	4.000	Stnd weight	0.226	3.548	0.06870	30.83
		40	0.226	3.548	0.06870	30.83
		X strong	0.318	3.364	0.06170	27.69
		80	0.318	3.364	0.06170	27.69
4	4.500	Stnd weight	0.237	4.026	0.08840	39.68
		40	0.237	4.026	0.08840	39.68
		X strong.	0.337	3.826	0.07986	35.84
		80 ·	0.337	3.826	0.07986	35.84·
		120	0.438	3.624	0.07170	32.18
		160	0.531	3.438	0.06647	29.83
		Dbl X strong	0.674	3.152	0.05419	24.32
5	5.563	Stnd weight	0.258	5.047	0.1390	62.39
		40	0.258	5.047	0.1390	62.39
		X strong	0.375	4.813	0.1263	56.69
		80	0.375	4.813	0.1263	56.69
		120	0.500	4.563	0.1136	50.99
		160	0.625	4.313	0.1136	50.99
		Dbl X strong	0.750	4.063	0.1015	45.56
6	6.625	Stnd weight	0.280	6.065	0.2006	90.04
		40	0.280	6.065	0.2006	90.04
		X strong	0.432	5.761	0.1810	81.24
		80	0.432	5.761	0.1810	81.24
		120	0.562	5.501	0.1650	74.06
		160	0.718	5.189	0.1467	65.84
		Dbl X strong	0.864	4.897	0.1308	58.71
8	8.625	20	0.250	8.125	0.3601	161.6
		30	0.277	8.071	0.3553	159.5
		Stnd weight	0.322	7.981	0.3474	155.9
		40	0.322	7.981	0.3474	155.9
		60	0.406	7.813	0.3329	149.4
		X strong	0.500	7.625	0.3171	142.3
		80	0.500	7.625	0.3171	142.3
		100	0.593	7.439	0.3017	135.4
		120	0.718	7.189	0.2817	126.4
		140	0.812	7.001	0.2673	120.0
		Dbl X strong	0.875	6.875	0.2578	115.7
		160	0.906	6.813	0.2532	113.6

TABLE A-1.—(continued)

Nominal Pipe Size (in.)	Outside Diameter[a] (in.)	Schedule Number[b]	Wall Thickness[a] (in.)	Inside Diameter[a] (in.)	Cross-sectional Area of Flow (sq ft)	Capacity at 1 ft/sec velocity (U.S. gpm)
10	10.750	20	0.250	10.250	0.5731	257.2
		30	0.307	10.136	0.5603	251.5
		Stnd weight	0.365	10.020	0.5475	245.7
		40	0.365	10.020	0.5475	245.7
		60	0.500	9.750	0.5185	232.7
		X strong	0.500	9.750	0.5185	232.7
		80	0.593	9.564	0.4987	223.8
		100	0.718	9.314	0.4729	212.3
		120	0.843	9.064	0.4479	201.0
		140	1.000	8.750	0.4176	187.4
		160	1.125	8.500	0.3941	176.9
12	12.750	20	0.250	12.250	0.8185	376.4
		30	0.330	12.090	0.7972	357.8
		Stnd weight	0.375	12.000	0.7854	352.5
		40	0.406	11.938	0.7773	348.9
		X strong	0.500	11.750	0.7530	338.0
		60	0.562	11.626	0.7372	330.9
		80	0.687	11.376	0.7056	316.7
		100	0.843	11.064	0.6674	299.5
		120	1.000	10.750	0.6303	282.9
		140	1.125	10.500	0.6013	269.9
		160	1.312	10.126	0.5592	251.0
14	14.000	10	0.250	13.500	0.9940	446.1
		20	0.312	13.375	0.9750	437.6
		30	0.375	13.250	0.9575	429.8
		Stnd weight	0.375	13.250	0.9575	429.8
		40	0.438	13.124	0.9397	421.8
		X strong	0.500	13.000	0.9218	413.7
		60	0.593	12.814	0.8957	402.0
		80	0.750	12.500	0.8522	382.5
		100	0.937	12.126	0.8017	359.8
		120	1.093	11.814	0.7610	341.6
		140	1.250	11.500	0.7213	323.7
		160	1.406	11.188	0.6827	306.4
16	16.000	10	0.250	15.500	1.3104	588.1
		20	0.312	15.375	1.2985	582.8
		30	0.375	15.250	1.2680	569.1
		Stnd weight	0.375	15.250	1.2680	569.1

TABLE A-1.—(continued)

Nominal Pipe Size (in.)	Outside Diameter[a] (in.)	Schedule Number[b]	Wall Thickness[a] (in.)	Inside Diameter[a] (in.)	Cross-sectional Area of Flow (sq ft)	Capacity at 1 ft/sec velocity (U.S. gpm)
16 (cont'd)		40	0.500	15.000	1.2272	550.8
		X strong	0.500	15.000	1.2272	550.8
		60	0.656	14.688	1.1766	528.1
		80	0.843	14.314	1.1171	501.4
		100	1.031	13.938	1.0596	475.6
		120	1.218	13.564	1.0032	450.3
		140	1.438	13.124	0.9394	421.6
		160	1.593	12.814	0.8953	401.8
18	18.000	10	0.250	17.500	1.6703	749.7
		20	0.312	17.375	1.6468	739.1
		Stnd weight	0.375	17.250	1.6230	728.5
		30	0.438	17.124	1.5993	717.8
		X strong	0.500	17.000	1.5763	707.5
		40	0.562	16.876	1.5533	697.2
		60	0.750	16.500	1.4849	666.5
		80	0.937	16.126	1.4180	636.4
		100	1.156	15.688	1.3423	602.5
		120	1.375	15.250	1.2684	569.3
		140	1.562	14.876	1.2070	541.7
		160	1.781	14.438	1.1370	510.3
20	20.000	10	0.250	19.500	2.0740	930.9
		20	0.375	19.250	2.0211	907.1
		Stnd weight	0.375	19.250	2.0211	907.1
		30	0.500	19.000	1.9689	883.7
		X strong	0.500	19.000	1.9689	883.7
		40	0.593	18.814	1.9302	866.3
		60	0.812	18.376	1.8417	826.6
		80	1.031	17.938	1.7550	787.7
		100	1.281	17.438	1.6585	744.4
		120	1.500	17.000	1.5763	707.5
		140	1.750	16.500	1.4849	666.5
		160	1.968	16.064	1.4071	631.6
24	24.000	10	0.250	23.500	3.012	1351
		20	0.375	23.250	2.948	1323
		Stnd weight	0.375	23.250	2.948	1323
		X strong	0.500	23.000	2.885	1295
		30	0.562	22.875	2.854	1277
		40	0.688	22.624	2.792	1253

TABLE A-1.—*(continued)*

Nominal Pipe Size (in.)	Outside Diameter[a] (in.)	Schedule Number[b]	Wall Thickness[a] (in.)	Inside Diameter[a] (in.)	Cross-sectional Area of Flow (sq ft)	Capacity at 1 ft/sec velocity (U.S. gpm)
24 *(cont'd)*		60	0.969	22.062	2.655	1192
		80	1.218	21.564	2.536	1138
		100	1.531	20.938	2.391	1073
		120	1.812	20.376	2.264	1016
		140	2.062	19.876	2.155	967.2
		160	2.343	19.314	2.034	912.9
28	28.000	10	0.312	27.376	4.087	1834
		20	0.500	27.000	3.976	1785
		30	0.625	26.750	3.903	1752
32	32.000	10	0.312	31.376	5.369	2410
		20	0.500	31.000	5.242	2353
		30	0.625	30.750	5.157	2315
		40	0.688	30.614	5.112	2294
36	36.000	10	0.312	35.376	6.826	3064
		20	0.500	35.000	6.681	2999
		30	0.625	34.750	6.586	2956
		40	0.750	34.500	6.492	2914

[a] ASA Standards B36.10–1959.
[b] Schedule 40(12 in. and larger) and schedule 80(10 in. and larger) do not agree with dimensions given for standard weight and extra strong weight.
[c] Schedules 40 and 80 apply to PVC schedule rated pipe according to the U.S. Dept. of Commerce Commercial Standard CS–207–60. Refer to CS–256–63 for information concerning uniformly pressure rated pipe (SDR rating system).

TABLE A-2.   Dimensions of Welded and Seamless Stainless Steel Pipe

Nominal Pipe Size (in.)	Outside Diameter[a] (in.)	Schedule Number[b]	Wall Thickness[a] (in.)	Inside Diameter[a] (in.)	Cross-sectional Area of Flow (sq ft)	Capacity at 1 ft/sec velocity (U.S. gpm)
1/8	0.405	10S	0.049	0.307	0.00051	0.2289
		40S	0.068	0.269	0.00040	0.1795
		80S	0.095	0.215	0.00025	0.1122
1/4	0.540	10S	0.065	0.410	0.00092	0.4129
		40S	0.088	0.364	0.00072	0.3232
		80S	0.119	0.302	0.00050	0.2244

TABLE A-2.—(continued)

Nominal Pipe Size (in.)	Outside Diameter[a] (in.)	Schedule Number[b]	Wall Thickness[a] (in.)	Inside Diameter[a] (in.)	Cross-sectional Area of Flow (sq ft)	Capacity at 1 ft/sec velocity (U.S. gpm)
3/8	0.675	10S	0.065	0.545	0.00162	0.7271
		40S	0.091	0.493	0.00133	0.5969
		80S	0.126	0.423	0.00098	0.4399
1/2	0.840	5S	0.065	0.710	0.00275	1.234
		10S	0.083	0.674	0.00248	1.113
		40S	0.109	0.622	0.00211	0.9470
		80S	0.147	0.546	0.00163	0.7316
3/4	1.050	5S	0.065	0.920	0.00461	2.069
		10S	0.083	0.884	0.00426	1.912
		40S	0.113	0.824	0.00371	1.665
		80S	0.154	0.742	0.00300	1.345
1	1.315	5S	0.065	1.185	0.00763	3.425
		10S	0.109	1.097	0.00656	2.944
		40S	0.133	1.049	0.00600	2.693
		80S	0.179	0.957	0.00499	2.240
1 1/4	1.660	5S	0.065	1.530	0.01277	5.732
		10S	0.109	1.442	0.01134	5.090
		40S	0.140	1.380	0.01039	4.663
		80S	0.191	1.278	0.00891	3.999
1 1/2	1.900	5S	0.065	1.770	0.01709	7.671
		10S	0.109	1.682	0.01543	6.925
		40S	0.145	1.610	0.01414	6.346
		80S	0.200	1.500	0.01225	5.498
2	2.375	5S	0.065	2.245	0.02749	12.34
		10S	0.109	2.157	0.02538	11.39
		40S	0.154	2.067	0.02330	10.45
		80S	0.218	1.939	0.02050	9.200
2 1/2	2.875	5S	0.083	2.709	0.04003	17.97
		10S	0.120	2.635	0.03787	17.00
		40S	0.203	2.469	0.03322	14.92
		80S	0.276	2.323	0.02942	13.20
3	3.500	5S	0.083	3.334	0.06063	27.21
		10S	0.120	3.260	0.05796	26.01
		40S	0.216	3.068	0.05130	23.03
		80S	0.300	2.900	0.04587	20.59

TABLE A-2.—(continued)

Nominal Pipe Size (in.)	Outside Diameter[a] (in.)	Schedule Number[b]	Wall Thickness[a] (in.)	Inside Diameter[a] (in.)	Cross-sectional Area of Flow (sq ft)	Capacity at 1 ft/sec velocity (U.S. gpm)
$3\frac{1}{2}$	4.000	5S	0.083	3.834	0.08017	35.98
		10S	0.120	3.760	0.07711	34.61
		40S	0.226	3.548	0.06870	30.83
		80S	0.318	3.364	0.06170	27.69
4	4.500	5S	0.083	4.334	0.1025	45.98
		10S	0.120	4.260	0.09898	44.43
		40S	0.237	4.026	0.08840	39.68
		80S	0.337	3.826	0.07986	35.84
5	5.563	5S	0.109	5.345	0.1558	69.93
		10S	0.134	5.295	0.1529	68.63
		40S	0.258	5.047	0.1390	62.39
		80S	0.375	4.813	0.1263	56.69
6	6.625	5S	0.109	6.407	0.2239	100.5
		10S	0.134	6.357	0.2204	98.92
		40S	0.280	6.065	0.2006	90.04
		80S	0.432	5.761	0.1810	81.24
8	8.625	5S	0.109	8.407	0.3855	173.0
		10S	0.148	8.329	0.3784	169.8
		40S	0.322	7.981	0.3474	155.9
		80S	0.500	7.625	0.3171	142.3
10	10.750	5S	0.134	10.482	0.5993	269.0
		10S	0.165	10.420	0.5992	265.8
		40S	0.365	10.020	0.5475	245.7
		80S	0.500[c]	9.750[c]	0.5185	232.7
12	12.750	5S	0.156	12.438	0.8438	381.0
		10S	0.180	12.390	0.8373	375.8
		40S	0.375[c]	12.000[c]	0.7854	352.5
		80S	0.500[c]	11.750[c]	0.7530	338.0
14	14.000	5S	0.156	13.688	1.022	458.7
		10S	0.188	13.624	1.013	454.7

Nominal Pipe Size (in.)	Outside Diameter[a] (in.)	Schedule Number[b]	Wall Thickness[a] (in.)	Inside Diameter[a] (in.)	Cross-sectional Area of Flow (sq ft)	Capacity at 1 ft/sec velocity (U.S. gpm)
16	16.000	5S	0.165	15.670	1.339	601.0
		10S	0.188	15.624	1.331	597.4
18	18.000	5S	0.165	17.670	1.703	764.4
		10S	0.188	17.624	1.694	760.3
20	20.000	5S	0.188	19.624	2.101	943.0
		10S	0.218	19.564	2.079	933.1
24	24.000	5S	0.218	23.564	3.029	1360
		10S	0.250	23.500	3.012	1352
30	30.000	5S	0.250	29.500	4.746	2130
		10S	0.312	29.376	4.707	2113

[a] ASA Standards B36.19–1957.
[b] Schedule 5S and 10S wall thicknesses do not allow threading (ASA Standards B2.1).
[c] In these sizes schedule 40S and 80S correspond to standard weight and extra strong weight of carbon and alloy steel pipe as given in ASA Standards B36.10–1959.

TABLE A-3. Dimensions of Cast Iron Pipe

Nominal Pipe Size (in.)	Outside Diameter[a] (in.) Pipe	Outside Diameter[a] (in.) Joint	Rating	Wall Thickness[b] (in.)	Inside Diameter (in.)	Cross sectional Area of Flow (sq ft)	Capacity at 1 ft/sec velocity (U.S. gpm)
3	3.96	7.62	c	0.32	3.32	0.0601	26.96
4	4.80	9.06	c	0.35	4.10	0.0917	44.88
6	6.90	11.06	c	0.38	6.14	0.2056	92.28
8	9.05	13.31	c	0.41	8.23	0.3694	165.8
10	11.10	15.62	d	0.44	10.22	0.5697	255.7
			Class 300, 300 psi	0.48	10.14	0.5608	251.7
			Class 350, 350 psi	0.52	10.06	0.5520	247.8

TABLE A-3.—*(continued)*

Nominal Pipe Size (in.)	Outside Diameter[a] (in.) Pipe	Joint	Rating	Wall Thickness[b] (in.)	Inside Diameter (in.)	Cross sectional Area of Flow (sq ft)	Capacity at 1 ft/sec velocity (U.S. gpm)
12	13.20	17.88	e	0.48	12.24	0.8171	366.7
			Class 250, 250 psi	0.52	12.16	0.8065	362.0
			Class 300, 300 psi	0.52	12.16	0.8065	362.0
			Class 350, 350 psi	0.56	12.08	0.7959	357.2
14	15.30	20.25	Class 50, 50 psi	0.48	14.34	1.122	503.6
			Class 100, 100 psi	0.51	14.28	1.112	499.1
			Class 150, 150 psi	0.51	14.28	1.112	499.1
			Class 200, 200 psi	0.55	14.20	1.100	493.7
			Class 250, 250 psi	0.59	14.12	1.087	487.9
			Class 300, 300 psi	0.59	14.12	1.087	487.9
			Class 350, 350 psi	0.64	14.02	1.072	481.1
16	17.40	22.50	f	0.54	16.32	1.453	652.2
			Class 200, 200 psi	0.58	16.24	1.439	645.9
			Class 250, 250 psi	0.63	16.14	1.421	637.7
			Class 300, 300 psi	0.68	16.04	1.403	629.7
			Class 350, 350 psi	0.68	16.04	1.403	629.7
20	21.60	27.00	Class 50, 50 psi	0.57	20.46	2.283	1025
			Class 100, 100 psi	0.62	20.36	2.261	1015
			Class 150, 150 psi	0.62	20.36	2.261	1015
			Class 200, 200 psi	0.67	20.26	2.239	1005

Nominal Pipe Size (in.)	Outside Diameter[a] (in.)		Rating	Wall Thickness[b] (in.)	Inside Diameter (in.)	Cross sectional Area of Flow (sq ft)	Capacity at 1 ft/sec velocity (U.S. gpm)
	Pipe	Joint					
20 (cont'd)			Class 250, 250 psi	0.72	20.16	2.217	995.1
			Class 300, 300 psi	0.78	20.04	2.190	982.9
			Class 350, 350 psi	0.84	19.92	2.164	971.3

[a] ASA Standard A21.11–1952.
[b] ASA Standards A21.6–1962, A21.8–1962.
[c] Wall thickness constant for all classes, i.e., class 50, 100, 150, 200, 250, 300 and 350.
[d] Wall thickness constant for classes 50, 100, 150, 200 and 250.
[e] Wall thickness constant for classes 50, 100, 150 and 200.
[f] Wall thickness constant for classes 50, 100 and 150.

TABLE A–4. Properties of

Material	Specific Gravity	Tensile Strength at 73°F (psi)	Modulus of Elasticity in Tension (psi $\times 10^5$)	Compressive Strength (psi)	Flexural Strength (psi)	Resistance to Cont. Heating (°F)
Polyvinyl chloride (PVC), type I, rigid	1.38	7000	4.15	9600	14,500	150
Polyvinyl chloride (PVC), type II, flexible	1.35	6000	3.50	8800	11,500	140
Polyethylene (PE), type I, low density	0.92	1750	0.19–0.35	—	1700	120
Polyethylene (PE), type III, high density	0.95	2800	1.50	—	2000	120
Polypropylene	0.90	5000	1.70	8500	81.00	160–212
Chlorinated polyether ("Penton")	1.40	6000	1.60	9000	5000	200–250
Polyvinyl dichloride (PVDC), high impact	1.50	7800	3.90	—	14,500	180–215
Acrylonitrile-butadiene-styrene (ABS), type I, high impact	1.03	5300	3.00	7000	8000	160
Acrylonitrile-butadiene-styrene (ABS), type II, extra high impact	1.08	8000	2.50	10,000	12,000	170
Vinylidene Fuoride ("Kynar")	1.76	7000	1.20	10,000	—	200–250
Tetrafluoroethylene ("Teflon")	2.20	2000	0.58	1700	2000	250–300
Cellulose-acetate-butyrate (CAB)	1.20	4200	1.30	5000	7000	150
Reinforced epoxy	1.70	9400	1.60	40,000	100,000	300

[a] Plastics Div., Cabot Corporation

[b] For thermal conductivities, coefficients of linear expansion, and specific heats, see Table A–5.

[c] Burning rate: SE = self extinguishing, VS = very slow, S = slow.
 Resistance to chemical attack: VR = very resistant, R = resistant, SL = slight attack, AOA = attacked by organic acids, A = attacked, Sol = soluble.

Plastic Piping Materials[a, b]

Burning Rate[c]	Heat Distortion Temperature at 264 psi (°F)	Water Absorption at 73°F (%/24 hr)	Effect of Weak Acids[c]	Effect of Strong Acids[c]	Effect of Weak Alkalis[c]	Effect of Strong Alkalis[c]	Effect of Organic Solvents[c]	Relative Cost[a]
SE	165	0.07	None	None	None	None	Sol	0.53
SE	155	0.07	None	None—SL	None	None	Sol	0.53
VS	175	0.01	R	AOA	R	R	>120°F Sol	—
VS	250	0	VR	SA	VR	VR	>120°F Sol	—
S	150	0.01	VR	SA	None	VR	>160°F Sol	0.40
SE	185	0.01	None	AOA	None	None	R	3.71
SE	215	—	None	None—SL	None	None	Sol	—
S	197	0.20	None	A	None	None	Sol	0.55
S	225	0.20	None	A	None	None	Sol	0.55
SE	195	0.04	None	None—SL	None	None—SL	Sol	—
SE	170	0	None	None	None	None	None	8.20
S	160	1.4–1.8	SL	D	SL	D	Sol	0.79
SE	300	0.03	None	None—SL	None	None—SL	Sol	—

TABLE A–5. Thermal Properties of Piping Materials

Material	Coefficient of Linear Expansion (in./in._°F) × 10⁶	Thermal Conductivity[b] (Btu/hr sq ft °F/ft)	Specific Heat[b] (Btu/lb °F)
Metals:			
Aluminum	13.3	129	0.233
Copper and copper alloys			
Copper, 99.9% pure	9.71	223	0.095
Brass, Admiralty, 71% Cu	10.2	64.2	0.090
Brass, red, 85% Cu	9.85	92.0	0.091
Brass, yellow, 65% Cu	10.4	69.2	0.090
Iron			
Cast	6.70	30.5	0.122
Wrought	6.32	27.5	0.110
Lead	15.1	19.3	0.032
Nickel	7.17	34.8	0.118
Steel			
0.20% C	6.75	30.0	0.110
0.43% C	6.50	33.5	0.108
Stainless, #302	9.63	9.38	0.125
Stainless, #304	9.60	8.75	0.120
Stainless, #310	8.51	8.63	0.110
Stainless, #316	8.40	8.75	0.124
Stainless, #410	5.48	14.4	0.110
Plastics:			
Acrylonitrile-butadiene-styrene (ABS)			
Type I, high impact	60	0.10	0.37
Type III, extra high impact	38	0.10	0.37
Cellulose acetate butyrate (CAB)	78	0.15	0.35
Chlorinated polyether ("Penton")	45	0.09	—
Polyethylene: (PE)			
Type I, low density	100	0.18	0.55
Type III, high density	120	0.18	0.52
Polypropylene	38	0.08	0.45
Polyvinyl chloride (PVC)			
Type I, rigid	28	0.085	—
Type II, flexible	56	0.085	—

TABLE A-5.—(continued)

Material	Coefficient of Linear Expansion (in./in. °F) $\times 10^6$	Thermal Conductivity[b] (Btu/hr sq ft °F/ft)	Specific Heat[b] (Btu/lb °F)
Polyvinyl dichloride (PVDC)	44	0.08	—
Polychlorotrifluoroethylene[a] ("Kel-F")	39	0.151	0.23
Polytetrafluoroethylene[a] ("Teflon")	57	0.140	0.25
Polyvinylidene chloride[a] ("Saran")	88	0.052	0.34
Polyvinylidene fluoride ("Kynar")	85	0.088	—

[a] Commonly used as a lining material.
[b] Values given are at 212 °F.

Index